The Ionisation of Carbon Acids

J. R. JONES

Department of Chemistry,
University of Surrey,
Guildford, Surrey

1973

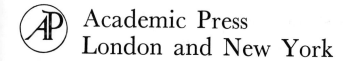

Academic Press
London and New York

ACADEMIC PRESS INC. (LONDON) LTD.
24/28 Oval Road,
London NW1 7DX

United States Edition published by
ACADEMIC PRESS INC.
111 Fifth Avenue
New York, New York 10003

Library of Congress Catalog Card Number: 72-9465
ISBN: 0-12-389750-5

PRINTED IN GREAT BRITAIN BY
WILLIAM CLOWES & SONS LIMITED
LONDON, COLCHESTER AND BECCLES

ACKNOWLEDGEMENTS

This book has come about as a result of work that I have become interested in over the last twelve to fifteen years. Being conscious of the attributes such a book should have, the task of writing has never been an easy one. However it has been made more pleasant by the knowledge that it provides an opportunity of expressing thanks to various people who have been of assistance to me during these years.

In the first place my thanks go to Dr C. B. Monk with whom I did my early research, and Professor C. W. Davies, who was Head of the Chemistry Department at Aberystwyth at that time. Although I have strayed somewhat from their own interests in classical electro-chemistry I hope that they will agree with me that the subject chosen is not one without interest.

I owe a particular debt of gratitude to Professor Ross Stewart with whom I had the privilege of working during the academic year 1966–67. I have also been assisted in my task by my colleagues at the University of Surrey and in particular Professors J. A. Elvidge and J. E. Salmon, both of whom have given me every encourage-ment.

The list of acknowledgements would be incomplete were I not to mention the help given to me over many years by my parents, and in more recent times by members of my own family. This book owes a great deal to them.

The typing of the manuscript has been left in the capable hands of Mrs D. Claxton and Mrs K. Warren. Likewise Mr D. Aldrich looked after the diagrams. The responsibility for the final outcome is, of course, my own.

J. R. JONES

Guildford, Surrey
January 1973

CONTENTS

1. Introduction

Carbon acids are organic compounds which, when treated with a base, undergo ionisation by cleavage of a carbon–hydrogen bond to give carbanions. These acids include most organic compounds, as media are now available which are sufficiently basic as to be able to abstract a proton from the most weakly acidic of compounds.

The ionisation of carbon acids is therefore a subject of much interest not only because of the central position occupied by these compounds in organic and bio-chemistry but also because the process of transferring a proton has so many distinguishing features such as the small mass of the proton and its low steric requirements. Two books, one by Cram on the *Fundamentals of Carbanion Chemistry* (1965), and the other by Bell, entitled *The Proton in Chemistry* (1959), have dealt with these various aspects in detail. Each in its own way, by examining different problems, evaluating advances and indicating future research trends, has been responsible for stimulating a great deal of new interest in carbanion chemistry and proton transfer reactions and indirectly, has been responsible for the appearance of this book.

The astonishingly rapid developments of the last few years are reflected in the fact that of the 650 references contained in the book 500 (or 77%) made their appearance during or after 1960 and nearly 450 during or after 1965. For illustrative purposes it may be best to compare the situation as it was just over a decade ago with the present situation by means of a few selected examples.

For the rates of acid–base reactions it was certainly true to say,[1] as Bell did, that "In general, measurements of isotopic exchange rates have not added greatly to our knowledge of the velocities of these reactions". Equally nobody familiar with recent developments would now dispute that the prediction that "The most useful field for obtaining new information is probably that of very weak acids and bases since by using the radioactive isotope tritium it is possible to measure extremely small exchanges . . ." has not materialised.

Studies of the rates of ionisation of carbon acids have led to a better appreciation of the importance of ion association[2] with the result that the situation is considerably different from as recently as

10 years ago when it was frequently asserted that ion pairs, at least in aqueous media, do not constitute an important factor in reaction kinetics. These studies have the added benefit of illustrating the important role which the solvent plays in reaction kinetics.

No less an authority than Melander in his book on *Isotope Effects on Reaction Rates* stated that "tunnelling seems to be without importance in the majority of well-investigated chemical reactions (and) it will not be discussed further". However, recent model calculations[3] suggest "that the observed variation of isotope effects . . . are determined mainly by the tunnel correction". Although this may be an overstatement there seems to be general agreement as to the importance of tunnelling, only in the manner in which the quantum mechanical correction to the rate is calculated does opinion tend to differ.

After a period of comparative neglect the study of solvent isotope effects has attracted a good deal of interest in recent years. Yet not so long ago it seemed as if "The complexity of the problem and the assumptions required make it doubtful that useful mechanistic conclusions can be drawn from observing rates in H_2O-D_2O mixtures".[4] This is certainly no longer the case.

Although the choice of material is to some extent governed by personal considerations it seems that to understand fully the nature of proton transfer processes from carbon acids it is necessary to study in a systematic manner not only their acidities but also the effect of different bases, and of temperature on the rates of both forward and reverse reactions. This information may be supplemented with the results of isotopic substitution as many unknown or poorly known factors cancel in the ratio of the rates. For these various reasons the book is organised on the following lines.

The various methods used to follow the rates of ionisation of carbon acids are described in Chapter 2. The recent development of the differential method, which enables rates to be measured with such high accuracy, seems likely to find wide application e.g. in studies of the temperature dependence of reaction rates and in H_2O-D_2O mixtures. Chapter 3 illustrates some of the many modes of carbanion stabilisation that are in operation as well as other factors important in the rates of ionisation of carbon acids.

In Chapter 4 various methods of determining the acidities of these acids, varying from the classical physical chemists approach (used for the more acidic compounds) to the more qualitative observations of the organic chemists (used for the weakly acidic compounds) are included and the results discussed in Chapter 5 in terms of the particular acidifying group(s).

Ideally the rates of ionisation of carbon acids should be studied over as wide a range of reactivity as possible. Too frequently in the past this has necessitated drastic structural modifications at or close to the reaction site, thus making the subsequent interpretation of the results difficult. Similarly only acidities covering a few pK units can be measured in a particular solvent system. The fact that dipolar aprotic solvents such as dimethyl sulphoxide can be used to alter the H_ values of aqueous hydroxide solutions by more than 14 units by gradually desolvating the hydroxide ion suggests a solution to the problem. Highly basic media (Chapter 6) seem destined to play an important part in future studies of both rates and acidities as well as being particularly well suited to studies of kinetic isotope effects.

Depending on the nature of the solvent the carbanion formed on ionisation can exist as a free ion or as an ion-pair of the solvent-separated kind or the contact variety; so can the base used for the ionisation reaction. The practical consequences of ion association are discussed in Chapter 7.

One aspect of the ionisation of carbon acids which has recently received increasing attention is the structure of the transition state and in particular the extent of proton transfer in this state. One can not, of course, directly determine the structure of the transition state and one of the main objectives of rate-equilibria correlations (Chapter 8) is to overcome this difficulty, if possible. Just as important is the problem of rationalising deviations from free energy relationships as these may be a sensitive probe for the presence of specific interactions between carbon acid and base.

Studies of kinetic hydrogen isotope effects (Chapter 9) provide another and probably more powerful method of investigating transition state structure. A satisfactory theory has been available for many years[5] but only with the development of large computers has it become possible to supplement the experimental findings with the results of model calculations.

The decade following the discovery of deuterium (1933–42) saw a good deal of interest in the study of solvent isotope effects (Chapter 10) but with the advent of war and the increasing use made of radioactive isotopes the subject was largely neglected. Recent experience has, however, shown[6] that for reactions where a certain amount is known about the mechanism solvent isotope effect studies can add a great deal to the detailed picture of the transition state.

Compounds labelled with deuterium or tritium are becoming increasingly important in reaction mechanism studies of both chemical and biological systems, and the need to prepare specifically labelled molecules has sometimes been presented as a considerable barrier to such investigations. In the final chapter it is shown how isotope exchange can be made to provide a convenient and versatile method for the preparation of a large number of labelled carbon acids. It provides an important example of the application of proton transfer reactions.

On reflection it may be argued that an account of *The Ionisation of Carbon Acids* would be incomplete without discussing in detail three other topics—techniques of fast reactions, stereochemical aspects of isotopic exchange and secondary deuterium isotope effects. However, a standard monograph[7] is available in the first case and there seems to be little that one can add to Cram's excellent account[8] of the second and Halevi's[9] of the third.

REFERENCES

1. Bell, R. P. (1959). *The Proton in Chemistry*, p. 123. Cornell University Press, Ithaca, N. Y.
2. Jones, J. R. (1973). *Progr. React. Kinetics* (Jennings, K. R. & Cundall, R. B. eds.) 7, 1.
3. Bell, R. P., Sachs, W. H. & Tranter, R. L. (1971). *Trans. Faraday Soc.* 67, 1995.
4. Saunders, W H. Jr. (1966). *Surv. Progr. Chem.* (Scott, A. F. ed.) 3, 109.
5. Bigeleisen, J. (1949). *J. Chem. Phys.* 17, 675.
6. Gold, V. (1969). *Adv. Phys. Org. Chem.* (Gold, V. ed.) 7, 259.
7. Caldin, E. F. (1964). *Fast Reactions in Solution*, Blackwell Scientific Publications, Oxford.
8. Cram, D. J. (1965). *Fundamentals of Carbanion Chemistry*, p. 85. Academic Press, N. Y.
9. Halevi, E. A. (1963). *Progr. Phys. Org. Chem.* (Cohen, S. G., Streitwieser, A. & Taft, R. W. eds.) 1, 109.

2. Rates of Ionisation—Methods

2.1. HALOGENATION

Amongst the many indirect methods of measuring rates of proton transfer reactions that of halogenation has been the subject of considerable study. Most of the work refers to the rates of bromination and serves to show that the method can, by suitable refinement, be made extremely versatile--reaction velocities from 10^{-8} to 10^{+7} M^{-1} s^{-1} can be measured.

The early work of Dawson[1] and Pedersen[2] using ketones and of Junell[3] with nitro-compounds showed that in the reaction of these carbon acids with bases the rate-determining step was the transfer of a proton to the catalysing species and that the rate was the same whether bromine or iodine was employed as the scavenger. The general scheme may be written as

$$RH_2 + B^- \xrightarrow{k_1} RH^- + BH \qquad (2.1)$$

$$RH^- + Br_2 \xrightarrow{fast} RHBr + Br^- \qquad (2.2)$$

$$RHBr + B^- \xrightarrow{k_2} RBr^- + BH \qquad (2.3)$$

$$RBr^- + Br_2 \xrightarrow{fast} RBr_2 + Br^- \qquad (2.4)$$

RH_2 being the carbon acid, and k_1 and k_2 first order velocity constants with the catalyst concentration remaining effectively constant. To follow rates of iodination it was customary to withdraw samples of reaction mixture at fixed time intervals and titrate with thiosulphate whereas for bromination any excess bromine could be removed by adding allyl alcohol and advantage taken of the fact that the bromo compound formed liberated iodine from potassium iodide solutions. This latter method is not always practical however as, for example, when the compound itself reacts with KI.

Several aspects of the halogenation method are worthy of comment. Thus although bromination usually proceeds quantitatively to products iodination in aqueous solution is frequently a reversible process going only partly to completion. Whilst it is possible to measure rates of bromination in the presence of a wide range of buffered solutions—these include acetate, trimethylacetate, chloro-acetate, phosphate and fluoride (the latter is of considerable practical interest since it is very unreactive towards oxidising and reducing agents as well as organic substances in general), both glycolate and benzoate buffers react slowly with bromine. Similarly iodine reacts slowly with pyridine presumably by nuclear iodination. Complex formation is also possible and in non-aqueous media evidence[4] in favour of the existence of the species $C_5H_5N . I_2$ has been found.

The halogenation reaction is best studied when only mono-substitution occurs as, for example, in the case of 2-carbethoxy-cyclopentanone bromination.[5] There are however many instances[6] where more than 1 mole of bromine is taken up per mole of carbon acid—ethyl nitroacetate, ethyl cyanoacetate, dinitromethane and malononitrile each take up 2 moles of bromine. In these examples the reaction continues to be first order with respect to substrate so that it is safe to assume that the monobromo compound is brominated much more rapidly than the original compound (i.e. $k_2 \gg k_1$). Work on acetylacetone,[7] however, shows that this is not always the case and Pedersen[8] found from the overall rate of bromination of ethyl acetoacetate that the α-bromoester was brominated about 12 times as fast as the original ester, which compares with a factor of 5 as determined by Bell and co-workers.[7]

In some cases it is possible to isolate RHBr and study its bromination separately so that k_1 can then be obtained fairly readily from the kinetics of bromination of RH_2. This approach is only satisfactory, however, when the ratio k_1/k_2 differs considerably from unity. Alternatively, the carbon acid e.g. acetylacetone, may be converted almost completely to the enolate ion by adding a slight excess of alkali. It is known that both the ion and enol react almost "instantaneously" with bromine so that on adding an excess of bromine to an alkaline solution of ketone the monobromoketone is formed immediately and is then brominated at a measurable rate, thereby enabling k_2 to be obtained directly. For slightly weaker acids than acetylacetone Bell and co-workers[7] have developed a method whereby k_2 can be obtained from partially neutralised solutions.

In the case of nitroacetone[9] 3 moles of bromine are taken up per mole of ketone and this has been accounted for by the following scheme:

$$CH_2(NO_2)COCH_3 + B^- \rightarrow [CH(NO_2)COCH_3]^- + BH \qquad (2.5)$$

$$[CH(NO_2)COCH_3]^- + Br_2 \rightarrow [CHBr(NO_2)COCH_3] + Br^- \qquad (2.6)$$

$$[CHBr(NO_2)COCH_3] + B^- \rightarrow [CBr(NO_2)COCH_3]^- + BH \qquad (2.7)$$

$$[CBr(NO_2)COCH_3]^- + Br_2 \rightarrow CBr_2(NO_2)COCH_3 + Br^- \quad (2.8)$$
$$CBr_2(NO_2)COCH_3 + H_2O \rightarrow CBr_2(NO_2)C(OH)_2CH_3 \quad (2.9)$$
$$CBr_2(NO_2)C(OH)_2CH_3 + B^- \rightarrow CBr_2NO_2^- + CH_3CO_2H + BH \quad (2.10)$$
$$CBr_2NO_2^- + Br_2 \rightarrow CBr_3NO_2 + Br^- \quad (2.11)$$

That reaction (2.5) is still rate-determining can be seen from the following analysis:

(a) Reactions (2.6), (2.8) and (2.11) represent the bromination of enols or aci-nitrocompounds, which are known to have high velocity constants.[10]

(b) The accelerating effect on the rates of ionisation of ketones of halogen substitution—the relative rates for CH_3COCH_3 $ClCH_2COCH_3$ and $Cl_2CH_2COCH_3$ are in the ratio 1:400:3000,[11] indicates that reaction (2.7) should be much faster than (2.5).

(c) Reaction (2.9) is known to be very fast for nitroacetone[6] and the introduction of two bromine atoms should certainly increase it.

(d) Reactions of gem-diols with different bases are known to be very fast.[12]

2.2. SPECTROPHOTOMETRIC

Such methods of following rates of halogenation are now widely used. Thus for bromination studies changes in the absorption band at 390 nm (ϵ_{Br_2} at this wavelength is 196) can be followed[13] but if either the products or reactants absorb in this region the absorption at 500 nm ($\epsilon_{Br_2} = 20$) or the tribromide absorption near 340 nm ($\epsilon = 860$) may be employed.[14] For studies of iodination changes in the tri-iodide absorption at 352 nm ($\epsilon = 26,400$) are most frequently used.[15] It is, however, necessary to take into account the slight dissociation of the tri-iodide ion in terms of the equilibrium constant $K = [I_3^-]/[I_2][I^-]$ which has a value of 714 at 25°. Changes in absorption at 436 nm[16] as well as the I_2/I_3^- isosbestic point[17] near 470 nm ($\epsilon = 675$) have also been used to measure the rates of iodination. Since both I_2 and I_3^- are capable of halogenating enols the rate of disappearance of ketone from solutions containing both species must be equal to the combined rates of halogenation. The enol content of ketones varies greatly (Table 2.1) and can in fact be determined by measuring the amount of bromine which reacts "instantaneously" with a solution of the ketone; the keto-form reacts at a much slower rate.

For slow reactions the hydrolysis of tri-iodide by, for example, carbonate, phosphate and succinate buffers is sufficiently fast as to make the observation of reaction between carbon acid and iodine virtually impossible.[22] In still more basic media, such as a solution of hydroxide ions, the halogens react to form the corresponding hypohalite (OBr^-, OI^-, OCl^-). All three are powerful halogenating agents although little use has been made of hypoiodite as it decomposes fairly rapidly. The hypobromite solutions are considerably more stable[23] and changes in the absorption spectrum at

TABLE 2.1

Percentage enol in aqueous solutions of some ketones

Ketone	% Enol	Reference
Methoxyacetone	1·1	19
Acetylacetone	17	20
Benzoylacetone	34	20
Methylacetylacetone	3·3	13
2-Acetylcyclohexanone	29·2	13
Cyclopentanone	$1·3 \times 10^{-3}$	18
Cyclohexanone	$4·1 \times 10^{-4}$	18
Bromoacetylacetone	7	21
2-Carbethoxycyclohexanone	~2–5	16
Ethylacetoacetate	0·4	7

330 nm ($\epsilon_{OBr^-} = 300$) have been used to follow the rates of bromination of a series of substituted acetophenones.[24] In all cases 1 mole of ketone reacts with three of hypobromite so that the overall rate represents that of tribromination. The reaction is zero-order with respect to OBr^- and first-order with respect to the ketone and hydroxide ion concentrations so that the rate of cleavage of the $\geq$C–H bond is rate-determining. The reaction mechanism is that given by Eqns (2.12) and (2.13). Assuming that $[R^-]$ is always extremely low the general rate equation (2.14) is obtained which

$$RH + OH^- \underset{k_{-1}}{\overset{k_1}{\rightleftharpoons}} R^- + H_2O \tag{2.12}$$

$$R^- + OX^- \overset{k_2}{\underset{H_2O}{\longrightarrow}} RX + 2OH^- \tag{2.13}$$

reduces to the usual second-order rate equation (2.15) when $k_2[OX^-] \gg k_{-1}[H_2O]$.

$$\frac{d[RX]}{dt} = \frac{-d[OX^-]}{dt} = \frac{k_1k_2[RH][OH][OX^-]}{k_{-1}[H_2O] + k_2[OX^-]} \tag{2.14}$$

$$= k_1[RH][OH^-] \tag{2.15}$$

Miller[25] however has drawn attention to the fact that if $k_{-1}[H_2O] \gg k_2[OX^-]$ Eqn (2.16) is obtained in which $K_1 = k_1/k_{-1}$.

$$\frac{-d[OX^-]}{dt} = K_1 k_2 [RH][OH^-][OX^-]/[H_2O] \qquad (2.16)$$

This equation has been found to apply to the base catalysed halogenation of phenylacetylene and di-isopropyl ketone.[26] On extending the work to nitroethane[27] neither second or third order kinetics but rather a rate law given by Eqn (2.17) was observed. Rate-determining

$$\frac{-d[OX^-]}{dt} = k_1 [RH][OX^-][OH^-]^{-1} \qquad (2.17)$$

attack of either hypochlorite on the nitronic acid $(CH_2CH=NO_2H)$ or hypochlorous acid on the nitronate ion $(CH_3CHNO_2^-)$ is suggested.

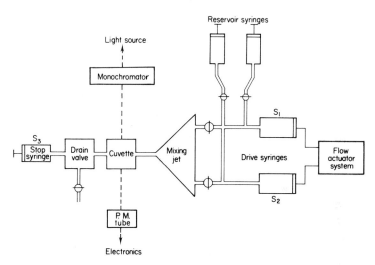

Fig. 2.1. Block diagram of stopped-flow mixing chamber plus accessories.

Carbon acids such as the nitro-compounds ionise much more slowly than one would predict from their acidities. It therefore becomes possible to measure rates of ionisation by following the appearance of the anion and this method, which does away with the need for a scavenger, has been successfully employed in several studies e.g. the ionisation of nitroethane,[28] ethylnitroacetate[29] and some phenylnitroethanes.[30]

In other cases where the reaction goes far enough over to observe the direct formation of the anion the rate is normally uncomfortably fast and a stopped-flow method, combining a rapid mixing device with spectrophotometric detection, may be necessary. The principle of the method can be seen by reference to Fig. 2.1. By correct manipulation of the appropriate valve settings the drive syringes S_1 and S_2 are filled with the reactants which were previously stored in the reservoir syringes. Then with the valves reset for following the reaction the actuator button is pressed thereby forcing equal volumes of the two reactants to mix in the mixing jet and flow into the cuvette. The flow is abruptly halted when the plunger of syringe S_3 strikes a limiting stop so that the reaction proceeds in the cuvette with minimum turbulence. Light from the monochromator is attenuated by the sample and detected by the photomultiplier, the output of which is fed into a storage oscilloscope. In principle there is no reason why changes in other properties such as infra-red absorption or optical rotation could not be observed.

Although the stopped-flow method has been extensively used to follow inorganic reactions relatively little work has been done using carbon acids. The ionisation of nitroethane in highly basic media has been followed by this means[31] as has also the reaction of aromatic nitro-compounds with different bases;[32] so also has the reaction between hydrocarbon acids and carbanions in dimethyl sulphoxide.[33,34]

If the reaction concerned is still too fast to be measured operation at much reduced temperatures may be necessary. For work in aqueous media this can be achieved by using large concentrations of salt e.g. 5·2M NaBr or 6·7M $NaClO_4$; depending on the kind of reaction under investigation difficulties may arise from increased ion association.[35] The alcohols are particularly good solvents for investigating reactions at low temperatures; thus the reaction between ethoxide ion and p-nitrobenzyl cyanide in an ethanol–ether mixture was studied down to $-124°C$ where the rate is $c.$ 4000 times slower than at $-60°$.[32] Low temperature thermostats using solid carbon dioxide in acetone as cooling agent down to $-70°$ and oxygen-free nitrogen for the lower temperatures can be readily constructed.[36]

2.3. ELECTROCHEMICAL

Several such methods of following rates of halogenation (particularly bromination) are in operation. Thus the bromination of nitroacetone was followed[9] by measuring the $Br_2-Br_3^-$ redox potential at a platinum electrode as a function of time. Bromine concentrations down to $10^{-7}-10^{-8}$M can be measured and this is of considerable benefit not only in extending the sensitivity of the classical Kurt Meyer method of determining the equilibrium enol content of ketones but also in enabling a wide range of reaction velocities to be measured. Thus for a relatively unreactive ketone it is possible to make accurate measurements on less than 15% of the total reaction by using a very low concentration of bromine in the presence of a large excess of ketone. On the other hand relatively fast reactions (second order rate constants $\sim 10^6$ M^{-1} s^{-1}) can be studied by following changes in bromine concentration through several powers of ten.

Bromine concentrations down to at least $5 \times 10^{-7} M$ can be measured using the "dead-stop" method[37,38] which depends on the depolarising effect of free halogen at a platinum cathode; the method has been used to follow the bromination of 2-carbethoxycyclopenta-none.[5] Polarographic as well as methods based on the electrolytic generation of bromine are also used.[39] The rates of bromination of several nitro-compounds have been followed by measuring changes in the conductivity of the solution.[40] Using this method it was possible to show that for the water-catalysed ionisation of nitroethane the rates of bromination and iodination were in good agreement as expected if the rate-determining step is the cleavage of a $\geq C-H$ bond.

Fairly rapid reactions with $t_{1/2}$ down to 3×10^{-2} s can be studied by making the rate of production (electrolytic) of reagent equal to that of consumption.[41] The hydroxide-catalysed ionisation of nitro-ethane was studied in this way, the hydroxide ions being generated at a platinum cathode (in the form of a gauze) with a platinum foil, immersed in a short bed of cation exchange resin in order to pick up the hydrogen ions produced by electrolysis, acting as an anode.

The same reaction has been studied by Bell and Goodall[42] but in this case a glass electrode was used to monitor the pH and control the addition of alkali so as to keep the pH constant during the experiment. The method, which has also been used by Coward and Bruice,[22] is particularly suitable for nitro-compounds as the rates of ionisation are relatively slow for compounds as acidic as these (pK_a values in the range 7–11). The consumption of alkali can be automatically recorded as a function of time and measures the extent of reaction. Because nitroethane is relatively soluble in aqueous media it is possible to make $[RH] \gg [OH^-]$; under these conditions the reaction follows a first-order course whereas with the consider-ably less soluble nitrocyclohexane an alternative approach using a stirred suspension containing several times the quantity of nitro-cyclohexane needed to form a saturated solution, is necessary.[42] As long as two phases exist the reaction follows a zero-order course with the rate of consumption of alkali given by $k_{OH}^H[OH^-][RH]_S$ where $[RH]_S$ is the solubility of nitrocyclohexane. Only when the reactions become quite slow ($t_{1/2} > 5 \times 10^4$ s) does pH drift become a problem and render the pH-stat inoperative.

It is possible to measure the rates of proton transfer reactions having half-lives in the range $3\,s < t_{1/2} < 200\,s$ by simply observing the temperature changes produced by the reaction.[43,44] The principle of the method is illustrated in Fig. 2.2. The full curve represents the temperature change which takes place if the reaction (exothermic) occurs adiabatically. The dotted curve refers to the same reaction under conditions where heat is lost continuously to the

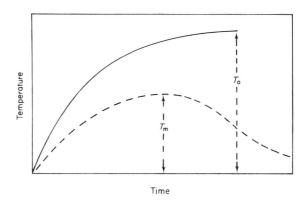

Fig. 2.2. Variation of temperature with time for an exothermic reaction under adiabatic and non-adiabatic conditions.[44]

surrounding thermostat. The ratio of T_m, the maximum temperature reached when heat transfer takes place, to T_0, the corresponding temperature change under adiabatic conditions, depends on the relationship between the rate of reaction and the rate at which heat is lost by the system. If the two rates can be represented by first order constants k_1 and k_2 with $k_1/k_2 = R$, it can be shown that

$$T_m/T_0 = R^{1/1-R} \tag{2.18}$$

Since the maximum is a flat one T_m can easily be determined without any measurements of time. By using this method a single observation can lead to a rate constant with an accuracy of ±2–3%.

Changes in conductivity have frequently been employed to follow the rates of ionisation of carbon acids and in particular nitrocompounds.[45] More recently such changes have been used to obtain very precise kinetic data.[46,47] This has been done by employing a differential method in which the ratio of rate constants for the same reaction taking place at two temperatures differing by 1–2° is measured. Usually a temperature difference of this order leads to a

10–20% difference in reaction rate. If one attempted to measure the reaction rates separately by a method having an experimental accuracy of 2%, then for a ratio of 1·10 one would obtain values varying from 1·08 to 1·12. However, in the differential method the error is not a percentage of the individual rates but of the difference between them. Many errors therefore cancel out and the results for a ratio of 1·100 would vary between 1·096 and 1·104. By this means very accurate values for the enthalpy of activation $\Delta H^{\ddagger}$ can be obtained as well as its variation with temperature, leading to values of $\Delta C_p^{\ddagger}$, the heat capacity of activation.

Given two reactions with first-order rate constants k and $k(1 + \alpha)$ the variation of conductance for the two reactions can be written:

$$(\lambda - \lambda_\infty)_t = (\lambda - \lambda_\infty)_0 \exp(-kt). \tag{2.19}$$

$$(\lambda' - \lambda'_\infty)_t = (\lambda' - \lambda'_\infty)_0 \exp -k(1 + \alpha)t. \tag{2.20}$$

Single conductance readings λ are taken at time t to obtain k in the usual manner. The difference in conductance between the two reactions λ'' is recorded at time $t + \Delta t$, where Δt is a constant time interval. Single and differential readings separated by Δt, are paired together to give from Eqns (2.19) and (2.20): ·

$$\frac{(\lambda'' - \lambda''_\infty)_{t+\Delta t}}{(\lambda - \lambda_\infty)_t} = \exp(-k\Delta t) - \frac{(\lambda' - \lambda'_\infty)_0}{(\lambda - \lambda_\infty)_0} \exp[-k(1 + \alpha)\Delta t - \alpha kt] \tag{2.21}$$

or

$$\ln\left[\exp(-k\Delta t) - \frac{(\lambda'' - \lambda''_\infty)_{t+\Delta t}}{(\lambda - \lambda_\infty)_t}\right] = \ln\frac{(\lambda' - \lambda'_\infty)_0}{(\lambda - \lambda_\infty)_0} - k(1 + \alpha)\Delta t - \alpha kt \tag{2.22}$$

A plot of the left hand side of Eqn (2.22) against t gives αk from which α and hence the ratio is obtained. The method has been used to study the hydrolysis of t-butyl chloride and the iodination of acetone; in the latter case changes in optical density were measured.

2.4. ISOTOPIC EXCHANGE

Not surprisingly in view of the fact that hydrogen has two isotopes, deuterium and tritium, the kinetics of isotope exchange reactions have been the subject of considerable study. McKay[48] was the first to show that the shape of the concentration versus time curve would be that for a first-order reaction, independent of whether the reaction is uni-, bi- or termolecular. Subsequently Harris[49] showed that provided the concentration of distinguishable isotope remains small this would still hold irrespective of the magnitude of any isotope effect associated with the reaction. More recently it has been concluded[50] that deviation from first-order kinetics was unlikely either as a result of isotopic fractionation or differences in kinetic form due to the mechanism of the exchange.

The first evidence for the existence of tritium came in 1934 from Rutherford's[51] work on the bombardment of a deuterium target with fast deuterons, only two years after the discovery by Urey[52] of deuterium in ordinary water and in samples of water concentrated by electrolysis. Tritium was later found to be radioactive,[53] being a weak β-emitter ($E_{avg} = 5{\cdot}7$ keV) with a half-life of 12·26 years.[54] Tritium–hydrogen exchange reactions can therefore be followed by using tracer concentrations of tritium–this makes it possible to measure very slow reactions where the collection of data for any appreciable extent of reaction is clearly impractical. In practice the initial rate method[55] is used in such a way that the rate of increase of radioactivity in the solvent can be followed. If the reaction is less than 3% complete the familiar equation for the first-order rate constant k (2.23) reduces to (2.24)

$$k = \frac{1}{t} \ln \frac{1}{1-x} \qquad (2.23)$$

$$k = x/t \qquad (2.24)$$

so that the increase in radioactivity with time is linear. The zero-order rate constant so obtained can then be converted to a first-order rate constant by making use of the total radioactivity of the substrate in solution.

Another advantage in the use of tritium can be seen from the work of Long et al.[56] on the detritiation of phenylacetylene in alkaline media. The rate-determining step for both labelled and unlabelled phenylacetylene is given by

$$C_6H_5C\equiv CH + OH^- \underset{k_{-1}}{\overset{k_1}{\rightleftarrows}} C_6H_5C\equiv C^- + H_2O \qquad (2.25)$$

$$C_6H_5C\equiv CT + OH^- \underset{k_{-2}}{\overset{k_2}{\rightleftarrows}} C_6H_5C\equiv C^- + HTO \qquad (2.26)$$

The general rate equation[50] is

$$\frac{d[C_6H_5C\equiv CT]}{dt} = \frac{k_2[\text{``}C_6H_5C\equiv CH\text{''}]}{1 - \beta \dfrac{k_{-1} - k_{-2}}{k_{-1}}} \left[\epsilon(1-\alpha)\beta - (1-\beta)\alpha \right] \qquad (2.27)$$

where ["C$_6$H$_5$C≡CH"] is the total concentration of phenylacetylene, α and β the atom fractions of tritium in the phenylacetylene and in the water, respectively, and ϵ the fractionation factor between substrate and water is defined by Eqn (2.28):

$$\epsilon = \frac{(1 - \beta_\infty)\alpha_\infty}{(1 - \alpha_\infty)\beta_\infty} \qquad (2.28)$$

The fact that tritium is present at tracer level concentrations permits some simplifications: thus both α and β are much less than unity, and ["C$_6$H$_5$C≡CH"] $\simeq$ [C$_6$H$_5$C≡CH]. Similarly [C$_6$H$_5$C≡CT] $\simeq$ α [C$_6$H$_5$C≡CH] and $\epsilon \simeq \alpha_\infty / \beta_\infty$. Consequently Eqn (2.27) simplifies to

$$\frac{d\alpha}{dt} = k_2 (\epsilon\beta - \alpha) \qquad (2.29)$$

which can be written as

$$\frac{d(\alpha_\infty - \alpha)}{dt} = k_2 \frac{["C_6H_5C≡CH"] + 2["H_2O"]}{2["H_2O"]} (\alpha_\infty - \alpha) \qquad (2.30)$$

As the total phenylacetylene concentration is small by comparison with the total amount of water and as α is proportional to the net observed count/min/aliquot, Eqn (2.30) reduces to

$$\frac{d \ln (C_\infty - C)}{dt} = -k_2 \qquad (2.31)$$

In other words the tritium label can either be initially in the phenylacetylene or in the water—in each case the plot of $\log_{10}$ ($C_\infty - C$) against time will yield k_2, the rate of rupture of the C–T bond. This has been found to hold good both in the case of phenylacetylene[56] and dimethyl sulphoxide.[57]

Most studies of the rates of detritiation of carbon acids have been made after the development of liquid scintillation counting. The method consists of dissolving the radioactive sample in a solution containing a scintillation solvent and solute. This liquid scintillator degrades and converts to light the energy emitted by the radioactive isotope. Then the light energy is transferred by the use of a photomultiplier tube to electrical energy which is amplified and detected. Other low energy β emitters (C^{14}, Ni^{63}, P^{32}, S^{35}) in addition to tritium can be readily detected by this method.

The scintillator solvent is chosen on the basis of its ability to absorb the energy of the β particle and transfer it efficiently to the solute. Experience shows that the alkyl benzenes, particularly toluene and to a lesser extent xylene are the most efficient although in some cases highly purified ethers such as dioxan and anisole are preferred. The energy transfer process probably occurs by migration of excitation energy from solvent molecule to solvent molecule but it is also possible that some of the energy is transferred through the solution by diffusion of the excited solvent molecules.

The excited solute molecules return to the various vibrational levels of the ground state with the emission of photons and it is customary for the wavelength distribution of light emitted by the scintillator to closely match the response of the cathode of the photomultiplier tube. If this is not the case a secondary solute such

TABLE 2.2

Primary solutes for liquid scintillation counting

Primary solute	Abbreviation	Fluorescence maximum (nm)	Comments
p-Terphenyl		344	Limited solubility
2,5 Diphenyloxazole	PPO	363	
2-(4-Biphenyl)-5-phenyl-oxadiazole	PBD	361	Limited solubility in the presence of water
2-(4'-t-Butylphenyl)-5-(4"-biphenyl)-1,3,4-oxadiazole	Butyl-PBD	366	Does not need a secondary solute

as 1,4-bis-(5-phenyloxazol-2-yl)benzene (POPOP) may be employed in order to shift the spectrum to a more favourable wavelength. Table 2.2 gives details of some of the most commonly used primary solutes. These are generally used at concentrations between 3–12 g/l. In some instances the use of naphthalene is beneficial because it has the property of accepting energy from an inefficient scintillator solvent and transferring it efficiently to the solute.

The liquid scintillation method offers a high detection efficiency, absence of self-absorption, ease of sample preparation, energy discrimination and short resolving time. The two major problems which one encounters are quenching effects and sample solubility. Quenching may be defined as a process taking place in the scintillator solution which results in attenuated pulse heights and lowered counting efficiency. It can occur in two forms—chemical quenching which arises when a substance in the scintillator solution interferes with the transfer of energy from the excited solvent to solute, and colour quenching which takes place when a coloured material is present in solution. The first effect is difficult to remove but because quenching increases with increasing concentration of quenching compound its effect may be minimised by operating at low concentrations e.g. a number of acetophenones have been counted without much difficulty at low concentrations although the carbonyl group is known to be a powerful quencher of light scintillations.[58] Where the effects still remain serious, correction may be made via the channel ratio method, external standard or internal standard methods.[59]

It is frequently necessary to count the tritium as tritiated water. In such circumstances a different solvent system is required. A mixture of toluene, xylene and ethanol has been employed but more water can be incorporated by using dioxan and naphthalene or, a mixture of dioxan, anisole and dimethoxyethane.

Prior to the development of liquid scintillation counting ionisation chambers, vibrating-reed electrometers and proportional counters were all used for the detection of tritium. In each case it is necessary to convert the tritiated material into a gaseous form and this, together with the filling of the detector, is rather time consuming. It is also not possible to measure the radioactivity of two soft β emitters simultaneously. On the other hand the efficiency of counting is high and with a radio-chromatography unit it is possible to simultaneously measure the rates of detritiation of several compounds.[60,61]

Another method of tritium detection not as yet widely used, is nuclear magnetic resonance spectroscopy.[62] Tritium has a spin of $\frac{1}{2}$ and its sensitivity to detection at constant field is higher than that for any other nucleus being 21% higher than that of the proton. Its n.m.r. frequency (45·414 MHz for a 10 K gauss field) is sufficiently different from that of the proton (42·577 MHz) for triton–proton spin–spin splitting to be first order so that the spectra can be readily interpreted.

Nuclear magnetic resonance methods have of course been extensively used to follow both hydrogen–deuterium and hydrogen–hydrogen exchange rates. Like polarography the method may be employed in two distinct ways. Firstly, changes in spectra as a function of time can be followed with normalisation of the integral amplitude corresponding to the reaction site being made by reference to a non-exchanging internal standard. Used in this way the method is limited to reactions with $t_{1/2}$ in excess of 1–2 min. There is also the need for relatively concentrated solutions of substrate ($\sim 0·1$–$0·5$ M) as well as solvents whose spectra do not overlap with the resonances of the exchanging groups(s) within the substrate. The method does however offer the opportunity of obtaining the orientation and rate of reaction from the same experiment. The deuterium exchange of $[2 - {}^2H]$-isobutyraldehyde[63] and methoxyacetone[64] as well as several other ketones[65-67] have been studied in this way. The experimental errors quoted are usually rather high (± 5–15%) and in some instances the presence of secondary kinetic isotope effects add to the uncertainty.

Secondly, nuclear magnetic resonance may be applied to the study of relatively fast reactions by line broadening techniques.[68] In its simplest form the method is based on one of two ideas:

(a) Two distinguishable protons will give rise to two lines in the n.m.r. spectra provided the frequency with which they exchange is small by comparison with the difference between the two absorption frequencies. These lines merge if the exchange frequency is large with respect to the difference between the absorption frequencies. With intermediate exchange frequencies intermediate line shapes are predicted.

(b) If a multiplet is caused by spin–spin coupling with a proton which is also exchanging, the multiplet will merge to a single line if the exchange is large with respect to the spin–spin coupling constant. Again intermediate line shapes are predicted for intermediate exchange rates. The deprotonation of several phenylacetylenes by hydroxide ion in aqueous t-butanol has been studied by this method.[69]

Line broadening techniques may also be used for measurements on systems at chemical equilibrium. In this way very fast reactions can be investigated and for some proton transfer reactions in hydroxylic solvents, it has been possible to obtain the actual number of solvent molecules participating in the reaction.[70] C^{13} satellite n.m.r. line broadening methods have also been used as, for example, in the exchange between dimethyl sulphoxide and the dimsyl ion in the presence of t-butyl alcohol, where the various possible exchange reactions are[71,72]

$$ROH + OR^- \rightleftharpoons OR^- + ROH \qquad (2.32)$$

$$CH_3SOCH_3 + C\bar{H}_2SOCH_3 \rightleftharpoons C\bar{H}_2SOCH_3 + CH_3SOCH_3 \qquad (2.33)$$

$$CH_3SOCH_3 + OR^- \rightleftharpoons C\bar{H}_2SOCH_3 + ROH \qquad (2.34)$$

The rate of process (2.34) can be obtained by observing the ROH line broadening and that of (2.32) plus (2.33) from the C^{13} satellite width of dimethyl sulphoxide. It is then possible to obtain the rate constant for process (2.33) at varying alcohol concentrations. The results obtained suggest that reaction (2.34) makes an important contribution to the exchange processes even in the presence of 10% t-BuOH.

It is common practice nowadays to use small digital computers in conjunction with n.m.r. spectrometers in order to improve the signal to noise ratio. This approach has recently been taken a step further by taking advantage of the fact that digitised spectra can be readily accepted by large computers specially programmed for spectral analysis. In this way a least-squares comparison of the whole of the observed and calculated spectra is possible; this was done in the study of the solvent-catalysed exchange of the methine proton of 1,1-bisethylsulphonylethane.[73]

Hydrogen–deuterium exchange reactions can normally be followed by the same methods, such as halogenation or pH-stat, that are used for the corresponding proton transfer reaction provided the site of exchange is fully deuteriated, or alternatively, if there is any hydrogen present it can be allowed for. When the percentage hydrogen is small a correction can be made to the observed rate of exchange using Eqn (2.35):

$$k_D = (k_{obs} - fk_H)/(1 - f) \qquad\qquad (2.35)$$

where f is the fraction of hydrogen in the exchange site. Only when the extent of reaction is $<30\%$ is the equation valid. In cases where the value of f is close to 0.5 it is possible to separate k_H and k_D by graphical means provided the reaction exhibits a large primary hydrogen isotope effect.[74]

All the other methods of following hydrogen–deuterium exchange depend on the measurement of deuterium concentration and this can be done in one of several ways. The falling drop method[75,76] for the analysis of deuterium in water consists of a graduated dropping tube containing o-fluorotoluene, maintained in a thermostat at $c.$ $27°$, the temperature being controlled to within $±0.001°$. A micropipette is used to deliver drops of uniform size into the tube and the times taken for these to fall between two points $c.$ 15 cm apart are recorded. A standard of distilled water, purified in the same manner as the samples,[77] is employed and the apparatus calibrated by measuring the drop times of solutions of known concentration. By using a calibration chart, made by plotting the difference in the reciprocals of the times taken by the samples and the standard it is possible to measure a sample containing 1.0% deuterium to within $±0.01\%$. The method can be easily adapted to measure the deuterium concentration of compounds other than water and has been used extensively in order to follow the rates of hydrogen–deuterium exchange of hydrocarbons in protophilic solvents such as liquid ammonia.[78]

Infra-red spectroscopy provides a simple and sensitive method of deuterium analysis as the replacement of hydrogen by deuterium lowers the stretching frequency by a factor of $2^{1/2}$. It has been extensively used in following the cyclohexylamide catalysed exchange reactions of aromatic hydrocarbons.[79] The deuterium-containing compound was extracted into carbon tetrachloride (or any other non-interfering solvent) and the intensity of the carbon-deuterium bond compared with the results of a calibration curve which itself confirms that the compound obeys Beer's law. A similar

TABLE 2.3

Infra-red absorption bands for liquid water,[82] HDO and D_2O. Fundamental, first overtone and simple combination frequencies given.

Vibration	Mode	H_2O cm^{-1}	HDO cm^{-1}	D_2O cm^{-1}
V_1		3430	2620	2500
V_3		3580	3400	2500
V_2		1615	1480	1220
$2V_1$		6800	5230	4996
$2V_3$		7050	7020	4960
$2V_2$		3230		
$V_1 + V_2$		5180	4100	
$V_3 + V_2$		5184	5000	3509
$V_1 + V_3$		6835		4878

approach has been used for measuring the deuterium content of benzene and other organic compounds.[80] Changes in the near infra-red have been used to follow hydrogen–deuterium exchange in amides[81] and also in the amine catalysed enolisation of acetone[15] where the iodination method may not be employed because of rapid and irreversible reaction of trimethylamine with iodine.

For hydrogen–deuterium exchange reactions performed in aqueous media the rates can be followed by measuring the appearance of deuterium in the solvent or, if the reaction is carried out in D_2O, the appearance of hydrogen in the solvent. Table 2.3 summarises the main absorption bands for liquid H_2O, HDO and D_2O arising from the fundamental, first overtone and simple combination frequencies of these molecules. For measurements carried out in heavy water i.e. D_2O content $> 99.5\%$, it can be assumed that nearly all of the light isotope is present as HDO. It is then possible to use the 3400 cm^{-1} (2940 nm) absorption band of HDO to detect hydrogen in heavy water. The method of analysis for D_2O in the 0 to 1% range is also based on detection of HDO. Although the 3400 cm^{-1} absorption band of HDO is now completely obscured by the 3430 cm^{-1} band of H_2O the 2620 cm^{-1} HDO band can be used although it tends to be partly obscured by atmospheric carbon dioxide absorption.

The accuracy of the measurements depends on what technique is employed. The Beer–Lambert law is given by

$$I/I_0 = 10^{-\epsilon cl} \tag{2.36}$$

where l is the cell thickness, c the concentration and ϵ the extinction coefficient. I_0 measures the intensity of the incident radiation and I the intensity after passing through the cell. If for sample A $I_0 = 100$ and $I_A = 10$ the percentage absorption is 90 as compared to 91 for sample B with $I_0 = 100$ and $I_B = 9$. This small difference will clearly be difficult to measure accurately. If, however, samples A and B are compared against a third sample C that has 89% absorption the differential absorption of sample $A = (I_C - I_A)/I_C \times 100 = 9\cdot1\%$ as compared to a value of $18\cdot2\%$ for sample B. In this differential method[83,84] source variation effects are reduced so that high signal amplification may be employed resulting in still further improvements in accuracy.

Another method, developed by Kreevoy,[85] for measuring the deuterium content of water, is based on the spectrum of water in the 800–1300 nm region. Liquid H_2O has peaks at 970 and 1192 nm and a valley at 1065 nm whereas for D_2O the absorbance at 1065 (I_{1065}) is the same as that at 1192 (I_{1192}). The quantity $I = I_{1192} - I_{1065}$ is therefore due to absorption by HOD and H_2O so that Eqn (2.37) can be written

$$I = x_{H_2O}\epsilon^{H_2O}b + x_{HOD}r\epsilon^{H_2O}b \tag{2.37}$$

where $r = \epsilon^{HOD}/\epsilon^{H_2O}$ and b is a path length. The mole fractions of H_2O and HOD, x_{H_2O} and x_{HOD} can be evaluated in terms of x_H and K, the equilibrium constant governing the redistribution reaction,

$$H_2O + D_2O \rightleftharpoons 2HOD \tag{2.38}$$

Assuming a value of 4 for K,

$$x_{H_2O} = x_H^2 \tag{2.39}$$

and

$$x_{HOD} = 2x_H(1 - x_H) \tag{2.40}$$

Combination of Eqns (2.37), (2.39) and (2.40) gives

$$x_H = \frac{(Q - 2rQ + r^2)^{1/2} - r}{1 - 2r} \tag{2.41}$$

where Q is $b_{H_2O}l/bI_{H_2O}$. Good agreement was obtained between x_H determined this way and by density measurements. The method offers an accuracy of 0·002 in x_H, the atom fraction of hydrogen and can be carried out in 1—5 cm quartz spectrophotometric cells which are frequently used for measurement of reaction rates.

The deuterium content of H_2O–D_2O mixtures may also be determined by converting the water to gaseous hydrogen (H_2–HD) and analysing this by thermal conductivity using a standard gas chromatography apparatus.[86] In practice a small aliquot of a H_2O–D_2O mixture is injected into a sample of calcium hydride in an evacuated tube. Since the selectivity for the reaction of calcium hydride with OH and OD bonds is practically unity the relative quantities of H_2 and HD that are formed from the reaction correspond very closely to the relative quantities of hydrogen and deuterium in the sample. A portion of the gas from the generation step is passed into, and measured in, a standard GLC gas sampler at atmospheric pressure. From here it is released into the stream of a standard GLC apparatus using hydrogen as the carrier gas. After passing through a short column of activated charcoal to remove any volatile impurities, the gas mixture enters the thermal conductivity cell and, since hydrogen is the carrier gas, only the HD content of the gas sample is detected by the cell. The size of the HD peak in the chromatogram is then directly proportional to the deuterium content of the original water sample. The method is precise (standard deviation ±0·1%) and may be used over the entire range of H_2O–D_2O solutions down to background levels.

Mass spectrometry is a frequently used method of determining the deuterium content of labelled compounds. For every compound the most suitable electron energy has to be determined. This is done by scanning the mass region of interest whilst decreasing, in a stepwise manner, the potential of the bombarding electrons. In the event of the molecular ion to be analysed losing one or more hydrogen atoms the spectrum is determined at an electron energy sufficient for the production of molecular ions but not of these fragments. Where there is a danger of hydrogen exchange taking place repeated equilibration of the instrument with the sample should preferably precede the actual determination.

The mass spectrum of nitroethane does not contain a parent peak and the determination of the isotopic content[42] of nitroethane-$1[^2H_2]$ was based upon the molecular ions $[CH_3CHD]^{+}$, $[CH_3CD_2]^{+}$. In another instance[87] different values of the isotopic content were obtained for the same sample when the electron voltage was varied from 6–70 eV, indicating probable fragmentation of $[CH_3CHD]^{+}$ or $[CH_3CD_2]^{+}$. The isotopic purity was ultimately established by proton magnetic resonance.

Low voltage mass spectrometry has been used to measure the deuterium content of triptycene and various ethyl benzenes.[79,88] For the deuterium analysis of 1,3,5-trimethoxy-benzene-2-$[^2H]$ an ionisation potential of 3·3 eV was sufficient to generate molecular ions.[89] In following the kinetics of de-deuteriation the heights of the parent ion peaks were compared and allowance made for the 1·11% natural abundance of ^{13}C.

2.5. MISCELLANEOUS

The tautomerism between nitro- and acinitro-cyclohexane has been studied polarographically with several acid–base pairs.[90] The system may be represented by Eqn (2.42):

$$RCH_2NO_2 + B^- \rightleftharpoons RCH:NO_2^- + BH \rightleftharpoons RCH:NO_2H + B^- \qquad (2.42)$$

Only the neutral nitro compound is active at the electrode and therefore the rate constants for the equilibrium between it, its anion and the acid–base pair can be found.

Relaxation methods of following the rates of ionisation of carbon acids have not been widely used. However, proton transfer from acetylacetone[91] to a variety of oxygen, nitrogen and sulphur bases, and from diacetylacetone[92] have been studied using the temperature jump method in which a system at equilibrium is displaced by application of a discharge from a high voltage condenser.

Electron spin resonance has been shown[93] to be a unique tool for the mechanistic study of selective stepwise deuteriation reactions and particularly useful for observing positional deuteriation during the initial rates of exchange in compounds where competing randomiz-ation can occur. Several deuteriated polycyclic hydrocarbons were converted into radical anions by reaction with sodium (or potassium) in 1,2-dimethoxyethane and deuterium analysis performed on these anions. Reasonably quantitative confirmation of the mass spectral distribution could be made under conditions where the n.m.r. of the deuteriated species did not differ from that of the parent unlabelled molecule. The only drawbacks of the method are that it is somewhat time consuming and that the range of compounds forming stable radical ions may be somewhat limited.

The rates of ionisation of carbon acids such as triphenylmethane can be measured by virtue of the fact that molecular oxygen reacts with a vigorously shaken solution of the acid in dimethyl sulphoxide-t-butyl alcohol containing potassium t-butoxide to give the corresponding carbinolate ion.[94] The process is first order in triphenylmethane and in base but independent of the partial pressure of the oxygen above 400 mm. These results imply that the rate of oxidation is equal to the rate of ionisation:

$$Ph_3CH + OR^- \xrightarrow{\text{slow}} Ph_3C^- + ROH \tag{2.43}$$

$$Ph_3C^- + O_2 \xrightarrow{\text{fast}} Ph_3CO^- + \tfrac{1}{2}O_2 \tag{2.44}$$

More acidic hydrocarbons like fluorene show an oxidation rate which is dependent on the oxygen pressure.

Some of the older methods of following rates of ionisation are still being used, e.g. the change in specific rotation of an optically active carbon acid can be followed as a function of time. As long ago as 1936 Hsü and Wilson[95] found the rates of acetate-catalysed halogenation and racemisation of 2-(carboxybenzyl)-indanone (1) to be equal and this finding has frequently been cited as evidence that enolisation is the rate-determining step. More recently the base-

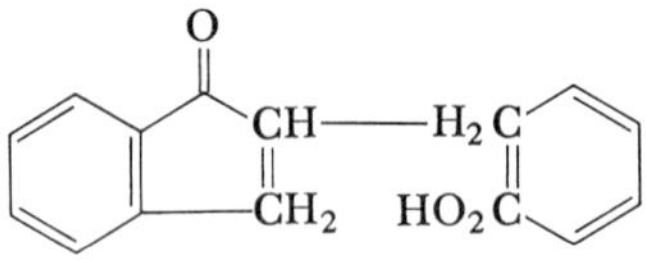

(1)

$$C_6H_5 \cdot CH(CH_3) \cdot CO \cdot C_6H_5$$

(3)

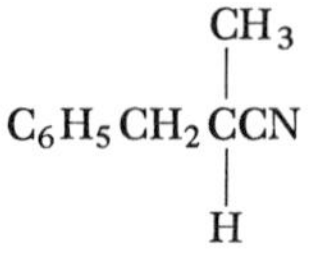

$$C_6H_5CH_2\underset{\underset{H}{|}}{\overset{\overset{CH_3}{|}}{C}}CN$$

(2)

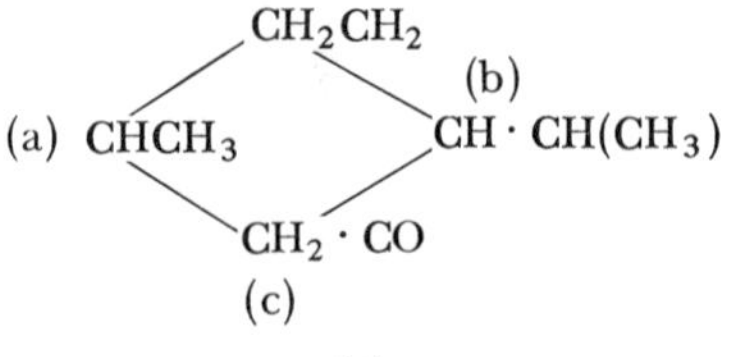

(4)

catalysed racemisation of (+)2-methyl-3-phenylpropionitrile[96] (2), d-methyldeoxybenzoin[97] (3) and (−)-menthone[98] (4) have been studied. The latter contains two centres of asymmetry (a) and (b) but as enolisation can proceed only from carbon atoms (b) and (c) only the former will lead to inversion. The reaction scheme is

$$(-)\text{menthone} + \text{OH}^- \underset{k_{-1}}{\overset{k_1}{\rightleftharpoons}} \text{enolate} + \text{H}_2\text{O} \underset{k_{-2}}{\overset{k_2}{\rightleftharpoons}} (+)\text{-isomenthone}$$

(2.45)

Difficulties in this kind of experiment arise when the total change in rotation is small either because of low solubility or because of the small difference in the specific rotation of the resolved compound and the racemised product.

REFERENCES

1. Dawson, H. M. & Powis, F. (1913). *J. Chem. Soc.* 2135.
2. Pedersen, K. J. (1933). *J. Phys. Chem.* 37, 751.
3. Junell, R. (1929). *Z. Phys. Chem.* 71A, 141.
4. Milliken, R. S. & Reid, C. (1954). *J. Amer. Chem. Soc.* 76, 3869.
5. Bell, R. P., Fendley, J. A. and Hulett, J. R. (1956). *Proc. Roy. Soc. Ser. A.* 235, 453.
6. Pearson, R. G. & Dillon, R. L. (1953). *J. Amer. Chem. Soc.* 75, 2439.
7. Bell, R. P., Gelles, E. & Möller, E. (1949). *Proc. Roy. Soc. Ser. A* 198, 308.
8. Pedersen, K. J. (1934). *J. Phys. Chem.* 38, 601.
9. Bell, R. P. & Robinson, R. R. (1962). *Proc. Roy. Soc. Ser. A.* 270, 411.
10. Bell, R. P. & Spiro, M. (1953). *J. Chem. Soc.* 429.
11. Bell, R. P. & Lidwell, O. M. (1940). *Proc. Roy. Soc. Ser. A.* 176, 88.
12. Bell, R. P., & Darwent, B. de B. (1950). *Trans Faraday Soc.* 46, 34.
13. Riley, T. & Long, F. A. (1962). *J. Amer. Chem. Soc.* 84, 522.
14. Bell, R. P. & Crooks, J. E. (1965). *Proc. Roy. Soc. Ser. A.* 286, 285.
15. Bender, M. L. & Williams, A. (1966). *J. Amer. Chem. Soc.* 88, 2502.
16. Bell, R. P. & Goldsmith, H. L. (1951). *Proc. Roy. Soc. Ser. A.* 210, 322.
17. Harper, E. T. & Bender, M. L. (1965). *J. Amer. Chem. Soc.* 87, 5625.
18. Bell, R. P. & Smith, P. W. (1966). *J. Chem. Soc. B*, 241.
19. Kenner, J. & Richards, G. N. (1953). *J. Chem. Soc.* 2240.
20. Eidinoff, M. L. (1945). *J. Amer. Chem. Soc.* 67, 2073.
21. Schwarzenbach, G. & Felder, E. (1944). *Helv. Chim. Acta* 27, 1701.
22. Coward, J. C. & Bruice, T. C. (1969). *J. Amer. Chem. Soc.* 91, 5339.
23. Polak, H. L., Feenstra, G. & Slagman, J. (1966). *Talanta* 13, 715.
24. Jones, J. R., Marks, R. E. & Subba Rao, S. C. (1967). *Trans. Faraday Soc.* 63, 111.
25. Li, R. R. & Miller, S. I. (1969). *J. Amer. Chem. Soc.* 91, 7524.
26. Li, R. R. & Miller, S. I. (1971). *J. Chem. Soc. B*, 2269.
27. Li, R. R. & Miller, S. I. (1971). *J. Chem. Soc. B*, 2271.
28. Dixon, J. E. & Bruice, T. C. (1970). *J. Amer. Chem. Soc.* 92, 905.
29. Barnes, D. J. & Bell, R. P. (1970). *Proc. Roy. Soc. Ser. A.* 318, 421.
30. Bordwell, F. G., Boyle, W. J. Jr. & Yee, K. C. (1970). *J. Amer. Chem. Soc.* 92, 5926.
31. Bell, R. P. & Cox, B. G. (1971). *J. Chem. Soc. B*, 783.
32. Caldin, E. F., Kasparian, M. & Tomalin, G. (1968). *Trans. Faraday Soc.* 64, 2802.

33. Uschold, R. E. & Ritchie, C. D. (1968). *J. Amer. Chem. Soc.* **90**, 3415.
34. Uschold, R. E. & Ritchie, C. D. (1969). *J. Amer. Chem. Soc.* **91**, 6749.
35. Jones, J. R. (1968). *Trans. Faraday Soc.* **64**, 440.
36. Caldin, E. F. (1964). *Fast Reactions in Solution*, p. 18. Blackwell Scientific Publications, Oxford.
37. Foulk, C. W. & Bawden, A. T. (1926). *J. Amer. Chem. Soc.* **48**, 2045.
38. Evans, D. P. (1947). *Analyst* **72**, 99.
39. Dubois, J. E. (1960). *Z. Elektrochem.* **64**, 143.
40. Pearson, R. G. & Dillon, R. L. (1950). *J. Amer. Chem. Soc.* **72**, 1692, 3574.
41. Pearson, R. G. & Piette, L. H. (1954). *J. Amer. Chem. Soc.* **76**, 3087.
42. Bell, R. P. & Goodall, D. M. (1966). *Proc. Roy. Soc. Ser. A.* **294**, 273.
43. Bell, R. P. & Clunie, J. C. (1951). *Nature (London)* **167**, 362.
44. Bell, R. P. & Clunie, J. C. (1952). *Proc. Roy. Soc. Ser. A.* **212**, 16.
45. Fukuyama, M., Flanagan, P. W. K., Williams, F. T. Jr., Frainier, L., Miller, S. A. & Shechter, H. (1970). *J. Amer. Chem. Soc.* **92**, 4689.
46. Albery, W. J. & Robinson, B. H. (1969). *Trans. Faraday Soc.* **65**, 980.
47. Albery, W. J. & Davies, M. H. (1969). *Trans. Faraday Soc.* **65**, 1067.
48. McKay, H. A. C. (1938). *Nature (London)* **142**, 997.
49. Harris, G. M. (1951). *Trans. Faraday Soc.* **47**, 716.
50. Bunton, C. A., Craig, D. P. & Halevi, E. A. (1955). *Trans. Faraday Soc.* **51**, 196.
51. Oliphant, M. L. E. Harteck, P. & Rutherford, E. (1934). *Proc. Roy. Soc. Ser. A.* **144**, 692.
52. Washburn, E. W. & Urey, H. C. (1932). *Proc. Nat. Acad. Sci. U.S.* **18**, 496.
53. Alvarez, L. W. & Cornog, R. (1939). *Phys. Rev.* **56**, 613.
54. Jones, W. M. (1955). *Phys. Rev.* **100**, 124.
55. Kresge, A. J. & Chiang, Y. (1961). *J. Amer. Chem. Soc.* **83**, 2877.
56. Halevi, E. A. & Long, F. A. (1961). *J. Amer. Chem. Soc.* **83**, 2809.
57. Stewart, R. & Jones, J. R. (1967). *J. Amer. Chem. Soc.* **89**, 5069.
58. Jones, J. R. (1966). *Int. J. Appl. Radiat. Isotop.* **17**, 666.
59. Evans, E. A. (1966). *Tritium and its Compounds*, p. 224. Butterworths, London.
60. Streitwieser, A. Jr. & Koch, H. F. (1964). *J. Amer. Chem. Soc.* **86**, 404.
61. Hofmann, J. E. & Schriesheim, A. (1962). *J. Amer. Chem. Soc.* **84**, 957.
62. Bloxsidge, J., Elvidge, J. A., Jones, J. R. & Evans, E. A. (1971). *Org. Mag. Reson.* **3**, 127.
63. Hine, J., Houston, J. G., Jensen, J. H. & Mulders, J. (1965). *J. Amer. Chem. Soc.* **87**, 5050.
64. Hine, J., Hampton, K. G. & Menon, B. C. (1967). *J. Amer. Chem. Soc.* **89**, 2664.
65. Sachs, W. H. (1971). *Acta Chem. Scand.* **25**, 2643.
66. Rappe, C. (1967). *Acta Chem. Scand.* **21**, 857.
67. Warkentin, J. & Cox, R. A. (1968). *J. Org. Chem.* **33**, 1301.
68. Reeves, L. W. (1965). *Adv. Phys. Org. Chem.* (Gold, V. ed.) **3**, 187.
69. Charman, H. B., Vinard, D. R. & Kreevoy, M. M. (1962). *J. Amer. Chem. Soc.* **84**, 347.
70. Grunwald, E. (1965). *Progr. Phys. Org. Chem.* (Cohen, S. C., Streitwieser, A. & Taft, R. W. eds.) **3**, 317.
71. Brauman, J. I. & Nelson, N. J. (1966). *J. Amer. Chem. Soc.* **88**, 2332.
72. Brauman, J. I., Nelson, N. J. & Kahl, D. C. (1968). *J. Amer. Chem. Soc.* **90**, 490.
73. Cox, B. G., Riddell, F. G. & Williams, D. A. R. (1970). *J. Chem. Soc. B*, 859.

74. Jones, J. R. (1967). *J. Chem. Educ.* **44**, 31.
75. Schloerb, P. R., Friis-Hansen, B. J., Edelman, I. S., Sheldon, D. B. & Moore, F. D. (1951). *J. Lab. Clin. Med.* **37**, 653.
76. Swain, C. G. & Labes, M. M. (1957). *J. Amer. Chem. Soc.* **79**, 1084.
77. Fetcher, E. S. Jr. (1944). *Anal. Chem.* **16**, 412.
78. Shatenshtein, A. I. (1963). *Adv. Phys. Org. Chem.* (Gold, V. ed.) **1**, 156.
79. Streitwieser, A. Jr., Van Sickle, D. E. & Langworthy, W. C. (1962). *J. Amer. Chem. Soc.* **84**, 244, 251.
80. Ashby, R. A. & Garnett, J. L. (1963). *Aust. J. Chem.* **16**, 549.
81. Klotz, I. M. & Frank, B. H. (1964). *J. Amer. Chem. Soc.* **86**, 3889.
82. Stevens, W. H. & Thurston, W. (1954). Atomic Energy of Canada Ltd. Rept. AECL-295.
83. Gaunt, J. (1954). *J. Sci. Instrum.* **31**, 315.
84. Gaunt, J. (1954). *Analyst (London)* **79**, 580.
85. Kreevoy, M. M. & Straub, T. S. (1969). *Anal. Chem.* **41**, 214.
86. Arnett, E. M. & McC. Duggleby, P. (1963). *Anal. Chem.* **35**, 1420.
87. Dixon, J. E. & Bruice, T. C. (1970). *J. Amer. Chem. Soc.* **92**, 905.
88. Streitwieser, A. Jr. & Ziegler, G. R. (1969). *J. Amer. Chem. Soc.* **91**, 5081.
89. Kresge, A. J. & Chiang, Y. (1967). *J. Amer. Chem. Soc.* **89**, 4411.
90. Zaitsev, P. M., Turyan, Ya. I. & Zaitzeva, Z. V. (1963). *Kinet. Katal.* **4**, 534.
91. Ahrens, M. L., Eigen, M., Kruse, W. & Maass, G. (1970). *Ber.* **74**, 380.
92. Stuehr, J. (1967). *J. Amer. Chem. Soc.* **89**, 2826.
93. Davis, K. P., Garnett, J. L. & O'Keefe, J. H. (1970). *Chem. Comm.* 1672.
94. Russell, G. A. & Beams, A. G. (1965). *Chemy Ind. (London)* 1262.
95. Hsü, S. K. & Wilson, C. L. (1936). *J. Chem. Soc.* 626.
96. Stewart, R., O'Donnell, J. P., Cram, D. J. & Rickborn, B. (1962). *Tetrahedron,* **18**, 917.
97. Earls, D. W., Jones, J. R. & Rumney, T. G. (1972). *J. Chem. Soc. (Faraday),* **68**, 925.
98. Bell, R. P. & Cox, B. G. (1970). *J. Chem. Soc. B* 194.

3. Rates of Ionisation—Results

3.1. FACTORS AFFECTING THE STABILISATION OF CARBANIONS

The rates of ionisation of carbon acids depend upon many factors and vary widely. For the sake of comparison it is necessary to consider a single solvent and water is usually chosen for this purpose not only because many rate constants are known for the "spontaneous" or water catalysed reaction but also because the process

$$\underset{\diagup}{\overset{\diagdown}{C}} - H + H_2O \underset{k_{-1}}{\overset{k_1}{\rightleftharpoons}} \underset{\diagup}{\overset{\diagdown}{C}}^- + H_3\overset{+}{O} \tag{3.1}$$

is used to define the thermodynamic equilibrium constant K_a. The first comprehensive compilation of the water catalysed rates of ionisation of carbon acids was made by Pearson and Dillon[1] and the findings have subsequently been discussed both by Bell[2] and Cram.[3] The former concludes that if the correlation between $\log k_1$ and pK_a is confined to the 17 ketonic substances for which data were reported the individual deviations still exceed the experimental uncertainties.

Several more recent results are now available[4] and together with some of the previously available data which were known with some certainty, are brought together in Table 3.1. The values of k_1 are known to within ±3% but the acidity constants, particularly for the most weakly acidic carbon acids may be subject to an uncertainty of ±0·5 pK units. The general shape of the $\log k - pK_a$ curve (Fig. 3.1) lends some hope that at the higher and lower acidities the slopes tend to the limiting theoretical values of zero and unity (see Chapter 8). Compounds, 16, 9, 7, 12, 3 and 14 give a fairly presentable straight line (slope + 0·4) whilst the less acidic compounds 14, 6, 17 and 1 give a straight line of slope +0·9. Alternatively the carbon acids 15, 5, 4, 27, 8 and 19 make up a line of slope 0·5.

The two compounds (20, 21) containing a cyano group ionise much faster than expected but the two nitro-containing compounds (nitroacetone, ethylnitroacetate) behave more like ketones and keto-esters than nitro-compounds. The sulphone (3) ionises faster than would be expected from its acid strength but the deviation is not as

TABLE 3.1

Rate and equilibrium data for carbon acids in water at $25°$

	Carbon acid	$k_1 (s^{-1})$	$pK_a{}^a$
1.	Acetone	$4·7 \times 10^{-10}$	19–20
2.	Bromoacetone	$2·9 \times 10^{-7}$	—
3.	Bis(ethylsulphonyl)ethane	$3·5 \times 10^{-5}$	14·6
4.	Methylacetylacetone	$9·6 \times 10^{-5}$	10·8
5.	2-Acetylcyclohexanone	$4·0 \times 10^{-4}$	9·8
6.	Sym-dichloroacetone	$3·6 \times 10^{-6}$	16
7.	2-Carbethoxycyclopentanone	$2·2 \times 10^{-3}$	$10·2^b$
8.	2-Carbethoxycyclohexanone	$4·2 \times 10^{-6}$	13
9.	Bromoacetylacetone	$3·3 \times 10^{-2}$	7·0
10.	Acetylacetone	$1·3 \times 10^{-2}$	9·0
11.	Ethyl 2-bromoacetate	$1·6 \times 10^{-2}$	—
12.	Ethyl acetoacetate	$1·2 \times 10^{-3}$	10·7
13.	Ethyl bromomalonate	$2·1 \times 10^{-4}$	—
14.	Ethyl malonate	$2·43 \times 10^{-5}$	$15·3^c$
15.	Ethyl nitroacetate	$1·5 \times 10^{-2}$	5·8
16.	Nitroacetone	$8·0 \times 10^{-2}$	5·1
17.	Ethyl pyruvate	$4·7 \times 10^{-7}$	16·6
18.	Potassium propan-2-one-1, 3-disulphonate	$2·4 \times 10^{-5}$	13·8
19.	Potassium propan-2-one-1-sulphonate	$1·9 \times 10^{-6}$	13·8
20.	t-Butylmalononitrile	$1·9 \times 10^{-3d}$	13·1
21.	Malononitrile	$2·5 \times 10^{-2d}$	11·2
22.	2-Bromopentan-3-one	$5·5 \times 10^{-8}$	—
23.	2-Chloropentan-3-one	$5·2 \times 10^{-8}$	—
24.	Cyclopentanone	—	16·7
25.	Cyclohexanone	—	16·7
26.	Methyl methylmalonate	$4·8 \times 10^{-7}$	—
27.	Ethyl methylacetoacetate	$1·1 \times 10^{-5}$	$12·7^e$

[a] Gross dissociation constant uncorrected for enol content.
[b] In D_2O.
[c] In propan-2-ol.
[d] Assuming $k_H/k_T = 6$.
[e] pK_a refers to $CH_3COCH(C_2H_5)CO_2Et$.

pronounced as for malononitrile. Clearly the insertion of different activating groups close to the carbon–hydrogen bond undergoing ionisation constitutes a drastic change and makes it impossible to set up a single satisfactory correlation between rate of ionisation and acid strength. In fact even when the correlation is confined to structurally similar carbon acids deviations may still occur. For a

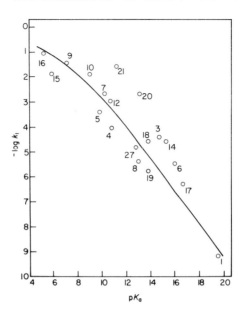

Fig. 3.1. Plot of $-\log k_1$ against pK_a for carbon acids in water at 25°. Numbers correspond to those in Table 3.1.

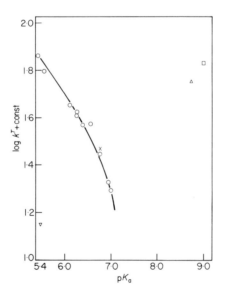

Fig. 3.2. Plot of $\log k^T$ against pK_a for several β-diketones.[5] o, meta and para-substituted benzoyltrifluoroacetones; x, acetyltrifluoroacetone; △, benzoylacetone; □, acetylacetone; ▽, hexafluoroacetylacetone

series of meta and para-substituted benzoyltrifluoroacetones[5] the logarithm of the water catalysed detritiation rate constant correlates well with the pK_a values (Fig. 3.2). The point for acetyltrifluoroacetone also fits on the curve but that for hexafluoroacetylacetone shows a sharp negative deviation. The points for benzoylacetone and acetylacetone on the other hand show a pronounced positive deviation. These findings can be rationalised in terms of the effect of fluorine substitution—on the one hand it should lead to an increase in acidity but on the other it brings about a greater tendency for hydrate formation which in turn makes the process of ionisation more difficult.

TABLE 3.2
Relative rates of isotopic exchange[a] for various
monohydrofluorocarbon acids[6,7]

Carbon acid	Relative rate
CF_3H	1
$CF_3(CF_2)_5CF_2H$	6
$(CF_3)_2CFH$	2×10^5
$(CF_3)_3CH$	10^9
	5×10^9

[a] In NaOMe — MeOH.

The results in Table 3.1 together with those presented by Pearson and Dillon show that the ability of groups to acidify carbon-hydrogen bonds is in the order $NO_2 > CO > SO_2 > CO_2H > CO_2R > CN \simeq CONH_2 > X > H > R$, where X is a halogen and R an alkyl group. The mechanism whereby a group or substituent stabilises a carbanion is a subject of much interest and Cram[3] has given an excellent account of the various types of stabilisation that may be operative. More recent studies of the effect of fluorine substitution on the rates of ionisation of carbon acids, and of isotopic hydrogen exchange in heterocyclic carbon acids have added further to our knowledge in this area.

Fluorine substitution can bring about large increases in the kinetic acidity of carbon acids[6] as shown in Table 3.2. In addition to a normal electron attracting inductive effect it has been suggested that the intermediate carbanion is stabilised by a negative hyper-conjugative effect of the kind

$$^-C-C\begin{smallmatrix}F\\|\\F\\|\\F\end{smallmatrix} \longleftrightarrow C=C\begin{smallmatrix}F^-\\|\\F\\|\\F\end{smallmatrix}$$

The larger the number of β-fluorines the larger the number of equivalent resonance structures that can be drawn and the more stabilised is the carbanion.

The carbanion formed by proton loss from 1-H-undeca-fluoro-bicyclo [2.2.1] heptane (Table 3.2), however, is forced to remain pyramidal[7] and hyperconjugation is therefore greatly reduced. Consequently the role of inductive effects is enhanced and if such hyperconjugation is an important factor in stabilising tris (trifluoromethyl) anion, base catalysed hydrogen exchange of tris (trifluoromethyl) methane should be much faster than for the above heptane. In fact it turns out that isotopic exchange is five times faster than for tris(trifluoromethyl) methane indicating that carbon–fluorine no-bond resonance plays no significant part in stabilising these anions. Another separate study[8] based on correlating the rates of detritiation of various 9-substituted fluorenes in methanolic sodium methoxide with the acidities of the corresponding acetic acids also shows that normal inductive effects alone are sufficient to rationalise the relative stability of the 9-trifluoromethyl fluorenyl anion.

Fluorine hyperconjugation also seems to be unimportant in the base catalysed isotope exchange of a series of 2-H-2-phenylhexa-fluoropropanes[9] [$C_6H_4 . X . CH(CF_3)_2$] as the anions most likely have a pyramidal configuration. The most important contribution in stabilising the carbanions seems to be the inductive effect as it has been estimated that $C_6H_5 CH(CH_3)_2$ is nearly 20 pK units less acidic than $C_6H_5 CH(CF_3)_2$. However the observed order of stabilisation within the series (X_m = Br $>$ I $>$ Cl $>$ F $>$ OCH$_3$, X_p = I $>$ Br $>$ Cl $>$ F $>$ OCH$_3$) can not be explained by inductive effects alone otherwise the order for X_m would be F $>$ Cl $>$ Br $>$ I $>$ OCH$_3$. Neither can resonance stabilisation by d orbital expansion to give

$$X^-=\underset{(1)}{\bigcirc}=C\begin{smallmatrix}CF_3\\|\\|\\CF_3\end{smallmatrix}$$

be important as this would predict that the p-substituted carbon acids ionise faster than the corresponding meta isomers, contrary to what is observed (Table 3.3). This finding is accounted for by the fact that inductive stabilisation is more effective in the meta position, but as the order of stabilisation by the meta substituents is different from that for the para substituents and as the meta/para ratios should be lowest for the most weakly inductive group (which it is not) this is probably not the complete answer. Klabunde and Burton[9] believe that conjugational destabilisation is important in the para series and as this would be in the order $OCH_3 > F > Cl > Br > I$ its presence would go some way to predicting the relative rates of ionisation of the para isomers and also the very large meta/para ratios for the fluorine and methoxy substituents.

TABLE 3.3

Relative rates of ionisation of some substituted
2-H-2-Phenylhexafluoropropanes[9]

Substituent	Relative rate	Meta/Para ratio
—	1·0	
$m-F$	18·5	
$p-F$	1·57	11·8
$m-Cl$	27·9	
$p-Cl$	10·9	2·56
$m-Br$	47·1	
$p-Br$	16·2	2·91
$m-I$	33·7	
$p-I$	19·1	1·76
$m-OCH_3$	1·06	
$p-OCH_3$	0·107	9·90

A striking observation[10] of the operation of different stabilisation effects was witnessed for the two hydrocarbons 9-fluorofluorene and α,α-difluorotoluene. The rate of isotopic exchange in sodium methoxide-methanol for the first compound was 8-fold slower than for fluorene itself whereas the corresponding 9-chloro and 9-bromo compounds reacted at rates which were 4×10^2 and 7×10^2 faster respectively. The decrease in rate for the fluoro compound is an example of conjugative destabilisation as the operation of an inductive effect alone should have resulted in a 10^5 increase in rate.

By contrast two α-fluorines increase the lithium cyclohexylamide catalysed exchange of toluene by a factor of 10^4. These apparently divergent results were explained by proposing that the 9-fluorofluorene anion is planar whereas the α,α-difluorobenzyl anion is pyramidal. The reactivity of the α,α-difluorotoluene is entirely consistent with the expected magnitude of the inductive stabilisation of a non-conjugating pyramidal difluoromethyl anion. Clearly the structural configuration of the carbanion is important in assessing the relative importance of the various stabilisation effects.

The effect of position and type of heteroatom(s) on the rates of ionisation of heterocyclic carbon acids offers the opportunity of being able to quantitatively dissect the various stabilisation effects.[11] Unlike many of the other carbon acids these compounds contain ionisable groups other than $\geqslant$C–H so that they are able to undergo reaction in a protonated or a deprotonated form rather than as the neutral molecule. Thus although many undergo isotopic exchange in the presence of water, the rate determining step no longer involves catalysis by water molecules. The rates of detritiation of [2-³H]-benzimidazole, for example, have been measured[12] over a pH range and the pH-rate profile accounted for in terms of rate determining attack by hydroxide ions on the benzimidazole cation with the formation of an ylide intermediate which then reacts with the solvent in a fast step:

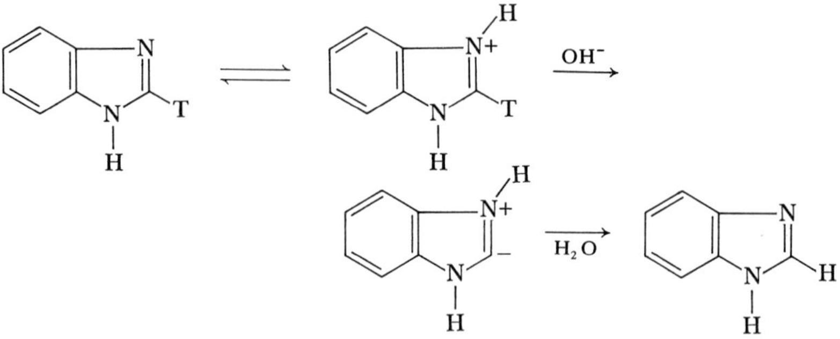

The kinetically equivalent possibility of a rate-determining attack by solvent molecules on the neutral benzimidazole molecule was ruled out by the observation that the second order rate constant for attack of hydroxide ions on [2-³H]-1,3-dimethylbenzimidazolium bromide was close to that for attack of OH⁻ on the benzimidazolium cation. The rates of detritiation of several 1-alkyl substituted benzimidazoles (benzyl ~ i-propyl > ethyl > methyl > hydrogen) are consistent with this mechanism which is common to many heterocyclic compounds.[11] Direct evidence for the existence of ylide intermediates in these reactions comes from the fact that many of the quaternary salts catalyse the benzoin and acetoin condensations.[13,14] 1,3-Dialkyltetrazolium salts as well as undergoing base catalysed isotope exchange also undergo ring scission to carbodiimides in a slower reaction thereby demonstrating the presence of an ylide intermediate.[15]

Hydrogen exchange of thiazole and thiazolium ions has received much attention since Breslow's observation[13,16] that thiamine, in the form of its pyrophosphate, cocarboxylase, exchanges its 2-H with a reaction half life of 20 min in D_2O at 28°C. The remarkable lability of this hydrogen has been ascribed to the combined effect of a number of factors. In addition to the high s character of the C—H bond and the operation of inductive effects the aromatic system has a great potential for enhancing resonance stability e.g. the ylide (2) can be stabilised by the contribution from the carbene-like structure (3). The stability of the ylide may also owe something to the interaction of a d orbital at sulphur with the σ orbital directed away from the ring at C-2, leading to (4).

This behaviour also accounts for the fact that the exchange rate of protons next to sulphur is invariably greater than the exchange rate of protons on carbon and next to nitrogen in contrast to what one would expect on the basis of reduced electronegativity. By comparing rates for the thiazolium cation and neutral thiazole it is clear that the positive charge on the α-nitrogen is worth more than a factor of 10^7 to the exchange rate and is therefore a major factor in contributing to the lability of the C-2 hydrogen.

Replacement of a carbon atom in the thiazolium ring by nitrogen to yield thiadiazolium salts increases the rate of hydrogen exchange by between 10^3 and 10^4. The 2- and 5-H of 5

exchanged with an increase in rate of 10^{10} and 10^6 respectively over the neutral 3,4-thiadiazole, illustrating once again the enormous rate enhancing effect of having positively charged nitrogen α and β to the exchange site.[17] The further addition of a nitrogen atom and the replacement of the sulphur atom by nitrogen to form tetrazolium salts further enhances the kinetic acidity of the C—H bond and in fact 1-substituted tetrazoles are amongst the strongest carbon acids of this type—the reaction half lives for the base catalysed deuterium incorporation at C-5 of a series of 1-aryl-4-ethyltetrazolium cations (6), in 9N CF_3CO_2D are of the order of 1–20 min, 10^9 times as fast as the corresponding imidazolium compounds.[15] The possibility

(6)

exists that the additional nitrogen atoms exert an effect which is more than purely inductive: they can stabilise the carbene form (7) of the zwitterion (8) by making new resonance forms possible in which the negative charge can be distributed over the additional electronegative atoms (9). Ionisation is thereby facilitated.

(9)   (8)   (7)

By contrast to these compounds those consisting of a 5-membered ring with one heteroatom only undergo exchange in highly basic media. Thus Shatenshtein's group found that the relative rates of exchange for the α-deuterium atom in furan, thiophene and seleno-phane in a $0.4M$ $K^+\bar{O}Bu$-t-CH_3SOCH_3 medium are 1:500:700, reflecting the enhanced stabilisation of the carbanions through d-σ overlap.[18]

The insertion of atoms possessing electron attracting inductive effects such as oxygen, fluorine or nitrogen into the benzene nucleus should facilitate the formation of carbanions at adjacent centres. In the case of pyridine however the reactivity order for hydro-gen–deuterium exchange in methanol–methoxide solution is $2(6) < 3(5) < 4$. Zoltewicz and co-workers[19] have ascribed the decreased reactivity of the positions adjacent to the nitrogen atom to the presence of two reinforcing factors. Firstly, the introduction of the heteroatom results in geometrical changes which lead to altera-tions in the s character of the various carbon–hydrogen bonds. In pyridine the endo-angle at C-2 is 4° larger, and at C-3 and C-4 1°24' and 1°54' smaller respectively than the 120° angle found in benzene.

The angle change at C-2 suggests a 5% reduction in the s character of the C(2)—H bond leading to a decreased acidity whereas the small increase in s character of the C(3)—H and C(4)—H bonds should be associated with an acidity increase. For comparison, a change from sp to sp^2 hybridisation is equivalent to a 17% reduction in s character and in going from acetylene to ethylene there is a fall in acidity of 11 pK units. Secondly, electrostatic repulsion between the coplanar electron pair and the electron pair of the adjacent anion, results in a destabilisation of the latter and hence leads to a reduced acidity of the C(2)—H bond. Pyridazine is another compound that does not have the regular geometry of benzene and the positional reactivity in this case is $4(5) > 3(6)$.

For isotopic hydrogen exchange in pyridinium salts the positional reactivity is considerably different from that exhibited by the pyridines e.g. for 3-methylpyridine methiodide it is $2 > 6 \gg 4, 5$. From a comparison of the rates of exchange for benzene Zoltewicz and co-workers[20] calculate that a positively charged annular nitrogen atom activates an aromatic ring for deprotonation via ylide formation by a factor of 10^{14}–10^{16}.

The mechanism of isotopic exchange in heterocyclic carbon acids made up of six-membered rings is invariably one involving attack of hydroxide ion on the protonated form to give an ylide intermediate which then reacts with the solvent in a fast step, or one in which the neutral molecule undergoes hydroxide-catalysed deprotonation to give a carbanion intermediate in the rate-determining step.

3.2. AROMATIC NITRO-COMPOUNDS[21,22]

In the interaction of the highly reactive aromatic nitro compounds with bases nuclear hydrogen abstraction is the least well characterised process. Usually these solutions are intensely coloured e.g. solutions of 1,3,5-trinitrobenzene and 1,3-dinitrobenzene in methanolic sodium methoxide are coloured orange and red respectively, but it is generally agreed that this is not due to the carbanion formed.

Several kinds of interaction have been recognised. Firstly, because of the high electron affinity of these compounds a partial transfer of electronic charge from the base to the aromatic nucleus depleted of its π electron density gives rise to a charge-transfer complex such as

(10)

Complete electron transfer leads to the formation of a radical anion such as

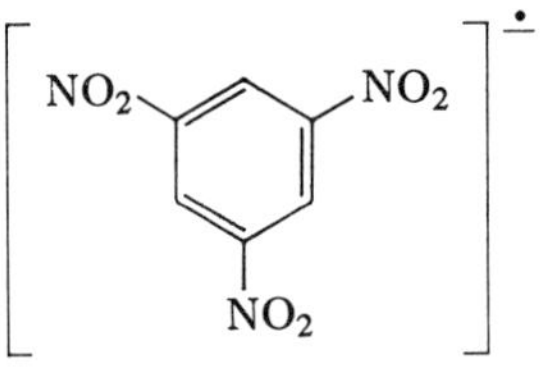

(11)

Anions of this type can be recognised by their electron spin resonance spectra and have been detected in basic solutions of nitrotoluenes and 1,3-dinitrobenzene.[23,24]

Secondly, the unshared electron pair of the base B^- may be used to form a covalent bond to an aromatic carbon atom e.g.

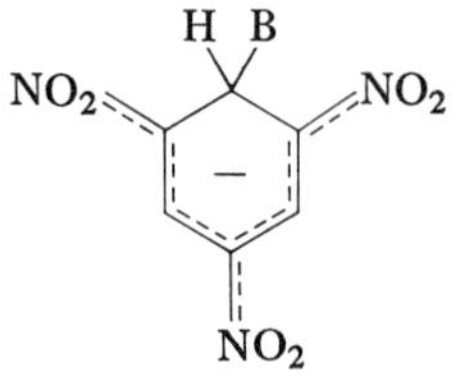

(12)

Compounds of this kind are known as Meisenheimer complexes and no longer have the benzenoid resonance intact. If the aromatic compound contains a displaceable group such as halogen the base may then act as a nucleophile and the reaction becomes an example of nucleophilic aromatic substitution. The tendency to form Meisenheimer complexes increases with the number of nitro groups and this explains why trinitro-substituted benzenes, for example, give small or zero concentrations of radical anions.

Because of the powerful electron withdrawing capability of the nitro groups proton abstraction from the aromatic nucleus remains a strong possibility. As long ago as 1937 the use of isotopic exchange as a tool for the study of proton transfer in aromatic nitro-compounds was reported.[25] Partial deuteriation of 1,3,5-trinitro-benzene using 0·02 M NaOH in ethanol-D_2O was observed although it has since been found[26] that nucleophilic displacement of a nitro group by alkoxide ion occurs even under milder conditions. From conductance and cryoscopy data it was concluded[27] that the same nitro compound reacted with 2-aminoethanol to give the anion

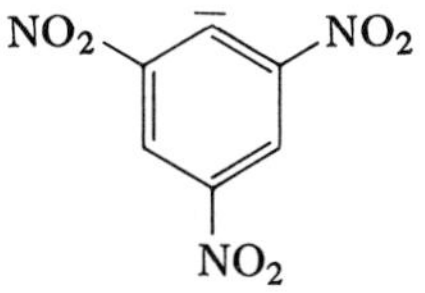

(13)

in contrast to the finding[28] that interaction of this substrate with piperidine in acetonitrile gave rise to an adduct

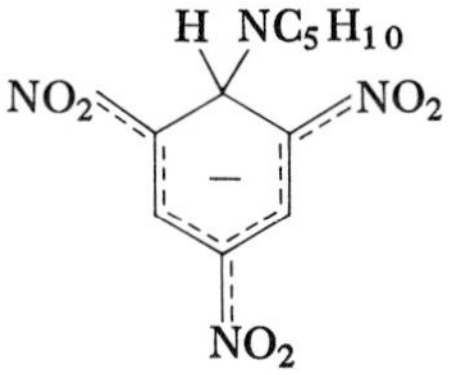

(14)

A recent study[29] shows that 1,3-dinitrobenzene undergoes hydrogen exchange at C-2 under mild conditions (NaOD in DMF-D$_2$O), the dependence of rate on medium composition and basicity (for anionic bases the order is OD$^-$ > OPh$^-$ > S$_2$O$_3^{2-}$ $\simeq$ CH$_3$COO$^-$ > N$_3^-$) being characteristic of a proton transfer reaction. Exchange seems to proceed more readily than for 1,3,5-trinitrobenzene[30] presumably because of the greater tendency for forming an unreactive Meisenheimer complex in the latter case.

Evidence for the formation of nitrobenzyl anions in basic media is also available. Thus 4-nitrobenzyl cyanide, when treated with sodium ethoxide in ethanol gives a red coloured solution. Kinetic data[31] as well as n.m.r. spectroscopy[32] have shown conclusively that the reaction is an example of a reversible proton transfer. The formation of the 2,4,6-trinitrobenzyl anion has also been reported[33] under similar conditions.

3.3. MECHANISM OF INTERNAL RETURN

Carbon acids such as ketones and nitro-compounds undergo ionisation in a step that involves considerable structural and solvent reorganisation :

$$\geq\!\!C\!-\!H + B^- \xrightleftharpoons[k_{-1}]{k_1} \geq\!\!C^- \ \cdots \ HB \xrightarrow{k_2} \text{exchange} \qquad (3.3)$$

Applying the steady-state treatment we find that

$$k_{obs} = k_1 k_2/(k_{-1} + k_2) \tag{3.4}$$

The protonation of a resonance-delocalised anion is fairly slow so that $k_2 \gg k_{-1}$, and

$$k_{obs} = k_1 \tag{3.5}$$

Acids of this kind are therefore subject to general base catalysis and the observed kinetic hydrogen isotope effects usually fall in the range $k_H/k_D = 3-8$ at room temperature.

However there are other carbon acids of the heterocyclic and aromatic kind in which the negative charge is extensively localised and where little solvent and structural reorganisation is necessary in order that exchange can take place. In such cases the energy barrier for reprotonation is low and the rate of protonation of the hydrogen bonded carbanion (k_1) competes favourably with the rate of replacement of hydrogen by deuterium (or tritium) from the solvent at the carbanion site (k_2) so that

$$k_{obs} = K k_2$$

The rate determining step now is the separation of the hydrogen bonded complex, preceded by an equilibrium for both of which the isotope effect should be small.[34] No buffer base catalysis should be observed in this case.

If the mechanism of internal return is operative there will be two further consequences. For two related compounds

$$\frac{k_{obs}}{k_{obs}^0} = (K/K^0)(k_2/k_2^0) \tag{3.7}$$

so that if the diffusion rate constant k_2 has the same value for both the last term in Eqn (3.7) reduces to unity and the observed relative rates are directly the ratio of the equilibrium acidities. The determination of the equilibrium acidity of one compound then enables one to determine that of a series of related compounds.[35]

Secondly the denominator of Eqn (3.4) has two terms of differing isotope effect, and if both are significant, k_{obs} can not give a normal inter-relationship between hydrogen, deuterium and tritium transfer (see p. 157). Streitwieser and co-workers[36,37] have used this approach in order to determine the amount of internal return taking place in various exchange reactions. The internal return ratio $(a = k_{-1}/k_2)$ was found to be insignificant for both 9-phenyl- and 9-methylfluorene but as high as 0·66 at 98°C for triphenylmethane.

Somewhat lower but still appreciable values were obtained for di-p-biphenyldiphenylmethane (0·21) and diphenylmethane (0·28).

Internal return also seems to be important in the ionisation of pentaflurobenzene[35] which shows no primary kinetic isotope effect ($k_D/k_T = 1·00 \pm 0·06$). The point has been made that the small entropy of activation for this reaction (−5·6 e.u) may also be diagnostic of internal return—the ionisation of ketones for example usually have more negative $\Delta S^{\ddagger}$ values. The entropy term is a composite of that for the equilibrium and diffusion steps and would therefore not be expected to be far from zero.

Internal return has been invoked to account for the low kinetic hydrogen isotope effects and lack of buffer base catalysis in the hydrogen–deuterium exchange reactions of N-substituted pyridinium ions and other heterocyclic carbon acids.[11,20] It may also be partly responsible for the widely different relative rates observed in different solvent systems.[4] Thus there is a million-fold rate difference between the α-hydrogens of toluene and ring hydrogens of benzene using the potassium t-butoxide-dimethyl sulphoxide system as compared to only a 200-fold difference for the lithium cyclohexylamide-cyclohexylamine system.

3.4. EXTENT OF HYDRATION[38]

Carbon acids containing a carbonyl group undergo hydration in aqueous media,

$$R_1R_2CO + H_2O \underset{k_d}{\overset{k_h}{\rightleftarrows}} R_1R_2C(OH)_2 \qquad (3.8)$$

and in this form there is no tendency for the ionisation of hydrogen attached to carbon. The process of hydration is reversible and catalysed by both acids and bases. The most common method of determining the extent of hydration is based on the fact that this process is usually accompanied by the disappearance or weakening of the characteristic ultra-violet absorption band of the carbonyl group at around 280 nm. The main difficulty lies in determining the exact extinction coefficient (ϵ) of the unhydrated carbonyl compound—if the rate of hydration is slow extrapolation of the absorption to zero time can be made but this is no longer satisfactory when the rate is fast. The frequently employed procedure of assuming that ϵ is independent of the nature of the solvent is not valid and can lead to large errors.[39]

A model compound may be used to determine the extinction coefficient of a carbonyl compound e.g. to calculate the ϵ of

4-methoxytrifluoroacetophenone the absorbance of the non-hydrating compound 4-methoxyacetophenone was measured both in a pure solvent and in the solvent mixture in which ϵ was desired. By assuming the same relative change to be applicable to the trifluoro

TABLE 3.4

Equilibrium constants for dehydration of some hydrates[38a]

Hydrate	Method	K_d
$CCl_3CH(OH)_2$	U.V.	$3 \cdot 6 \times 10^{-5}$
$CH_2(OH)_2$	Polarography	$5 \cdot 5 \times 10^{-4}$
$CH_3CH(OH)_2$	U.V.	$0 \cdot 65$
	N.M.R.	$0 \cdot 67$
	N.M.R.	$0 \cdot 81$
$(CH_2Cl)_2C(OH)_2$	U.V.	$0 \cdot 10$
$(CH_3)_2C(OH)_2$	N.M.R.	$\sim 5 \times 10^2$
$CH_3C(OH)_2 . CHCl_2$	U.V.	$0 \cdot 35$
$CH_2Cl . CH(OH)_2$	U.V.	$0 \cdot 027$
$CH_3CH_2 . CH(OH)_2$	U.V.	$1 \cdot 4$

[a] In aqueous solution at 25°.

ketone the ketone absorption measured in the pure inert solvent was corrected to give the ϵ value for the solvent mixture.[40]

Nuclear magnetic resonance is also a very useful technique as one can determine the concentration of both hydrate and ketone directly from the peak areas. Furthermore the reaction velocity in both directions can be determined, leading to an independent estimate of the equilibrium position. Table 3.4 gives the equilibrium constant for dehydration ($K_d = k_d/k_h$) for several hydrates from which it can be seen that K_d decreases in the presence of electron attracting substituents (de-stabilisation of the carbonyl compound) but increases in the presence of bulky groups (steric strain in the hydrate).

It is generally agreed that the mechanism for hydration involves the formation of a transition state containing one or more water molecules in excess of the one that reacts. For base catalysis the mechanism proposed by Bell[41] is

$$\text{>CO} + H_2O + B^- \longrightarrow \text{>C(OH)O}^- + HB \tag{3.9}$$

$$\text{>C(OH)O}^- + HB \rightleftharpoons \text{>C(OH)}_2 + B^- \tag{3.10}$$

the first termolecular step being rate determining. Any attempt to split it up into two consecutive bimolecular processes leads to conclusions incompatible with experimental findings. The various possibilities[38] are

$$B^- + H_2O \rightleftharpoons HB + OH^- \tag{3.11}$$

$$\text{>CO} + OH^- \rightleftharpoons C(OH)O^- \tag{3.12}$$

$$\text{>CO} + B^- \rightleftharpoons \text{>C(B)O}^- \tag{3.13}$$

$$\text{>C(B)O}^- + H_2O \rightleftharpoons \text{>C(OH)O}^- + BH \tag{3.14}$$

$$\text{>CO} + H_2O \rightleftharpoons \text{>C(O}^-)\overset{+}{O}H_2 \tag{3.15}$$

$$\text{>C(O}^-)\overset{+}{O}H_2 + B^- \rightleftharpoons C(OH)O^- + HB \tag{3.16}$$

If reaction (3.11) or (3.15) is rate determining the reaction velocity in the first case would be independent of the concentration of ketone, and in the second would not be catalysed by different bases. Reaction (3.12) would exhibit specific hydroxide ion catalysis if it were rate determining. Reactions (3.13) and 3.14) might well be slow but their rates depend upon the nucleophilic reactivity of the catalyst towards carbon rather than on its basic strength. Reaction (3.16) is an example of proton transfer from oxygen and would therefore be expected to be fast.

A more detailed consideration of the rates of the individual processes concerned together with the wide range of velocities over which the Brönsted relationship was obeyed led Eigen[42] to suggest that steps (3.9) and (3.10) could be replaced by a concerted process involving the participation of two extra water molecules so that the critical stage in the reaction could be written as

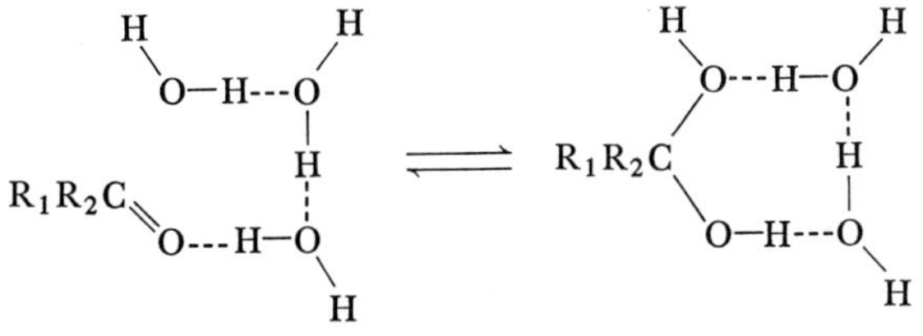

$$\tag{3.17}$$

where the broken lines indicate hydrogen bonds. Evidence in favour of this mechanism comes from studies[43,44] of proton exchange between carboxylic acids and water (or methanol), and also from a study[45,46] of the hydration of 1,3-dichloroacetone over a range of water concentrations in both dioxan and acetonitrile with and without added catalyst. The order with respect to water in dioxan and in the absence of added catalyst are close to 3 and 2 for the hydration and dehydration reactions respectively. When the reaction is catalysed by triethylamine in aqueous dioxan the order with respect to water falls, being now c. 2 and 1 for the hydration and dehydration reactions respectively. This suggests that the catalyst can replace one of the water molecules in the transition state proposed in the absence of catalyst.

Recently Stewart and Van Dyke[40,47] have looked into the possibility of setting up an hydration scale for dimethyl sulphoxide-water and sulpholane-water mixtures, analogous to the acidity function H_-. The equilibrium constant for dehydration (K_d) can be written

$$K_d = \frac{[\text{ketone}]}{[\text{hydrate}]} \frac{f_{\text{ket}}}{f_{\text{hyd}}} \cdot a_{H_2O} \tag{3.18}$$

or

$$pK_d = -\log\left(\frac{[\text{ketone}]}{[\text{hydrate}]}\right) - \log\left(\frac{f_{\text{ket}}}{f_{\text{hyd}}} \cdot a_{H_2O}\right) \tag{3.19}$$

The function W_0 defined as

$$W_0 = -\log\left(\frac{f_{\text{ket}}}{f_{\text{hyd}}} \cdot a_{H_2O}\right) \tag{3.20}$$

represents the effect of the dipolar aprotic solvent on the hydration equilibrium. For pure water W_0 is zero and rises to a value of 2·72 in 99 mol % sulpholane, in contrast to the dimethyl sulphoxide-water mixtures where negative values of W_0 are obtained from 0-85 mol % dimethyl sulphoxide. These latter systems hydrate the ketones to a greater extent than does pure water, whereas sulpholane has a greater dehydrating action than dimethyl sulphoxide, in sharp contrast to their effect on hydroxide ion basicity (see Chapter 6).

3.5. INTRAMOLECULAR CATALYSIS

This kind of catalysis becomes possible when the active $\geqslant$C–H group and a basic group are suitably orientated within the same molecule. Various systems have been specifically designed so as to make possible the active participation of intramolecular catalytic groups in the transition state. Thus Bell and co-workers[48,49] studied the rates of iodination of a series of keto acids of the form $CH_3CO[CH_2]_n$-CO_2H (n = 2-5 and 11) and found that some or all of the observed rate could be attributed to intramolecular catalysis of ionisation by the carboxy group. The intramolecular rate passed through a maximum when $n = 3$, corresponding to a 6-membered cyclic transition state. This finding was subsequently supported by the results of calculations pertaining to the probability of forming a cyclic transition state.[50] Furthermore the "water-catalysed" rates of iodination of levulinic acid and 5-ketohexanoic acids[51] were greater by factors of 7 and 100 respectively, than for ethyl levulinate and ethyl 5-ketohexanoate where of course intramolecular catalysis is not possible.

Catalysis of this kind is not as well established for pyruvic acid as was once thought. Bell and Ridgewell[52] found the "water-catalysed" rates of iodination of ethyl pyruvate to be approximately the same as for pyruvic acid, as also did Meany.[53] In addition a comparative study[54] of the hydration of pyruvic acid and methyl and ethyl pyruvates shows that the rates at $0°$ are very similar so that intramolecular catalysis by the neighbouring carboxyl group,

$$CH_3C \overset{\displaystyle O\text{---}H}{\underset{\displaystyle \overset{C}{\underset{O}{\|}}}{\diagdown}} O$$

(15)

is not important

Provided that the proton donor and acceptor were suitably orientated it would be expected that intramolecular catalysis would be more important in a stereochemically fixed system than in a more flexible arrangement and this seems to be borne out by the work of Harper and Bender[55] on the enolisation of o-isobutyrylbenzoic acid. In the pH region 2·5–10 the reaction is dependent only on the anionic form of the substrate and independent of external buffer catalysts, the predominant pathway being via intramolecular base catalysis:

$$\text{(3.21)}$$

Support for this finding comes from the fact that the rate of halogenation is faster than for o-acetylbenzoate whereas for the intermolecular general base catalysed iodination of acetophenone and isobutyrophenone (or acetone and di-isopropyl ketone) the reverse is true.

The results of a similar study[56] on the iodination of o-carboxy-acetophenone also show that in self-buffered solutions the first order rate constant (the observed zero order rate constant divided by the ketone anion concentration) is independent of anion concentration and of hydrogen ion concentration over a wide range even when a large proportion of the substrate is in the protonated form. The rate constant $(2 \times 10^{-6}\ s^{-1})$ is much too great to be attributed to intermolecular catalysis by water molecules since for ketones as weakly acidic as the acetophenones the latter process has rate constants of the order of $10^{-10}\ s^{-1}$. A kinetically equivalent process would be the transfer of methyl protons from the undissociated acid to hydroxide ions but calculation shows that the observed rate corresponds to a rate constant of $1{\cdot}4 \times 10^4\ M^{-1}\ s^{-1}$. Measurements of proton transfer to hydroxide ion from a number of substituted acetophenones[57,58] gives rate constants of the order $1\ M^{-1} s^{-1}$ so that the observed rate is primarily due to the abstraction of protons from the acetyl group by the o-carboxylate group. This conclusion is supported by the fact that the rate constant for the corresponding para-substituted acetophenone is nearly 300 times slower.

3.6. STATISTICAL FACTORS

The relative rates of ionisation of carbon acids may be affected by purely statistical considerations. Thus in comparing acetone and acetophenone account must be taken of the different number of methyl groups. A similar situation exists when dealing with the groups $-CH_3$, $>CH_2$ and $>CH$. The same criteria apply when different basic catalysts such as CH_3COO^- and $CH_2(COO^-)_2$ are involved.

The way in which the corrections should be applied has been the subject of some disagreement[59] and this has been made worse by the difficulty of obtaining experimental evidence. Brönsted[60] originally pointed out that the catalytic coefficient k of an acid was related to its acid strength K by the equation

$$k/p = G(qK/p)^\alpha \qquad (3.22)$$

where G and α are constants, p and q are statistical factors, the former representing the number of equivalent acidic hydrogen atoms in the acid and the latter the number of equivalent sites for proton attachment in the conjugate base. Bell[61] modified this by taking p to be the number of equivalent acidic hydrogen atoms attached to different atoms e.g. p is 1 for NH_4^+ but 2 for $(COOH)_2$. It has since been pointed out[62] that this procedure lends itself to an inconsistency if one considers the relative reactivity of ions such as H_3O^+,

H_2DO^+ and HD_2O^+ for proton transfer; p would be taken as unity in each case whereas statistical factors in the ratio 3:2:1 are required.

An alternative procedure for evaluating p and q in terms of symmetry numbers has been given by Benson.[63] For the ionisation

$$HA \rightleftharpoons H^+ + A^- \qquad (3.23)$$

the equilibrium constant may be expressed by

$$K = (\sigma_{HA}/\sigma_{A^-})K^0 \qquad (3.24)$$

where the σ's are symmetry numbers and K^0 is a modified constant from which the symmetry numbers have been extracted. In an analogous way the rate constant can be expressed by

$$k = (\sigma_{HA}/\sigma^{\neq})k^0 \qquad (3.25)$$

If it is now assumed that the quantities k^0 and K^0 are related by the simple equilibrium

$$k^0 = G(K^0)^{\alpha} \qquad (3.26)$$

it follows that

$$k\sigma^{\neq}/\sigma_{HA} = G[K(\sigma_A^-/\sigma_{HA})]^{\alpha} \qquad (3.27)$$

so that $\sigma_{HA}/\sigma^{\neq}$ is identified with p and p/q with σ_{HA}/σ_{A^-}. This procedure is entirely satisfactory except in the case where optical isomerism in the transition state is a possibility.[64]

More recently Bishop and Laidler[65] have shown that for any chemical equilibrium the ratio of symmetry numbers is equal to the ratio of statistical factors. These statistical factors represent the number of different sets of products that can be formed if identical atoms in the reactant are labelled. Equation (3.25) is replaced by

$$k = l^{\neq}/k^0 \qquad (3.28)$$

and the Brönsted equation takes the form

$$k/l^{\neq} = G[K(\sigma_{A^-}/\sigma_{HA})]^{\alpha} \qquad (3.29)$$

An analogous equation applies to base catalysis. The use of statistical factors in this way offers several advantages not least being the fact that they are easily evaluated by direct counting.

REFERENCES

1. Pearson, R. G. & Dillon, R. L. (1953). *J. Amer. Chem. Soc.* **75**, 2439.
2. Bell, R. P. (1959). *The Proton in Chemistry*, Chapter 10. Cornell University Press, New York.
3. Cram, D. J. (1965). *Fundamentals of Carbanion Chemistry*. Chapter 1. Academic Press, New York.
4. Jones, J. R. (1972). *Progr. Phys. Org. Chem.* (Streitwieser, A. & Taft, R. W. eds. **9**, 241.
5. Jones, J. R. & Patel, S. P. (1973) unpublished results.
6. Andreades, S. (1964). *J. Amer. Chem. Soc.* **86**, 2003.
7. Streitwieser, A. Jr. & Holtz, D. (1967). *J. Amer. Chem. Soc.* **89**, 692.
8. Streitwieser, A. Jr., Marchand, A. P. & Pudjaatmaka, A. H. (1967). *J. Amer. Chem. Soc.* **89**, 693.
9. Klabunde, K. J. & Burton, D. J. (1972). *J. Amer. Chem. Soc.* **94**, 820.
10. Streitwieser, A. Jr., & Mares, F. (1968). *J. Amer. Chem. Soc.* **90**, 2444.
11. Elvidge, J. A., Evans, E. A., Jones, J. R., O'Brien, C. & Sheppard, H. C. (1973). *Adv. Heterocyclic Chem.* (Katritzky, A. R. & Boulton, A. J. eds.) in press.
12. Elvidge, J. A., Evans, E. A., Jones, J. R., O'Brien, C. & Turner, J. C. (1973). *J. Chem. Soc. (Perkin II)* 432.
13. Breslow, R. (1958). *J. Amer. Chem. Soc.* **80**, 3719.
14. Ugai, T., Tanaka, S. & Dokawa, S. (1944). *J. Pharm. Soc. Jap.* **63**, 3.
15. Rochat, A. & Olofson, R. A. (1969). *Tetrahedron Letters*, 3377.
16. Breslow, R. (1957). *J. Amer. Chem. Soc.* **79**, 1762.
17. Olofson, R. A. & Landesberg, J. M. (1966). *J. Amer. Chem. Soc.* **88**, 4263.
18. Shatenshtein, A. I., Kamrad, A. G., Shapiro, I. O., Ranneva, Yu. I. & Zvyagintseva, E. N. (1966). *Dokl. Akad. Nauk. SSSR* **168**, 364.
19. Zoltewicz, J. A., Grahe, G. & Smith, C. L. (1969). *J. Amer. Chem. Soc.* **91**, 5501.
20. Zoltewicz, J. A. & Helmick, L. S. (1970). *J. Amer. Chem. Soc.* **92**, 7547.
21. Crampton, M. R. (1969). *Adv. Phys. Org. Chem.* (Gold, V., ed.) 7, 211.
22. Buncel, E., Norris, A. R. & Russell, K. E. (1968). *Quart. Rev. Chem. Soc.* **22**, 123.
23. Russell, G. A. & Janzen, E. G. (1962). *J. Amer. Chem. Soc,* **84**, 4153.
24. Russell, G. A., Janzen, E. G. & Strom, E. T. (1964). *J. Amer. Chem. Soc.* **86**, 1807.
25. Kharasch, M. S., Brown, W. G. & McNab, J. (1937). *J. Org. Chem.* 2, 36.
26. Crampton, M. R. & Gold, V. (1966). *J. Chem. Soc. (B)* 498.
27. Baliah, V. & Ramakrishnan, V. (1959). *Rec. Trav. Chim.* **78**, 783 (1960). **79**, 1150.
28. Briegleb, G., Liptay, W. & Cautner, M. (1960). *Z. Phys. Chem. (Frankfurt am Main)* **26**, 55.
29. Buncel, E. & Zabel, A. W. (1967). *J. Amer. Chem. Soc.* **89**, 3082.
30. Buncel, E. & Symons, E. A. (1967). *Chem. Comm.* 771.
31. Caldin, E. F., Kasparian, M. & Tomalin, G. (1968). *Trans. Faraday Soc.* **64**, 2802.
32. Crampton, M. R. (1967). *J. Chem. Soc. B* 85.
33. Caldin, E. F. & Long, G. (1955).*Proc. Roy. Soc. Ser. A* **228**, 263.
34. Cram, D. J., Kingsbury, C. A. & Rickborn, B. (1961). *J. Amer. Chem. Soc.* **83**, 3688.

35. Streitwieser, A. Jr., Hudson, J. A. & Mares, F. (1968). *J. Amer. Chem. Soc.* 90, 648.
36. Streitwieser, A. Jr., Hollyhead, W. B., Pudjaatmaka, A. H., Owens, P. H., Kruger, T. L., Rubenstein, P. A., MacQuarrie, R. A., Brokaw, M. L., Chu, W. K. C. & Niemeyer, H. M. (1971). *J. Amer. Chem. Soc.* 93, 5088.
37. Streitwieser, A. Jr., Hollyhead, W. B., Sonnichsen, G., Pudjaatmaka, A. H., Chang, C. J. & Kruger, T. L. (1971). *J. Amer. Chem. Soc.* 93, 5096.
38. Bell, R. P. (1966). *Adv. Phys. Org. Chem.* (Gold, V. ed.) 4, 1.
39. Greenzaid, P., Rappoport, Z. & Samuel, D. (1967). *Trans. Faraday Soc.* 63, 2131.
40. Stewart, R. & Van Dyke, J. D. (1972). *Can. J. Chem.* 50, 1992.
41. Bell, R. P. & Higginson, W. C. E. (1949). *Proc. Roy. Soc. Ser. A* 197, 141.
42. Eigen, M. (1965). *Discuss. Faraday Soc.* 39, 7.
43. Grunwald, E., Jumper, C. F. & Meiboom, S. (1963). *J. Amer. Chem. Soc.* 85, 522.
44. Grunwald, E. & Meiboom, S. (1963). *J. Amer. Chem. Soc.* 85, 2047.
45. Bell, R. P., Millington, J. P. & Pink, J. M. (1968). *Proc. Roy. Soc. Ser. A* 303, 1.
46. Bell, R. P. & Critchlow, J. E. (1971). *Proc. Roy. Soc. Ser. A* 325, 35.
47. Stewart, R. & Van Dyke, J. D. (1970). *Can. J. Chem.* 48, 3961.
48. Bell, R. P. & Fluendy, M. A. D. (1963). *Trans. Faraday Soc.* 59, 1623.
49. Albery, W. J., Bell, R. P. & Powell, A. L. (1965). *Trans. Faraday Soc.* 61, 1194.
50. Fluendy, M. A. D. (1963). *Trans. Faraday Soc.* 59, 1681.
51. Bell, R. P. & de Maria, P. (1970). *Trans. Faraday Soc.* 66, 930.
52. Bell, R. P. & Ridgewell, H. F. F. (1967). *Proc. Roy. Soc. Ser. A* 298, 178.
53. Meany, J. E. (1971). *J. Phys. Chem.* 75, 150.
54. Pocker, Y., Meany, J. E. & Zadorojny, C. (1971). *J. Phys. Chem.* 75, 792.
55. Harper, E. & Bender, M. L. (1965). *J. Amer. Chem. Soc.* 87, 5625.
56. Bell, R. P., Cox, B. G. & Henshall, J. B. (1972). *J. Chem. Soc. (Perkin II)* 1232.
57. Jones, J. R., Marks, R. E. & Subba Rao, S. C. (1967). *Trans. Faraday Soc.* 63, 111.
58. Jones, J. R., Marks, R. E. & Subba Rao, S. C. (1967). *Trans. Faraday Soc.* 63, 993.
59. Bishop, D. M. & Laidler, K. J. (1965). *J. Chem. Phys.* 42, 1688.
60. Brönsted, J. N. & Pedersen, K. J. (1924). *Z. Phys. Chem (Leipzig)* 108, 185.
61. Bell, R. P. (1941). *Acid-Base Catalysis*, Chapter 5. Oxford Univ. Press, London.
62. Wynne-Jones, W. F. K. (1935). *Chem. Rev.* 17, 115.
63. Benson, S. W. (1958). *J. Amer. Chem. Soc.* 80, 5151.
64. Gold, V. (1964). *Trans. Faraday Soc.* 60, 738.
65. Bishop, D. M. & Laidler, K. J. (1970). *Trans. Faraday Soc.* 66, 1685.

4. The Acidities of Carbon Acids—Methods

The intrinsic acidity constant of a carbon acid is measured by the equilibrium constant for the reaction

$$RH \rightleftharpoons R^- + H^+ \tag{4.1}$$

$$K_a = a_{R^-} a_{H^+} / a_{RH} = \frac{[R^-][H^+]}{[RH]} \frac{f_{R^-} f_{H^+}}{f_{RH}} \tag{4.2}$$

a's refer to activities, f's to activity coefficients on the molar concentration scale and [ ] to concentration. Provided the carbon acid is sufficiently acidic K_a can be measured in water and this solvent then acts as the standard state. If, for some reason or other, another solvent is necessary, the acidities in the different media can be related by

$$K_{a(H_2O)} = K_{a(S)} [f_{R^-} f_{H^+} / f_{RH}] \tag{4.3}$$

where the last term represents the activity coefficients of the particular species in solvent S relative to a standard state in water and can be equated to the free energy required to transfer 1 mole of the species from its standard state in water to its standard state in solvent S.

4.1. ELECTROCHEMICAL

One of the simplest and most widely used methods[1] of determining the acidity constants of the more acidic carbon acids ($pK_a \sim 4$–10) is that in which the acid is partially neutralised by the addition of sodium hydroxide solution and the pH measured. If the concentration of acid is very low the activity coefficient term can be neglected and Eqn (4.2) reduced to

$$K_a' = \frac{[R^-][H^+]}{[RH]} \tag{4.4}$$

or

$$pH = pK_a' + \log_{10} \frac{[R^-]}{[RH]} \tag{4.5}$$

K_a' is the concentration dissociation constant and values can be calculated for various degreees of neutralisation. If on the other hand the activity coefficients must be retained Eqn (4.2) takes the form

$$pH = pK_a + \log_{10} \frac{[R^-]}{[RH]} + \log_{10} f_{R^-} - \log_{10} f_{RH} \qquad (4.6)$$

RH is an uncharged species and f_{RH} is usually taken as unity; f_{R^-} can be estimated in a number of different ways e.g. from the Debye-Hückel theory the activity coefficient (f_i) of an ion of valency z is given by

$$-\log_{10} f_i = \frac{A z^2 \sqrt{I}}{1 + B a_i \sqrt{I}} \qquad (4.7)$$

where I is the ionic strength of the medium, A and B are constants which vary with the dielectric constant of the solvent and temperature, and a_i is an ion size parameter.

During the course of the titration the ionic strength increases and pK_a' changes. It is therefore preferable if a medium of constant ionic strength, such as $0.1M$ NaCl, is employed. The thermodynamic acidity constant K_a can then be obtained from Eqn (4.8).

$$pK_a' = pK_a + \log_{10} f_{R^-} \qquad (4.8)$$

the value of f_{R^-} being 0.78.

Recent work by Ritchie and Uschold[2] has shown that the glass electrode functions reversibly even in highly basic media ($H_- \sim 28$). The apparatus consists essentially of an H cell assembly, one arm of which contains the solution to be titrated and in which the glass electrode is immersed. This arm was connected to the silver reference electrode (immersed in a $5 \times 10^{-2} M$ solution of silver perchlorate in dimethyl sulphoxide) by a salt bridge filled with $0.1M$ tetraethylammonium perchlorate in dimethyl sulphoxide. The reversibility of the electrode system was verified by titrating various acids with solutions of dimsylcesium; excellent adherence to the Nernst equation was observed. Potentiometric titration of various acids with a standardised solution of dimyslcesium enabled the pK_a's to be determined with a precision of ± 0.2 pK unit.

The classical conductance and electromotive force methods of determining acidity constants as developed over the last half-century have been thoroughly discussed in a number of standard works[3-7] and will not be considered here. In fact the majority of carbon acids are so weak that these methods are not very suitable—the conductance method, for example, can not be used for acids with

$pK_a > 5$ because of the long extrapolation that is required to obtain λ_∞.

Changes in conductivity can, however, be used in another way to determine the acidities of acids in the pK_a range 10–15. The principle of the method developed by Ballinger and Long[8] can be seen from the following illustration. If to an aqueous solution of sodium hydroxide an excess of a weak acid RH ($K_a = 1 \times 10^{-12}$) is added there will be a transformation of NaOH to NaR through the reaction

$$RH + OH^- \rightleftharpoons R^- + H_2O \tag{4.9}$$

The equilibrium constant at 25° for the reaction is $K = K_a/K_W = 100$. With stoichiometric concentrations of 0·01M RH and 0·002M NaOH almost 50% of the alkali is transformed to NaR. Since the equivalent conductivities of these two electrolytes are c. 245 and 80 the addition of acid to the alkali solution produces a large and easily measured change in conductivity so that the pK_a of RH can be obtained with some accuracy.

Although it is customary to characterise the stability of carbanions by their pK_a values this is far from being the sole criterion. In principle any method which reflects the affinity of carbanions for electron acceptors may be employed and Reutov and co-workers[9] have used the tendency of carbanions to associate with mercuric ions according to the equilibrium

$$R_2Hg + 2e \longrightarrow Hg + 2R^- \xrightarrow{2H^+} 2RH \tag{4.10}$$

for this purpose. The electrochemical reduction of symmetrical organomercuric compounds at the mercury electrode is (usually) an irreversible process for which the relevant equation is

$$E_{1/2} = \frac{RT}{\alpha n_a F} \ln \frac{0 \cdot 886 k_f^0}{D^{1/2}} + \frac{RT}{2\alpha n_a F} \ln t \tag{4.11}$$

n_a being the number of electrons in the potential-determining stage, k_f^0 the rate constant of reduction at the potential $E = 0$, D the diffusion coefficient of R_2Hg, t the drop time and R, T and F have their usual significance. This equation can be more conveniently written as

$$\alpha E_{1/2} = a \log_{10} k_f^0 + b \tag{4.12}$$

By making the drop time constant and assuming that the diffusion coefficients for two R_2Hg compounds are the same it can be seen that

$$\Delta(\alpha E_{1/2}) = a \Delta(\log_{10} k_f^0) \tag{4.13}$$

$\alpha E_{1/2}$ values have been found to be linearly related to the basicities of different oxygen and nitrogen bases and it seems realistic to assume that the affinity of carbanions for the mercuric ion should be similarly related to the pK_a values of RH. Figure 4.1 illustrates the dependence of $\alpha E_{1/2}$ upon pK_a, the latter values having been obtained from the well known MSAD scale. In this way a polarographic scale of carbon acidities has been set up.

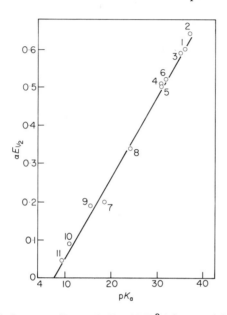

Fig. 4.1. Relationship between $\alpha E_{1/2}$ and pK_a of RH.[9] (1) C_2H_4; (2) C_6H_6; (3) $C_6H_5CH_3$; (4) C_6Cl_5H; (5) $CH_2=CHCl$; (6) $CH_2=CH-CH_3$ (α position); (7) $C_6H_5C\equiv CH$; (8) CH_3COOCH_3; (9) cyclo-C_5H_6; (10) $CH_3COCH_2CO_2C_2H_5$; (11) HCN.

Polarography may be employed to determine acidities in another more direct manner as illustrated by the work of Zuman and co-workers.[10] The carbanions formed from compounds bearing an electro-negative grouping on the α carbon atom can accept a proton in one of two ways, for example

$$RCO.CH_2X + H_2O \underset{k_{-1}}{\overset{k_1}{\rightleftharpoons}} RCO.\bar{C}HX + H_3O^+ \qquad (4.14)$$

$$\underset{OH}{\overset{|}{RC}}=CHX + H_2O \underset{k_{-2}}{\overset{k_2}{\rightleftharpoons}} \underset{O^-}{\overset{|}{RC}}=CHX + H_3O^+ \qquad (4.15)$$

The ratio of [enol]/[keto] is given by $K_{a(1)}/K_{a(2)}$ and the overall acidity constant $K_{a(T)}$ by

$$K_{a(T)} = K_{a(1)} K_{a(2)}/K_{a(1)} + K_{a(2)} \qquad (4.16)$$

which simplifies to

$$K_{a(T)} = K_{a(1)} \{1 + [\text{enol}]/[\text{keto}]\} \simeq K_{a(1)} \qquad (4.17)$$

when $[\text{keto}] \gg [\text{enol}]$. For a rapidly established equilibrium (4.14) $K_{a(T)}$ can be determined from the shift with pH of the half-wave potential of the single observed wave of $RCO.CH_2X$, the height of which is practically pH-independent. For a slowly established equilibrium on the other hand two waves for $RCOCH_2X$ and $(RCOCHX)^-$ are observed, the ratio of whose heights changes with pH in such a way that $K_{a(T)}$ can be obtained from the inflexion point. The situation where the time needed for establishment of the equilibrium (4.14) is comparable to the drop time (~ 3 s) has also be discussed.

Polarography may also be used in conjunction with other electrochemical methods to provide data that enables the acidities of such weak acids as triphenylcyclopropene ($pK_a \sim 51$) to be determined and where no other methods are currently available.[11,12] The approach is based on the fact that the thermodynamics of direct conversion of a carbon acid such as a hydrocarbon to its anion can also be determined from the thermodynamics of indirect conversion, through the sequence.

$$R\!-\!H \xrightarrow{\ 1\ } R\!-\!OH \xrightarrow{\ 2\ } R^+ \xrightarrow{\ 3\ } R\cdot \xrightarrow{\ 4\ } R^- \qquad (4.18)$$

Only for step 1 are data not easily available and Breslow assumes that the difference in heat of formation of a hydrocarbon and its related alcohol is constant, at least for closely similar compounds. In fact, variations in the relative heat of formation of hydrocarbons and alcohols are sufficiently small that the resulting error is unlikely to exceed 3–4 pK units. For step 2 the commonly available thermodynamic parameter is the pK_{R^+}. For steps 3 and 4 the $E_{1/2}$'s for the successive addition of two electrons can be determined by polarographic and other methods e.g. cyclic voltammetry is particularly convenient in obtaining reversible potentials with very reactive species. To obtain absolute pK_a's the value of 33 obtained by McEwen[13] for triphenylmethane was used.

4.2. SPECTROPHOTOMETRIC

Under conditions where the activity coefficients can either be calculated or neglected and where the activity of the hydrogen ion can be measured the task of determining the acidity constant simplifies to one in which only the ratio of anion to acid concentrations needs to be found. Fortunately many carbon acids have ultraviolet and visible absorption spectra which undergo significant alteration on ionisation. Consequently spectrophotometric methods of determining acidity constants have been widely employed although the exact manner in which this has been done differs a great deal.

Firstly, there is the competitive method in which the acid, in the presence of suitable solvent, is treated with the conjugate base of another acid and the relative concentrations of the two acids and conjugate bases produced at equilibrium, measured. This method which was used many years ago by Conant and Wheland,[14] and McEwen,[13] provides a direct measure of the difference in the acidity of two compounds as expressed in the equilibrium

$$RH + B^-M^+ \rightleftharpoons R^-M^+ + HB \tag{4.19}$$

$$K = \frac{[R^-M^+][HB]}{[RH][B^-M^+]} \tag{4.20}$$

$$\log K = pK_{(HB)} - pK_{(RH)} \tag{4.21}$$

In McEwen's work a hydrocarbon was mixed with an organosodium (or potassium) salt in ether (or benzene) and the position of equilibrium estimated by visible means or by quenching with carbon dioxide. On the basis of these early experiments with several hydrocarbons McEwen gave estimates of pK_a values which are only now being made more quantitative.

In the realisation that few of the methods then available were generally applicable to the weakly acidic hydrogens found in simple hydrocarbons Applequist and O'Brien[15] undertook research to see whether the halogen–metal interchange reaction

$$RX + R'M \rightleftharpoons RM + R'X \tag{4.22}$$

could be used to obtain quantitative data on acidities. The reaction is formally similar to the acid–base equilibrium traditionally used except that the two bases compete for a halogen atom rather than a hydrogen atom. A somewhat similar study by Salinger and Dessy[16] of carbanion stabilities was made via the exchange reactions of organomercury and organomagnesium compounds:

$$RMg + R'Hg \rightleftharpoons RHg + R'Mg \tag{4.23}$$

In Streitwieser's more recent and extensive studies[17-20] of the equilibrium acidities of hydrocarbons a mixture of two hydrocarbons is treated with an insufficient amount of cesium (or lithium) cyclohexylamide in cyclohexylamine. All of the hydrocarbons studied were more acidic than cyclohexylamine so that equilibrium (4.19, $M^+ = Li^+$ or Cs^+, $B^- = C_6H_{11}NH^-$) lies well over to the right. The ultraviolet and visible spectrum of the mixture was compared with the spectra of the individual metal salts in cyclohexylamine. From these spectral determinations and the known amounts of starting hydrocarbons the equilibrium constants could be determined.

The disadvantage of the competitive method is that it gives the difference in acid strength so that one of the pK_a's must be determined by other means before an absolute value may be quoted. The use of a specific solvent–base system also means that only acids covering a pK range of something less than 10 units can normally be studied. In addition the dielectric constants of the solvents most widely used in this method are usually low so that complications may arise from the effects of ion association.

Secondly, the spectrophotometric method may be used to obtain pK_a values in a more direct manner.[21] For the more acidic carbon acids ($pK_a \sim 12\text{-}14$) it is possible to measure the equilibrium constant for the reaction (4.9) provided there is a pronounced shift in the absorption maximum on ionisation and that Beer's law is obeyed. For solutions of low ionic strength it can be assumed that $f_{OH^-}/f_{R^-} = 1$. It can then be shown[22] that

$$\epsilon = \epsilon_{R^-} - \epsilon K_W/K_a[OH^-] \tag{4.24}$$

if RH does not absorb at the wavelength used and if $K_a[OH^-] \gg K_W$; ϵ is the apparent extinction coefficient and ϵ_{R^-} the extinction coefficient of the anion. A plot of ϵ against $\epsilon/[OH^-]$ therefore gives a straight line of slope $-K_W/K_a$ and intercept ϵ_{R^-}.

The acidities of the vast majority of carbon acids have been determined either by competitive means or by the acidity function approach[23,24] which is dealt with in more detail in Chapter 6 in connection with the setting up of H_- scales. Suffice to say that the method is based on first of all determining the basicity of a medium as expressed by the H_- acidity function.

$$H_- = -\log_{10}a_{H^+}f_{R^-}/f_{RH} = pK_{RH} + \log_{10}[R^-]/[RH] \tag{4.25}$$

by using an acid of known strength and then using this H_- value to determine the acidity of another structurally similar acid. The procedure can then be used in a stepwise manner so that the acidities of acids covering a wide pK range can be determined. With reasonable assumptions concerning activity coefficient ratios the derived acidity values can be related to a standard state such as water.

Finally the spectrophotometric method may be used to determine the acidities of some weak acids by using a solvent system such as a solution of the amide ion in liquid ammonia.[25] This medium is so basic that such weak carbon acids as triphenylmethane, diphenylmethane and xanthene are virtually completely ionised in it. For still weaker acids the equilibrium constant K for the ionisation

$$RH + NH_2^- \rightleftharpoons R^- + NH_3 \qquad (4.26)$$

is given

$$K = a_{R^-}a_{NH_3}/a_{RH}a_{NH_2^-} \qquad (4.27)$$

Many conjugate bases are highly coloured in this medium so that it is usually possible to monitor the position of equilibrium by using the characteristic absorption band of R^-.

Because of the low dielectric constant of the medium ion association is an important factor even when the concentration of base is low. Unfortunately the ion pairs can not be distinguished spectrophotometrically from the corresponding free ions[26] as both absorb at 335 nm. The equilibrium constant (K_d) for the reaction between free ions and ion pairs,

$$K^+NH_2^- \rightleftharpoons K^+ + NH_2^- \qquad (4.28)$$

can however be determined from conductance measurements; so also can K_d', resulting from the fact that the potassium salt of the conjugate base can exist as an ion pair or as free ions:

$$R^-K^+ \rightleftharpoons R^- + K^+ \qquad (4.29)$$

By using this information and assuming that the activities can be replaced by concentration terms pK_a values for both di-(tolyl)methane and di-(4-methoxyphenyl)methane were determined.

4.3. KINETIC

Acidity constants may be determined from kinetic measurements in a number of different ways. For a series of carbon acids it has been shown[27,28] that the water catalysed rates of ionisation are related to their acid strengths, the plot of $-\log k$ against pK_a taking the form of a curve the slope of which increases with decreasing acid strength. This particular example of the Brönsted relationship (Chapter 8) can then be used to give a rough estimate of the acid strength of a carbon acid the pK_a of which is not known. Alternatively the rate of ionisation itself may be used to describe its "kinetic acidity". This latter approach has been widely adopted.[29,30]

Acidity constants may be obtained if it is possible to assume that the rate, not of ionisation, but of the reverse step (ion recombination) is diffusion controlled. A value of 27 was obtained for the pK_a of phosphine in this way.[31] More recently the rate of the hydroxide catalysed detritiation of dimethyl sulphoxide in water at 25° has been found[32] to be $10^{-8} M^{-1} s^{-1}$. The rate of reaction of dimethyl sulphoxide itself under these conditions will be greater by the amount of the isotope effect k_H/k_T (which is probably between 5 and 10), giving a value $c.$ $10^{-7} M^{-1} s^{-1}$.

For such a weak acid the rate of the reverse process must be close to the limiting value of $10^{10} M^{-1} s^{-1}$ —a value of 10^8 was estimated by Long and Halevi[33] for the reaction between water and the anion of phenylacetylene, a much weaker base. Assuming a value of 10^{10} the pK_a of dimethyl sulphoxide works out at between 32 and 33 in close agreement with the revised value of 32·9 obtained by Steiner[34] from indicator measurements.

The effect of dipolar aprotic solvents in being able to increase the basicity of aqueous hydroxide solutions and also the rates of many reactions carried out in such media provides another method[35] of determining acidity constants. As an example, the rates of detritiation of a "standard" acid such as 9-t-butylfluorene have been measured over a wide H_- range and then repeated in the presence of a second acid which is appreciably ionised under these conditions. The resulting decrease in hydroxide ion concentration (and hence H_-) is reflected in a decrease in the rate of detritiation of the "standard" acid. Assuming that the second-order rate constant for detritiation for a fixed mole percent. of aprotic solvent is indeed constant, and that no catalysis of the detritiation by the anion formed from the more acidic acid (HR_2) occurs, the new hydroxide ion concentration is given by

$$[OH^-]_2 = [OH^-]_1 \times \frac{k_2^T}{k_1^T} \tag{4.30}$$

k_1^T and k_2^T are the pseudo-first-order rate constants for detritiation of the "standard" acid in the absence and in the presence of the other acid, respectively. Then

$$[R_2^-] = [OH]_1 - [OH]_2 \tag{4.31}$$

and

$$[R_2H]_{final} = [R_2H]_{initial} - [R_2^-] \tag{4.32}$$

which on substitution in Eqn (4.33) gives the required pK_a

$$H_- = pK_{R_2H} - \log_{10}[R_2^-]/[R_2H]_{final} \tag{4.33}$$

4.4. THEORETICAL

The acidities of many carbon acids may be calculated by means of the Hückel molecular orbital (HMO) theory[36] if, as is the case for many hydrocarbons, they form planar anions on ionisation. For the reaction given by Eqn (4.1) the π-bond energy of the acid is given by

$$E_\pi = n\alpha + M\beta \qquad (4.34)$$

where n is the number of π electrons, M a dimensionless number obtained from the HMO calculations, and β the bond integral. For the anion

$$E_\pi^- = (n + 2)\alpha + M^-\beta \qquad (4.35)$$

so that the change in π-bond energy on forming the anion is

$$\Delta E_\pi = 2\alpha + \Delta M\beta \qquad (4.36)$$

It is customary practice to neglect electron repulsion and solvation terms as well as steric interactions; all carbon–carbon double bonds are assumed to have the same bond lengths. Changes in σ-bond energies are either neglected by comparison with the π-bond energy changes or treated as constant for a series of similar acids. The free energy for the ionisation is given by Eqn (4.37):

$$\Delta G_0 = -RT \ln K_a = \Delta H_0 + \int_0^T \Delta C_p \, dT - T \int_0^T \frac{\Delta C_p}{T} dT \qquad (4.37)$$

In practice the last two terms tend to cancel out so that

$$-RT \ln K_a \simeq \Delta H_0 \qquad (4.38)$$

If the above assumptions are correct a linear relationship between pK_a and ΔM would be expected with higher acidities being associated with the higher ΔM values. Results[37] show that the method accounts satisfactorily for the pK_a values obtained by McEwen[13] and also for other hydrocarbons able to form planar or nearly planar carbanions. In cases where the carbanion is known to exist as an ion-pair or as a non-planar entity marked deviations in either direction are observed. The same applies for carbon acids containing one or more heteroatoms thereby serving to demonstrate the need for a more refined theory in which the carbon–heteroatom bond overlap integrals are not equal to zero and where allowance for inductive effects is made. Dewar[38] has already shown that the self consistent field (SCF) methods introduced by Pople[39] are superior in some respects to the older HMO methods.

4.5. MISCELLANEOUS

Nuclear magnetic resonance methods have been used in a competitive way to determine the relative acidities of a series of substituted anilines in liquid ammonia.[40] Although the work refers to nitrogen acids it also has important implications for the study of carbon acids as not only does this method permit the ratio $[R^-]/[RH]$ to be determined but the spectra reveal whether or not the anions are formed by simple proton loss. If this is the case it enables one to assign the ultraviolet spectra of the carbanions; if not it strongly suggests that more than one analytical technique be employed in

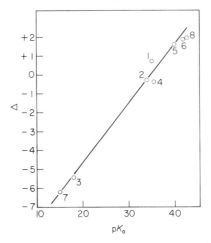

Fig. 4.2. Relationship between pK_a's of carbon acids and Δ, the difference in chemical shift for the carbon acid and its lithium salt.[42] (1) Toluene; (2) diphenylmethane; (3) indene; (4) propene; (5) methane; (6) ethane; (7) cyclopentadiene; (8) propane. pK_a's are on the MSAD scale.[43]

determining the acidity constants. Support for this viewpoint comes from the results of a recent study[41] on the interaction of several nitrophenylmethanes with base-spectral shifts brought about by solvent changes are now known to be due to radical anion formation resulting from electron transfer from the carbanion.

Schaeffer[42] has used the n.m.r. method in another way in order to determine the acidities of carbon acids that cover over 24 pK_a units. The method is based on the fact that n.m.r. spectroscopy provides a measure of the electron density in the vicinity of a proton or group of protons. In practical terms it was found that the acidity was related to the difference in chemical shift between a compound of the type $X-CH_2-Y$ (where X and/or Y are H, alkyl, or aryl) and its lithium salt, $X-CHLi-Y$ (Fig. 4.2). In contrast there is no correlation of pK_a with either the chemical shift of the acid or that of the lithium salt.

Although it has been known for some time[43] that the stability of carbanions with localised charge depends, at least qualitatively, on the amount of s character in the lone pair relatively few attempts have been made to correlate the relative rates of hydrogen exchange with parameters known to be a valid measure of s character e.g. $J(^{13}C-H)$ coupling constants. In at least two studies[44,45] good correlations have been reported.

The possibility that there may be a direct relationship between the acidity and basicity of various compounds has been considered by Arnett,[46] who makes the point that as different resonance and solvation factors must be operating only a limited correlation can at best be expected. Such a correlation has been observed for the benzoic acids where the base strengths are influenced in a manner nearly equal and opposite to the acid strengths.[47,48]

Fluoroadene is one of the most acidic of hydrocarbons (probably because of its high symmetry and complete conjugation in the anion) and a quantitative measure of its acidity was obtained from a study of its distribution between hexane and 97% aqueous methanol as a function of pH.[49]

Mainly because of the lack of theoretically predictable migration distances paper electrophoresis has, until very recently, only been applied to the qualitative separation of various organic and inorganic substances. However, a general equation derived by Kiso et al.[50] relates the relative electrophoretic mobilities of substances to their molecular weight and pK, and the pH of the background solution. A plot of migration distance $vs.$ pH curves for substances of known molecular weight allows the pK to be calculated.[51]

REFERENCES

1. Albert, A. & Serjeant, E. P. (1962). *Ionization Constants of Acids and Bases*, Chapter 2. Methuen, London.
2. Ritchie, C. D. & Uschold, R. E. (1967). *J. Amer. Chem. Soc.* **89**, 1721, 2752 (1968). **90**, 2821.
3. Harned, H. S. & Owen, B. B. (1958). *The Physical Chemistry of Electrolytic Solutions*. Reinhold, New York.
4. Robinson, R. A. & Stokes, R. H. (1959). *Electrolyte Solutions*. Butterworths, London.
5. Monk, C. B. (1961). *Electrolytic Dissociation*. Academic Press, London.
6. Davies, C. W. (1962). *Ion Association*. Butterworths, London.
7. Prue, J. E. (1966). *Ionic Equilibria*. Pergamon Press, London.
8. Ballinger, P. & Long, F. A. (1959). *J. Amer. Chem. Soc.* **81**, 1050.
9. Butin, K. P., Beletskaya, I. P., Kashin, A. N. & Reutov, O. A. (1967). *J. Organometal. Chem.* **10**, 197.

10. Nisli, G., Barnes, D. & Zuman, P. (1970). *J. Chem. Soc. (B)* 764.
11. Breslow, R. & Chu, W. (1969). *J. Amer. Chem. Soc.* 90, 2165.
12. Breslow, R. & Balasubramanian, K. (1969). *J. Amer. Chem. Soc.* 90, 5183.
13. McEwen, W. K. (1936). *J. Amer. Chem. Soc.* 58, 1124.
14. Conant, J. B. & Wheland, G. W. (1932). *J. Amer. Chem. Soc.* 54, 1912.
15. Applequist, D. E. & O'Brien, D. F. (1963). *J. Amer. Chem. Soc.* 85, 743.
16. Salinger, R. M. & Dessy, R. E. (1963). *Tetrahedron Lett.* 729.
17. Streitwieser, A. Jr., Brauman, J. I., Hammons, J. H. & Pudjaatmaka, A. H. (1965). *J. Amer. Chem. Soc.* 87, 384.
18. Streitwieser, A.Jr., Hammons,J. H., Ciuffarin, E. & Brauman,J. I. (1967). *J. Amer. Chem. Soc.* 89, 59.
19. Streitwieser, A. Jr., Ciuffarin, E. & Hammons, J. H. (1967). *J. Amer. Chem. Soc.* 89, 63.
20. Streitwieser, A. Jr., Chang, C. J. & Hollyhead, W. B. (1972). *J. Amer. Chem. Soc.* 94, 5292.
21. Stearns, R. S. & Wheland, G. W. (1947). *J. Amer. Chem. Soc.* 69, 2025.
22. Bell, R. P. & Cox, B. G. (1971). *J. Chem. Soc. (B)* 652.
23. Rochester, C. H. (1966). *Quart. Rev. Chem. Soc.* 20, 511.
24. Bowden, K. (1966). *Chem. Rev.* 66, 119.
25. Takemoto, J. H. & Lagowski, J. J. (1969). *J. Amer. Chem. Soc.* 91, 3785.
26. Cuthrell, R. E. & Lagowski, J. J. (1967). *J. Phys. Chem.* 71, 1298.
27. Pearson, R. G. & Dillon, R. L. (1953). *J. Amer. Chem. Soc.* 75, 2439.
28. Jones, J. R. (1971). *Quart. Rev. Chem. Soc.* 25, 365.
29. Shatenshtein, A. I. (1963). *Adv. Phys. Org. Chem.* (Gold, V. ed) 1, 156.
30. Streitwieser, A. Jr. & Hammons, J. H. (1965). *Progr. Phys. Org. Chem.* (Cohen, S. G., Streitwieser, A. & Taft, R. W. eds.) 3, 41.
31. Weston, R. E. & Bigeleisen, J. (1955). *J. Amer. Chem. Soc.* 76, 3074.
32. Stewart, R. & Jones, J. R. (1967). *J. Amer. Chem. Soc.* 89, 5069.
33. Long, F. A. & Halevi, E. A. (1961). *J. Amer. Chem. Soc.* 83, 2809.
34. Steiner, E. C. & Starkey, J. D. (1967). *J. Amer. Chem. Soc.* 89, 2751.
35. Cockerill, A. F., Earls, D. W., Jones, J. R. & Rumney, T. G. (1973), unpublished results.
36. Streitwieser, A. Jr. (1961). *Molecular Orbital Theory for Organic Chemists*, p. 33. J. Wiley, New York.
37. Streitwieser, A. Jr. (1960). *Tetrahedron Lett.* 23.
38. Dewar, M. J. S. & Thompson, C. C. Jr. (1965). *J. Amer. Chem. Soc.* 87, 4414.
39. Pople, J. A. (1953). *Trans. Faraday Soc.* 49, 1375.
40. Birchall, T. & Jolly, W. L. (1966). *J. Amer. Chem. Soc.* 88, 5439.
41. Fyfe, C. A., Albagli, A. & Stewart, R. (1970). *Can. J. Chem.* 48, 3721.
42. Schaeffer, D. J. (1970). *Chem. Commun.* 1043.
43. Cram, D. J. (1965). *Fundamentals of Carbanion Chemistry*, p. 48. Academic Press, New York.
44. Closs, G. L. & Larrabee, R. B. (1965). *Tetrahedron Lett.* 287.
45. Streitwieser, A. Jr., Caldwell, R. A. & Young, W. R. (1969). *J. Amer. Chem. Soc.* 91, 529.
46. Arnett, E. M. (1963). *Progr. Phys. Org. Chem.* (Cohen, A., Streitwieser, A. & Taft, R. W. eds.) 1, 223.
47. Stewart, R. & Granger, M. R. (1961). *Can. J. Chem.* 39, 2508.
48. Stewart, R. & Yates, K. (1960). *J. Amer. Chem. Soc.* 82, 4059.
49. Rapoport, H. & Smolinsky, G. (1958). *J. Amer. Chem. Soc.* 80, 2910.
50. Kiso, Y., Kobayashi, M., Kitaoka, Y., Kawamoto, K. & Takada, J. (1968). *J. Chromatogr.* 36, 215.
51. Mori, I., Shinogi, M., Falk, E. & Kiso, Y. (1972). *Talanta* 19, 299.

5. The Acidities of Carbon Acids—Results

5.1. CYANO COMPOUNDS

By simple structural modifications the acidities of cyanocarbon acids (Table 5.1) may be made to cover a wide range $(-5 < pK_a < 30)$ resulting in some compounds being more acidic than mineral acids e.g. tetracyanopropene is a stronger acid than perchloric acid. In general the compounds are very stable to hydrolysis and the process of ionisation seems both uncomplicated, and readily reversible. The pK_a's of the more acidic compounds are usually determined from ultraviolet or visible spectra in solutions of strong mineral acids since the strong characteristic electronic absorptions of the anions disappear on protonation.

The remarkable strength of the polyfunctional compounds can be ascribed[2] to the high degree of resonance stabilisation in the anions, which is not possible in the protonated form:

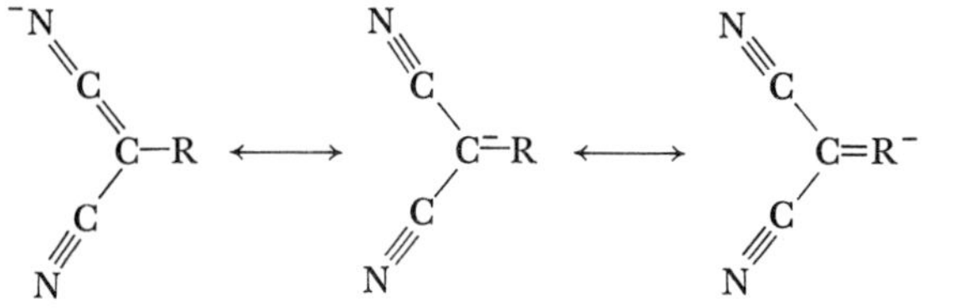

If structure (1) can resonate through conjugation with the R group i.e. if (2) is a good resonance structure, then the acid will be relatively strong. The situation where structures (1) and (2) are identical should also be particularly favourable and in fact the simplest of such structures (pentacyanopropene, tetracyanopropene) are exceptionally strong acids. The particular case of cyanoform is interesting in that structure (2) reduces to one of three structures with the charge on the cyano group.

The thermodynamic aspects of the ionisation of several cyanocarbon acids have been investigated[6] from which it appears that a good correlation between ΔH_0 and pK_a exists and that the major contribution to the variation of pK_a is from the enthalpy term. This result is consistent with the fact that the large variations in acidity are due primarily to variations in resonance stabilisation of the anion and the effect of cyanide group electronegativity on the C—H bond strength.

The effect of cyano groups on acidity can be clearly seen by reference to compounds No. 1, 4, 10, and 13 in Table 5.1. There is little evidence of the "saturation effect" so noticeable for the nitro compounds (p. 74). Somewhat similar behaviour has been observed[7]

TABLE 5.1

Acidities of cyanocarbon acids in aqueous solutions[1,2] at 25°

	Acid	$pK_a(H_2O)$
1.	Methyl cyanide	∼ 25[a]
2.	1,4-Dicyano-2-butene	20–21[b]
3.	t-Butylmalononitrile	13·1[c]
4.	Malonitrile	11·20[d]
5.	Hydrogen cyanide	9·21[d]
6.	Bromomalononitrile	∼ 5[a]
7.	p-(Tricyanovinyl)-phenyldicyanomethane	0·75[d], 0·60[2]
8.	Methyl dicyanoacetate	− 2·8[d]
9.	Hexacyanoheptatriene	− 3·55[e], − 3·90[f]
10.	Cyanoform	− 5·13[e], − 5·0[f]
11.	Bis-(tricyanovinyl)-amine	−6·07[e], − 5·98[f]
12.	Tricyanovinyl alcohol	− 5·3[e], − 5·0[f]
13.	Tetracyanopropene	< − 8[e]
14.	Pentacyanopropene	< − 8·5[e]
15.	Hexacyanoisobutylene	< − 8·5[e]

[a] quoted in ref 3; [b] ref. 4; [c] ref. 5; [d] ref. 6; [e] refer to aqueous perchloric acid; [f] refer to aqueous sulphuric acid.

for a series of cyanated cyclopentadienes (Table 5.2) which have been prepared by taking advantage of the high reactivity of sodium hydride to slightly acid hydrogens but low reactivity to other bonding situations. Reaction of cyanogen chloride, sodium hydride and cyclopentadiene can be stopped at the mono-, di-, or tri-cyano stage merely by limiting the amount of cyanogen chloride; further reaction of the tricyano-compound requires a Friedel–Craft's catalyst.[8] The stability of the white potassium salts increases gradually from the unstable monocyano- to the very stable pentacyanocyclopentadiene.

Not all the pK_a's of the cyanocyclopentadienes could be measured in water. For these compounds calculated values were obtained by subtracting 9·1 from the pK_a value in methyl cyanide as this was the difference found for the pK_a of 3,4-dicyanocyclopentadiene in the two solvents.

TABLE 5.2

Acidities of cyanocyclopentadienes in water and methyl cyanide[7]*

Acid	$pK_a(H_2O)$	$pK_a(CH_3CN)$	$pK_a(H_2O)$ calc
Cyclopentadiene	15		
Cyanocyclopentadiene	9·78		
2,5-Dicyanocyclopentadiene	2·52		
3,4-Dicyanocyclopentadiene	1·11	10·17	1·1
1,3,4,-Tricyano-5-methyl-cyclopentadiene		3·40	−5·7
1,3,5,-Tricyanocyclopentadiene		3·00	−6·1
1,2,5-Tricyanocyclopentadiene		1·44	−7·8
		1·99	−7·2
2,3,4,5-Tetracyanocyclopentadiene		~0·0	−9·1
		~0·2	−8·9
Pentacyanocyclopentadiene		<−2	<−11

* Temperature not specified but probably close to 25°.

5.2. NITRO COMPOUNDS

The acidities of nitro compounds have been, with the possible exception of the hydrocarbons, the most extensively studied of the various carbon acids. Whilst estimates of the pK_a of methane vary greatly (a value of 58 has been mentioned),[9] the introduction of a single nitro group brings about a much higher acidity—nitromethane has a pK_a of 10·2 at 25° in water.[10] In contrast to what is usually found *methyl* substitution leads to an increase in acidity [CH_3NO_2 (10·2), $CH_3CH_2NO_2(8·60)$, $(CH_3)_2CHNO_2(7·74)$][10] whereas the rates of reaction with hydroxide ion decrease in the same sequence. Successive introduction of methyl groups are expected to decrease the acidity through the operation of the inductive effect but increase it by hyperconjugative stabilisation of the nitronate anion—clearly the second contribution is more important that the first in these compounds.

For a series of 1-aryl-1-nitroethanes ($ArCHCH_3NO_2$) electron withdrawing substituents decrease whereas electron donating substituents in the meta and para positions increase the acidity

(Table 5.3). A Hammett correlation with the substituent constant σ gives a ρ value of 1·62, which is reduced to 1·06 if σ values of substituted benzoic acids, determined in the same medium [50% (v/v) dioxane–water] as employed for the pK_a determinations, are used.[11] The value of ρ in 50% (v/v) methanol–water[12] is 1·07.

Substituent effects on the acidities of 1-aryl-2-nitropropanes in 50% (v/v) methanol–water (Table 5.4) parallel those in the 1-aryl-1-nitroethane series (despite the fact that direct conjugative effects are

TABLE 5.3

Acidities of 1-aryl-1-nitroethanes ($ArCHCH_3NO_2$)

Substituent	pK_a		
	in 50% (v/v) H_2O–MeOH[12] at 23° ± 1°	in water[13] at 25° $I = 0.10$	in 50% (v/v) dioxane–H_2O[11] at 20°
p-Me	(8·55)[a]		10·47
m-Me	8·62	7·49	10·53
H	(8·52)[a]	7·39	10·30
m-MeO	8·48		10·38
p-F	8·36		
p-Cl	8·23		9·81
m-F	8·22	7·05	
m-Cl	8·20	7·05	
p-CF$_3$	8·05		
m-CF$_3$	8·12	6·96	
m-Br			9·93
p-Br			10·00
m-NO$_2$	7·73	6·67	9·18
p-NO$_2$	7·49	6·51	9·06
m,m'-(NO$_2$)$_2$		(5·95)[b]	

[a] Uncertain due to sample decomposition; [b] estimated value.

only possible for the latter) although they are much smaller ($\rho = 0.395$) than for the former. These compounds are the carbon acid analogues of the benzoic acids with respect to the distance between the ring substituents and the acidic hydrogen atoms whilst the 1-aryl-1-nitroethanes are the carbon acid analogues of phenols or amines where the effect of substituents are much more pronounced— for ArOH $\rho = 3.2$ and for ArNH$_3^+$ $\rho = 3.4$, both in the same medium (30% ethanol–water). The principal reason for the difference lies in the way in which substituents affect the acidity of the carbon acid and the basicity of its conjugate base in the same manner whereas for the oxygen and nitrogen acids substituents probably affect the acidity of the acid and the basicity of its conjugate base in an opposite manner.

Thus a m-NO_2 substituent increases the rate of deprotonation of $ArCHCH_3NO_2$ but it also increases the rate of protonation of $ArCCH_3=NO_2^-$. On the other hand the same substituent increases the effectiveness of benzoic acid as a catalyst for the dehydration of acetaldehyde hydrate by 2·6 fold[14] but decreases the catalytic effect of benzoate ion on the base-catalysed bromination of ethyl aceto-acetate by 2·3 fold.[15] The positions of the equilibria for reactions of

TABLE 5.4

Acidities of 1-aryl-2-nitropropanes[12] ($ArCH_2CHCH_3NO_2$)

Substituent	pK_a in 50% (v/v) H_2O–MeOH at $23° \pm 1°$
p-MeO	9·20
p-Me	9·20
m-Me	9·18
H	9·13
p-F	9·06
m-MeO	9·09
p-Cl	9·05
m-F	9·03
m-Cl	9·00
m-CF_3	9·02
p-CF_3	8·94
m-NO_2	8·85
p-NO_2	8·76

$ArCO_2H$ and $ArOH$ with water are determined primarily by the deprotonation rates however since the reverse protonations of $ArCO_2^-$ and ArO^- by H_3O^+ are essentially diffusion controlled.[16]

The acidities of some arylnitromethanes in water (Table 5.5) are between 0·6 and 1·1 pK units lower than in 50% (v/v) methanol-water. A similar difference (1·0–1·1 pK units) is observed for the 1-arylnitroethanes, but on going to 50% (v/v) dioxane-water this is increased to between 1·4 and 2·0 pK units (Table 5.3). Similar findings have been reported for some β-diketones (p. 78).

The effect of substituents, and in particular fluorine, on the acidities of some nitro-aliphatics, have been studied by Kamlet.[17] Data for three series of mononitromethanes as well as literature

values for dinitromethane and the halodinitromethanes are summarised in Table 5.6. In contrast to the findings of several
workers[18,19] from deuterium exchange studies that α-fluorine substitution increases the kinetic acidity of polyhaloaliphatic hydrocarbons, similar substitution in the nitromethanes leads to a decrease
in acidity in all four series. It is also evident from Table 5.6 that the
magnitudes of α-fluorine as well as α-chlorine influences on pK_a
depend strongly on the nature of the third substituent Y. Acid
weakening by α-fluorine increases in the order, $Y = CO_2Et$, $CONH_2$,
Cl, NO_2, while acid strengthening by α-chlorine decreases in almost
the same sequence. Moreover, in the nitroacetates and nitro-
acetamides, where fluorine's effects are small, chlorine's effects are

TABLE 5.5

Acidities of arylnitromethanes[13] $(ArCH_2NO_2)$

Substituent	pK_a	
	in water at 25° $I = 0.05$	in 50% (v/v) H_2O–MeOH at 25° $I = 0.01$
o-Me	7·60	8·70
m-Me	6·97	8·00
H	6·88	7·93
m-Cl	6·63	7·48
m-NO$_2$	6·30	7·05
p-NO$_2$	5·89	6·49

large; in the chloronitromethanes the chlorine effect decreases while
the fluorine effect becomes larger, and this trend continues in the
dinitromethanes where fluorine substitution increases the pK_a by 4
units while the chlorine effect has become very small.

In these compounds acid strengthening contributions composed
mainly of inductive effects, increased anion size with greater dis-
persal of the negative charge, and d-orbital stabilisation of the
carbanion must be operative but it seems unlikely than any of these
are sufficiently different to account for the observed changes in
pK_a. The probable explanation lies more with the acid-weakening
factors operative in the fluorine compounds. Decreased acidity on
replacement of α hydrogen by halogen may result from either
destabilisation of the carbanion conjugate base or stabilisation of the
unionised acid. The central carbon atom in these nitro-carbanions is
sp^2 hybridised with the negative charge delocalised over the π
system formed by this carbon atom, the nitro group and the negative

substituent Y. The proximity of fluorine and to a lesser extent chlorine may lead to repulsion of charge between the π system and their p electrons, leading to destabilisation of the fluoronitrocarbanion relative to the chloro compound.

Another factor stems from the suggestion by Hine[20] that the halogen bond to sp^2 carbon is weaker than to sp^3 carbon because the former is more electronegative. This effect, which depends on the square of the electronegativity difference between the atoms involved, is larger for fluorine than for chlorine. Since such a change to sp^2 hybridisation occurs on ionisation of the nitromethanes, this

TABLE 5.6

Acidities of substituted nitromethanes[17]

$$\left(\begin{array}{c} O_2N \diagdown \quad \diagup H \\ \quad C \\ Y \diagup \quad \diagdown H(X) \end{array}\right)$$

Substituent	pK_a in water at $25°$ $I = 0.06$
Y = COOEt	
X = Cl	4·16
H	5·75
F	6·28
Y = CONH$_2$	
X = Cl	3·50
H	5·18
F	5·89
Y = Cl	
X = Cl	5·99
H	7·20
F	10·14
Y = NO$_2$	
X = Cl	3·80
H	3·57
F	7·70

would again tend to destabilise the fluoro relative to the chloro or parent nitrocarbanion unless the increase in electronegativity of carbon is compensated by a decrease due to the partial negative charge on carbon.

Factors which influence the stability of the free acid include double bond—no bond resonance[21] and intra-molecular hydrogen bonding (particularly by fluorine). Although the importance of the first factor has been questioned[21] it does go some way to explaining the observed trend in pK_a's. Fluoronitromethane should be stabilised relative to the chloro or parent nitromethane because of fluorine's greater ability to share one of its lone pairs in halogen double bonding (canonical structures 4–6). Much of this stabilisation would be lost in the anion where the negative charge discourages electron donation

(4)   (5)   (6)

by fluorine. The relative contribution of 6 to the resonance hybrid should increase with the ability of Y to form a stable anion; chlorine and nitro, being much better leaving groups than carbethoxyl and carbamyl, stabilisation of the unionised species would be greatest for Y = Cl and NO_2.

The acidities of dinitroalkanes $(RCH(NO_2)_2)$ have been the subject of considerable study by various workers. In all cases attempts have been made to relate the measured pK_a's to the Taft σ^* values of nonconjugated substituents R and assess the significance of deviations from the relationship. Thus Novikov and co-workers[22] express their results in terms of Eqn (5.1) whereas Kamlet and co-workers[23] favour a slightly different expression [Eqn (5.2)].

$$pK_a = 5\cdot22 - 1\cdot74\sigma^* \qquad (5.1)$$

$$pK_a = 5\cdot24 - 3\cdot60\sigma^* \qquad (5.2)$$

$$pK_a = 5\cdot23 - 3\cdot29\sigma^* \qquad (5.3)$$

More recently the acidities of a large number of these compounds have been measured[24] (Table 5.7) and related to the σ^* values by means of Eqn (5.3).

Inductive substituent effects in systems where R is once removed from the atom bearing the ionising proton, such as RCOOH or RCH_2OH, give ρ^* values in the range 1·3–1·7 but in circumstances where it is directly fixed to the atom bearing the ionising proton, such as RNH_2, ρ^* values are higher (2·6–3·3) and similar to those quoted in Eqns (5.2), (5.3).

Serious deviations from the pK_a–σ^* relationship (Fig. 5.1), are observed in several instances and may be discussed in terms of the stabilities of the carbanions which are primarily governed by various resonance contributions, and Kamlet and Glover[25] have suggested

(7)   (8)   (9)

TABLE 5.7

Acidities of dinitro-compounds[24] $(R–CH(NO_2)_2)$

No.	Compound R =	pK_a in water at 20°	No.	R =	pK_a
1.	$(CH_3)_2CH$	6·77, 6·71[a]	23.	$(CH_3)_3CNHCO(CH_2)_2$	4·43
2.	$(o–CH_3C_6H_4)_2CH$	5·80	24.	$CH_3OCO(CH_2)_2$	4·43
3.	CH_3CH_2	5·61, 5·49[a]	25.	$CH_3NHCO(CH_2)_2$	4·41
4.	$CH_3(CH_2)_3$	5·45, 5·34[a]	26.	$N≡C(CH_2)_3$	4·34
5.	$(CH_3)_2CHCH_2$	5·40, 5·36[a]	27.	$CH_3CONH(CH_2)_2$	4·28
6.	$^-OCO(CH_2)_2$	5·35	28.	$HOCH_2$	4·24
7.	CH_3	5·30, 5·13[a]	29.	$CH_3OCONH(CH_2)_2$	4·23
8.	$CH_3CH=CHCH_2$	5·26	30.	$CH_3COO(CH_2)_2$	4·19
9.	$NH_2COCH_2CH(CH_3)$	5·24	31.	$N^+H_3NHCO(CH_2)_2$	4·15
10.	$HO(CH_2)_3$	5·06	32.	$CH_3CONHCH_2$	4·00
11.	$(CH_3)_3CCH_2$	5·05	33.	$CH_3COCH(OH)CH_2$	3·98
12.	$N≡C(CH_2)_4$	5·00	34.	$N^+H_3(CH_2)_3$	3·93
13.	$(C_6H_5)_2CH$	4·97	35.	$o–NO_2C_6H_4CH_2$	3·89
14.	$CH_2=CHCH_2$	4·92, 4·95[a]	36.	$m–N≡CC_6H_4CH_2$	3·88
15.	$Cl_3C(CH_2)_3$	4·79	37.	$m–NO_2C_6H_4CH_2$	3·77
16.	$NH_2CO(CH_2)_3$	4·75	38.	$CH_3C(NO_2)_2(CH_2)_2$	3·72
17.	$HO(CH_2)_2$	4·73, 4·44[a]	39.	$NH(NO_2)(CH_2)_2$	3·71
18.	$CH_3CO(CH_2)_2$	4·73	40.	$O_2NO(CH_2)_2$	3·67
19.	$C_6H_5CH_2$	4·54	41.	H	3·63, 3·57[a]
20.	$NH_2CO(CH_2)_2$	4·49	42.	Br	3·58
21.	$(CH_3)_2NCO(CH_2)_2$	4·49	43.	CH_3OCH_2	3·56, 3·48[a]
22.	$CH_3C(=NOH)(CH_2)_2$	4·46	44.	$Cyclo–C_6H_{11}N(NO_2)CH_2$	3·55

No.	Group	Value	No.	Group	Value
45.	$N{\equiv}C(CH_2)_2$	2·50, 3·45[a]	64.	$CH_3OCH_2C(NO_2)_2CH_2$	1·45
46.	$CH_3N(NO_2)(CH_2)_2$	3·45	65.	$CH_3C(NO_2)_2CH_2$	1·37, 1·35[a]
47.	$C_6H_5CH_2OCH_2$	3·44	66.	NH_2CO	1·30
48.	NH_2COCH_2	3·41	67.	$NH_2CO(CH_2)_2C(NO_2)_2CH_2$	1·16
49.	$NO_2(CH_2)_2$	3·37, 3·24[a]	68.	$CH_3OCO(CH_2)_2C(NO_2)_2CH_2$	1·13
50.	$2,4\text{-}(NO_2)_2C_6H_3CH_2$	3·35	69.	CH_3OCO	0·98
51.	$N{\equiv}CCH(CH_3)CH_2$	3·27	70.	$N{\equiv}C(CH_2)_2C(NO_2)_2CH_2$	0·90
52.	I	3·19	71.	NO_2	0·14
53.	$N\text{-(Phthalimido)-}CH_2$	3·17	72.	$N^+(CH_3)_3CH_2$	-1·87
54.	CH_3OCOCH_2	3·08, 3·08[a]	73.	$N{\equiv}C$	-6·22
55.	$CH_3CH_2CH(NO_2)CH_2$	2·96	74.	$CH_3(CH_2)_2$	5·35[a]
56.	$CH_3CH(NO_2)CH_2$	2·94	75.	$CH_3(CH_2)_4$	5·37[a]
57.	$(N\text{-Succinimido)-}CH_2$	2·92	76.	$CH_3(CH_2)_5$	5·46[a]
58.	$N^+H_3(CH_2)_2$	2·71	77.	$CH_3(CH_2)_6$	5·46[a]
59.	$CH_3N(NO_2)CH_2$	2·69	78.	$CH_3(CH_2)_7$	5·46[a]
60.	$CH_3CH_2N(NO_2)CH_2$	2·44	79.	$CH_3(CH_2)_8$	5·45[a]
61.	$N{\equiv}CCH_2$	2·34, 2·27[a]	80.	C_6H_5	3·71[a]
62.	$CH_3C(Cl)(NO_2)CH_2$	2·32	81.	$CH(NO_2)_2CH_2$	1·09[a]
63.	$CH_3CH_2C(NO_2)_2CH_2$	1·47			

[a] Data of ref. 23 at 25° in H_2O.

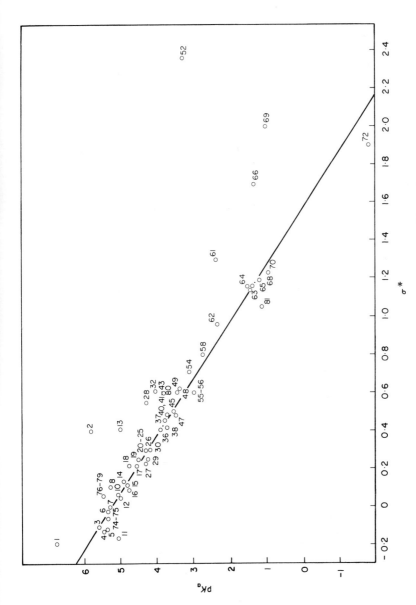

Fig. 5.1. Dependence of pK_a for 1,1-dimitro-compounds on polar substituent constants.[24] The numbers correspond to those in Table 5.7.

that oxygen–oxygen repulsion would impart a tendency toward skewing of the C—N(—O)—O planes from the R—C(—N)—N planes, in consequence of which, resonance contributions of the individual nitro groups in the preferred conformations would be less than in totally coplanar situations. Where steric considerations permit, an alternative mechanism for relief of O—O repulsions would involve spreading of the N—C—N angle from the normal $120°$ with corresponding contraction of the R—C—N angles. Such an effect, by increasing the O—O distances, would allow lesser nitro group skews in the preferred conformation than would be the case if the N—C—N angle were $120°$. It follows that the greater the steric requirements of R in $RC(NO_2)_2^-$ the more difficult it becomes to contract the R—C—N angles and expand the N—C—N angle. The O—O repulsions manifest themselves in greater angles of skew of the C—N(—O)—O planes from the R—C(—N)—N plane and lesser contributions of resonance structures 8 and 9 to the structure of the carbanion.

It has also been pointed out that skewing resulting from such O—O repulsions could account for the "saturation effect" noted by Pearson and Dillon[3] in the pK_a's of the polynitromethanes but absent in the corresponding cyanocompounds i.e.

	pK_a		pK_a
CH_4	~40 (58)		
CH_3NO_2	10·2	CH_3CN	~25
$CH_2(NO_2)_2$	3·6	$CH_2(CN)_2$	11·5
$CH(NO_2)_3$	0	$CH(CN)_3$	−5

The linear cyano groups exert fully additive resonance effects in all cases but the nitro groups exert fractionally smaller resonance effects as the degree of substitution and the consequent extent of skewing increases.

Amongst the compounds that deviate markedly from the pK_a–σ^* plot are those that are branched at the α-carbon atoms (nos. 1, 2, 9 and 13)—the steric effect of the substituent prevents coplanar disposition of the nitro groups; so also do compounds branched at the β carbon atom (nos. 11 and 72) and also the halogenodinitromethanes (nos. 42 and 52) for reasons mentioned previously.

5.3. SULPHONES

Although Pearson and Dillon[3] from an extrapolation based on the relationship between rates of ionisation and pK_a's of ketones estimated the pK_a of dimethyl sulphone to be 23 more recent work[26] shows that in dimethyl sulphoxide at least it is considerably less acidic than was thought (Table 5.8). Methyl substitution for hydrogen causes an increase of 1·5–2 pK_a units (compare 4 and 5 and also 2 and 3) whilst phenyl substitution causes a decrease of 6·5 pK_a units (compare 1 and 4). Substitution of phenyl group for a methyl group at a β position causes a decrease of 1·5 pK_a units (compare 1 and 2).

Bordwell and Steiner[26] have compared these effects with those observed for other oxygenated carbon acids for which equilibrium

TABLE 5.8

Acidities of sulphones in dimethyl sulphoxide[26] at 25°

Acid	Formula	pK_a (DMSO)
1. Dimethyl sulphone	$CH_3SO_2CH_3$	28·5
2. Methyl phenyl sulphone	$CH_3SO_2C_6H_5$	27
3. Ethyl phenyl sulphone	$CH_3CH_2SO_2C_6H_5$	29
4. Dibenzyl sulphone	$(C_6H_5CH_2)_2SO_2$	22
5. Di-α-methyl benzyl sulphone	$[C_6H_5CH(CH_3)]_2SO_2$	23·5
6. Trimethylene sulphone		>30
7. Tetramethylene sulphone		>31
8. Pentamethylene sulphone		>31

data are available, such as the nitro compounds. As discussed previously methyl substitution in this series causes a decrease, rather than an increase, in pK_a (CH_3NO_2, 10·2; $CH_3CH_2NO_2$, 8·6; $(CH_3)_2CHNO_2$, 7·7). Phenyl substitution causes a decrease in pK_a (CH_3NO_2, 10·2; $C_6H_5CH_2NO_2$, 6·88) as in the sulphone series but of only 3·3 units, as compared to 6·5 units. Substitution of a phenyl group for a methyl group at a β position appears to have relatively little effect $\{CH_3(CH_2)_2NO_2$, $pK_a = 8·98$; $C_6H_5(CH_2)_2NO_2$, $pK_a = 8·68\}$.

A number of factors must be operating to make NO_2 and CH_3SO_2 of about equal effectiveness in promoting the acidity of oxygen acids (nitric and methanesulphonic acids are of similar acidity) but markedly different for carbon acids produced by substitution of these two groups in methane. Undoubtedly one of the most important is the degree of resonance stabilisation in the conjugate bases. In the oxygen series the conjugate bases, NO_3^- and $CH_3SO_3^-$ each have three equivalent resonance contributions but this is not so for $CH_2NO_2^-$ and $CH_3SO_2CH_2^-$. However the $CH_2{=}NO_2^-$ contribution is important not only because of the concentration of the negative charge on oxygen but also because of the near equivalence of the C=N and N=O bond energies, and compares favourably with the poor conjugative stabilisation provided by the $2p$-$3d$ overlap in the $[CH_3SO_2{=}CH_2]^-$ contribution.

TABLE 5.9

Acidities of some disulphones in water[27] at $25°$

Acid	Formula	$pK_a(H_2O)$
Bis(ethylsulphonyl) ethane	$(CH_3CH_2SO_2)_2CHCH_3$	14·6
Bis(methylsulphonyl) methane	$(CH_3SO_2)_2CH_2$	12·6
Bis(ethylsulphonyl) methane	$(CH_3CH_2SO_2)_2CH_2$	12·2
Bis(ethylsulphonyl) phenylmethane	$(CH_3CH_2SO_2)_2CHC_6H_5$	12·1
Bis(ethylsulphonyl) bromomethane	$(CH_3CH_2SO_2)_2CHBr$	10·7

The disulphones are, as expected, considerably more acidic than the monosulphones and in the few cases reported[27] the electron-donating and -withdrawing effects of substituents, such as CH_3 and Br follow the customary behaviour (Table 5.9).

5.4. KETONES

Unlike the rates of ionisation, which have been extensively studied, very little work has been done on the acidities of ketones. These compounds differ from other carbon acids in that they can and frequently do exist in two forms, keto and enol, having different acidities e.g. the enol of cyclopentanone in water has a pK_a of 11·8, 4·6 units more acidic than the keto form.[28]

The acidities of β-diketones have however been subjected to greater study[29,30] as the pK_a's are frequently required with some accuracy in order to make better comparisons of the formation constants of chelate compounds formed between metal ions and the β-diketones. The results in Table 5.10 show that most of the pK_a's

TABLE 5.10

Acidities of β-diketones (RCOCH$_2$COR$'$) in water at 20°C

R	R$'$	pK_a	Ref.
CH$_3$	CH$_3$	8·84, 8·82	31, 32
C$_6$H$_5$	C$_6$H$_5$	8·95[a]	35
C$_2$H$_5$	C$_2$H$_5$	9·55	31
(CH$_3$)$_2$CH	(CH$_3$)$_2$CH	9·82	31
(CH$_3$)$_3$C	CH$_3$	10·00	31
(CH$_3$)$_3$C	(CH$_3$)$_3$C	11·57, 11·77	31, 33
CH$_3$(CH$_2$)$_2$	CH$_3$(CH$_2$)$_2$	9·67	34
CH$_3$(CH$_2$)$_3$	CH$_3$(CH$_2$)$_3$	9·72	34
CH$_3$(CH$_2$)$_4$	CH$_3$(CH$_2$)$_4$	9·71	34
(CH$_3$)$_2$CH.CH$_2$	(CH$_3$)$_2$CH.CH$_2$	9·88	34
C$_6$H$_5$	CH$_3$	8·7[a]	36
C$_6$H$_5$	CF$_3$	6·56[a]	37
CH$_3$	CF$_3$	6·79	37
CF$_3$	CF$_3$	5·35	37
C$_4$H$_3$S	CF$_3$	6·1[a]	3

[a] At 25°.

are in the range 8–11 and vary in a predictable manner as one or both of the R groups is changed.

Replacement of a CH$_3$ group by a trifluoromethyl group increases the acidity by close to 2 pK units. In contrast the replacement of one of the carbonyl groups by a sulphone grouping makes the carbon acid, (CH$_3$SO$_2$CH$_2$COCH$_3$)[38] less acidic than acetylacetone by 1pK

TABLE 5.11

Acidities of β-diketones[30] (RCOCH$_2$COR$'$) and monothio-β-diketones (RCSCH$_2$COR$'$) in 74·5 vol % dioxan at 30°

R	R$'$	β-Diketone	Thio-β-diketone
C$_6$H$_5$	C$_6$H$_5$	13·75	11·14, 11·40
CH$_3$	C$_6$H$_5$	12·85	10·43, 10·40
CH$_3$	CH$_3$	12·60	10·26, 10·20
C$_4$H$_3$S	CF$_3$	8·64	7·05
C$_4$H$_3$S	CH$_3$		10·40
C$_4$H$_3$S	C$_4$H$_3$S		10·80
CH$_3$	(CH$_3$)$_3$C		10·65
(CH$_3$)$_3$C	CH$_3$		12·02
CH$_3$	C$_{10}$H$_7$		11·20
C$_6$H$_5$	C$_{10}$H$_7$		11·45

unit; the disulphone $(CH_3SO_2CH_2SO_2CH_3)$ has a pK_a of 12·50 under similar conditions.[39]

The acidities of β-diketones in dioxane–water mixtures[40] vary linearly with the mole fraction of dioxan, the pK_a values in 74·5 vol % dioxan being from 1–4 units higher (Table 5.11) than in water. Similar behaviour has been reported for monothio-β-diketones[41] $(RCSCH_2COR)$, the pK_a's of which are from 2·0–2·7 units lower than those of their oxygen analogues.

5.5. HYDROCARBONS

Whilst the literature abounds with qualitative and semi-quantitative observations relating to syntheses and relative ease of metallation of hydrocarbons only recently have quantitative values of acidities become available. In this short time interval however a considerable amount of data has been accumulated[42,43] partly prompted by the fact that the molecules frequently lend themselves to theoretical considerations and partly because of the interest in the absorption spectra of the anions.

The extensively studied fluorenes owe their acidities to the planarity as well as the anion stabilising properties of the cyclopenta-dienyl ring system. Measurements have been made in several solvents and show a remarkable consistency, irrespective of the importance of ion association. This result stems from extensive charge delocalisation in the highly conjugated carbanions so that specific solvent effects and hydrogen bonding are kept to a minimum. 9-Phenyl-fluorene, for example, one of the most thoroughly studied of carbon acids and frequently used as an anchor in the acidity function approach, has pK_a values of 18·59 (DMSO-EtOH),[44] 18·49 (sulpholane–water),[45] 18·38 (DMSO–water),[44] 18·1 (DMSO)[46] and 16·4 (DMSO).[47,48] The good agreement may, however, be some-what fortuitous as it has been pointed out[49] that the value of 18·59 for example was not obtained without some difficulty. A transition from water to ethanol and the use of a number of nitrodiphenyl-methane and nitrotriphenylmethane indicators, the spectra of which were highly solvent sensitive, was involved. Consequently it is frequently the case that more information can be obtained from a comparison of relative acidities than of absolute values.

The pK_a's of 2-substituted fluorenes[50] (Table 5.16, nos. 1, 3, 6, 7, 10, 11) can be correlated with the Hammett σ substituent constant by assuming that the substituents in this position can be considered as meta-substituents. The reaction constant ρ lies between 6 and 7, higher than that for substituted phenols[51] (2·23) and anilines[52] (4·07) and consistent with the increased delocalisation achieved as the electronegativity of the atom bonded to the ionisable proton is decreased.

The pK_a's of the 9-substituted fluorenes[50] (Table 5.16, nos. 9, 12, 13, 14, 21) correlate well with Taft σ^* values, the reaction constant ρ^* again being large (4·6) and higher than that obtained for the ionisation of both thiols[53] (3·5) and alcohols[53] (3·9) in water. The correlation is further improved if the point for the unsubstituted fluorene is removed, as was also found when the pK_a's measured in cesium cyclohexylamide–cyclohexylamine[54] (CsCHA–CHA) are plotted against σ^*; the reaction constant in this case was very similar (4·55) to that observed in DMSO–H_2O. It could be that the secondary hydrogens of fluorene correspond to a different acidity

TABLE 5.12

Acidities of substituted 9-phenylfluorenes[56] in dimethyl sulphoxide–water solutions at 25°

Acid	pK_a^*(H_2O)
4-Cyano-9-phenylfluorene	15·40
9-Phenyl-3,4-benzofluorene	16·60
9-(m-Chlorophenyl)fluorene	17·66
9-(m-Trifluoromethylphenyl)fluorene	17·69
9-(p-Chlorophenyl)fluorene	18·10
9-(m-Anisyl)fluorene	18·47
9-(m-Tolyl)fluorene	18·84
9-(p-Tolyl)fluorene	18·96
9-(p-Anisyl)fluorene	19·01
9-(p-N,N-Dimethylaminophenyl)fluorene	19·61

* Relative to 9-phenylfluorene (18·59).

order than the tertiary hydrogens of the 9-alkylfluorenes. 9-t-Butyl-fluorene is less acidic than expected, presumably because of the increase in steric strain in going from hydrocarbon to anion.

The pK_a's of substituted 9-phenylfluorenes[55] (Table 5.12) in DMSO–H_2O do not exhibit a linear relationship with the Hammett σ substituent constant presumably because the 9-phenyl group is unable to attain coplanarity with the fluorene nucleus in the carbanion. Thus only part of the mesomeric effect of the substituent is transmitted to the site of ionisation. The modified Hammett equation (Eqn 5.4)

$$\log K/K_0 = \rho(\sigma_I + n\sigma_R) \tag{5.4}$$

allows for this reduction in transmission and provides a satisfactory explanation of the results. The substituent constant is divided into its inductive and mesomeric components and the factor n allows partial transmission of the latter. The results suggest that the 9-phenyl ring is displaced from planarity with the fluorene nucleus by $c.$ 39°, close to the value predicted from molecular orbital calculations.

Although the inductive effect of alkyl substituents is still a matter of some controversy[56] there seems to be a good deal of evidence that alkyl groups are generally electron donating relative to hydrogen. However, in both ionic and ion-pair systems 9-methyl-fluorene is more acidic than fluorene itself (Table 5.13) and various

TABLE 5.13

Acidities of 9-alkylfluorenes in various media

Carbon acid	pK_a*		
	CsCHA–CHA[54]	LiCHA–CHA[54]	$(CH_3)_4N^+OH^-$–DMSO–H_2O[50]
Fluorene	22·74	22·55	22·10
9-Methylfluorene	22·33	22·60	21·80
9-Ethylfluorene	22·60	22·96	22·22
9-i-Propylfluorene	23·20	23·75	22·70
9-t-Butylfluorene	24·25	24·82	23·41
9-Benzylfluorene	21·27	—	21·20

    * Relative to 9-phenylfluorene.

explanations have been offered. Bowden and co-workers[50] suggest that in the fluorene series the inductive effect of all the alkyl groups is almost the same but is opposed by "anti-hyperconjugation" of any α-carbon hydrogen bonds present:

$$\underset{\underset{H}{|}}{\overset{\overset{H}{|}}{R-C-C^-}}\diagdown \quad \longleftrightarrow \quad \overset{H^-}{\underset{\underset{R}{|}}{R-C=C}}\diagdown$$

This latter effect reaches a maximum for the methyl group which has three α-hydrogens.

The observed trend in acidities may also be rationalised in terms of alkyl group stabilisation of carbanions by dispersion interactions[47] but a more likely explanation, favoured by Streitwieser,[54] is based on changes in σ-bond strength on ionisation. In the case of fluorene the bond changes on ionisation involves going from C_{sp^3}–H to C_{sp^2}–H and there are several instances where putting more s character into a C–C bond provides greater stabilisation than in a C–H bond.

The two factors, inductive effect and bond stabilisation, should vary with structure in a predictable way—in the case of the fluorenyl anion the negative charge is so delocalised that the bond stabilisation effect dominates slightly for methyl substitution but for the higher alkyl substituents, the inductive effect becomes increasingly important. On this basis toluene would be expected to be more acidic than ethylbenzene.

The pK_a's of the 9-alkylfluorenes in CsCHA—CHA and DMSO—H_2O are in good agreement[54] (<1 pK unit apart) despite the great differences between the two systems. Another aspect of considerable interest is the pK_a differences observed for the CsCHA—CHA and LiCHA—CHA systems.[54] Similar findings have been observed for

TABLE 5.14

Acidities of hydrocarbons in cyclohexylamine

Carbon acid	pK_a*	
	CsCHA—CHA[58]	LiCHA—CHA[57]
3,4-Benzfluorene	19·45	19·38
Indene	19·93	20·24
1,2-Benzfluorene	20·05	19·97
Benzanthrene	21·17	20·67
4,5-Methylenephenanthrene	22·63	22·60
2,3-Benzfluorene	23·17	23·16
1,1,3-Triphenylpropene	26·59	26·39
1,1,3,3-Bis(4,5-phenanthrylene) propene	13·26	12·21
1,1,3,3-Bis(biphenylene) propene	13·79	12·80
1,3-Diphenylindene	13·92	13·92

* Relative to 9-phenylfluorene.

hydrocarbons[57,58] other than the fluorenes (Table 5.14), and rationalised in terms of ion association in these solutions. Fluorenyllithium as well as idenyllithium has been shown[59] to exist as a mixture of solvent separated and contact ion pairs in a cyclohexylamine-diethylamine mixture whereas fluorenylcesium, idenylcesium and triphenylmethylcesium in cyclohexylamine exist primarily as contact ion pairs. The equilibria should then be represented as

$$RH + Li^+\bar{N}HC_6H_{11} \rightleftharpoons R^- \| Li^+ + C_6H_{11}NH_2 \qquad (5.5)$$

$$RH + Cs^+\bar{N}HC_6H_{11} \rightleftharpoons R^-Cs^+ + C_6H_{11}NH_2 \qquad (5.6)$$

In Eqn (5.5) the equilibrium involves a solvent separated ion pair competing with a contact ion pair whereas only the latter are involved in Eqn (5.6).

The larger charge separation in Eqn (5.5) accounts for the effectively lower acidity of hydrocarbons toward LiCHA than toward CsCHA and the relationship has recently been put on a more quantitative basis by Streitwieser and co-workers.[59] For several carbanions expected to be planar the electrostatic ion pair energies have been calculated and found to be linearly related to the differences in the pK_a values in LiCHA–CHA and CsCHA–CHA (Fig. 5.2). The electrostatic interaction is greatest for the indenyl ion pair, and it has the highest relative acidity toward CsCHA and the contact ion pair. Conversely benzanthryl anion shows the smallest

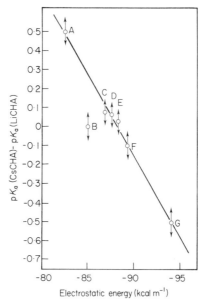

Fig. 5.2. Plot of pK_a (CsCHA)–pK_a (LiCHA) for several hydrocarbons against the calculated ion pair electrostatic energies.[59] Points are A, benzanthrene; B, 2,3-Benzfluorene; C, 1,2-Benzfluorene; D, 3,4-Benzfluorene; E, 4,5-Methylenephenanthrene; F, Fluorene; G, Indene.

electrostatic interaction in an ion pair, and it has the highest relative acidity toward LiCHA and the solvent-separated ion pair.

In solvents where ion association is unimportant but in which dielectric constants and hydrogen bonding abilities vary widely large differences in acidities may be observed (Table 5.15). Although the differences may be interpreted in a qualitative manner it is not as yet possible to quantify the various contributions. In taking the case of the two solvents, dimethyl sulphoxide and water, the pK_a's in the two solvents can be related by Eqn (5.7)[47]:

$$pK_a(H_2O) - pK_a(DMSO) = \log f'_{RH} - \log f'_{R^-} - \log f'_{H^+} \qquad (5.7)$$

Equivalence of pK_a values requires that the right hand side of Eqn (5.7) is equal to zero. It seems most unlikely that each term (f'_{RH}, the degenerate activity coefficient of the acid, f'_{R-}, that of the conjugate base and f'_{H^+}, that of the proton) is equal to zero. Because the dielectric constant of DMSO is considerably less than that of water the electrostatic effect alone should make f'_{H^+} and f'_{R-}, greater than unity. As the solubility of organic compounds is in general greater in DMSO than in H_2O, f'_{RH} is less than unity. The exact magnitude of the electrostatic effect is however difficult to evaluate since the correct radius to be used for the proton is difficult to determine.

TABLE 5.15

Acidities of carbon acids in various media

Carbon acid	pK_a		
	DMSO[47,60]	H_2O	MeOH[60]
9-Cyanofluorene	8·4		14·2
9-Carbomethoxyfluorene	10·3	12·9	15·8
Fluoradene	10·5		17·0, 18·2[61]
Benzoylacetone	12·1	8·7[36]	
Nitromethane	15·9	10·2[10]	

Dimethyl sulphoxide is considerably more basic than water (1·8 pK units) and this would help to decrease f'_{H^+}. Taken in conjunction with the relative concentration of H_2O in H_2O and DMSO in DMSO, the expected pK_a difference in going from H_2O to DMSO would be −1·2 units.[47]

Hydrogen bonding is more important in H_2O than DMSO but for a highly delocalised carbanion this effect is unlikely to be a significant contribution to the observed acidity differences. Dispersion interactions between highly coloured anions and the solvent are other factors which have to be considered. Since DMSO is more polarisable than is H_2O this kind of interaction will result in a decrease in f'_{R-} but the magnitude of the effect is difficult to calculate. If this term is important it at least goes some way towards explaining the pK_a difference in DMSO and H_2O for compounds such as nitromethane or benzoylacetone whose conjugate bases are not intensely coloured.

5.6. THEORETICAL VALUES

It was shown earlier (p. 59) that under certain conditions the acidity of a carbon acid was proportional to the change in the π-bond energy resulting from the difference in conjugation between RH and the corresponding anion, R^-:

$$pK_a = 2\alpha + \Delta M\beta \tag{5.8}$$

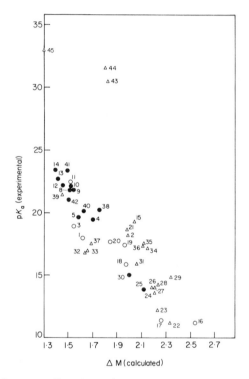

Fig. 5.3. Relation between pK_a values of some carbon acids and ΔM[50] (numbers as in Table 5.16). •' Planar carbanions; △, non-planar carbanions; ○, carbanions possessing heteroatoms.

In the first $pK_a - \Delta M$ correlation reported[62] the pK_a data covered a small range and were obtained by approximation methods or in solvents where ion association is known to be important. Bowden and Cockerill[50] have, however, recently assessed the validity of the relation using pK_a values which have been obtained in more polar solvents and over a larger range of acidities. Their findings are summarised in Table 5.16 and Fig. 5.3. All the pK_a's quoted are relative to that of 9-phenylfluorene (18·59).

The results can be most conveniently discussed in terms of those carbon acids which (a) form planar or nearly planar carbanions; (b) form non-planar carbanions; or (c) possess one or more heteroatoms. For those in the first group [acids 4, 5, 8, 10, 25, 30, 38, 40–42] a good correlation between pK_a and ΔM exists, similar to that found by Streitwieser.[62] Clearly the calculated change in π-electron density on ionisation is a good measure of the acidity of these hydrocarbons.

The second group of acids [2, 16, 21–24, 26–29, 31–37, 39, 43–45] often deviate quite markedly from the relationship although the extent of the deviation is more serious for the diphenyl and triphenylmethanes than for the fluorenes, where part of the molecule is held co-planar by the interannular bond. Steric interactions usually produce a decrease in the expected acidity due to the lack of coplanarity and incomplete conjugation.

TABLE 5.16

Experimental pK_a values and molecular orbital calculations for carbon acids[50]

	Carbon acid	pK_a	M_{RH}	ΔM
1.	2-Nitrofluorene	17·96	23·49	1·62
2.	9-Biphenyl-4-yl-fluorene	18·21	32·77	1·99
3.	2-Cyanofluorene	18·96	19·05	1·54
4.	Phenalene	19·45	16·13	1·70
5.	7H-Benzo[c]-fluorene	19·62	22·08	1·58
6.	2-Bromofluorene	20·56	16·46	4·48
7.	2-Chlorofluorene	20·59	16·52	5·43
8.	4H-Cyclopenta[def]phenanthrene	21·79	19·49	1·51
9.	9-Methylfluorene	21·80	21·90	1·54
10.	Fluorene	22·10	16·38	1·52
11.	2-Methoxyfluorene	22·36	26·11	1·51
12.	9-Ethylfluorene	22·22	21·90	1·45
13.	9-Isopropylfluorene	22·70	21·90	1·41
14.	9-t-Butylfluorene	23·41	16·38	1·39
15.	9-(1-Naphthyl)fluorene	19·20	30·05	2·04
16.	Malononitrile	11·20	4·35	2·54
17.	9-Cyanofluorene	11·41	18·56	2·26
18.	4,4′-Dinitrodiphenylmethane	15·85	30·15	1·97
19.	2,4′-Dinitrodiphenylmethane	17·38	30·15	1·96
20.	3,4′-Dinitrodiphenylmethane	17·62	30·15	1·84
21.	9-Phenylfluorene	18·59	24·38	1·98
22.	3,4,5,6-Biph-CHCH=CBiph	11·2		2·29
23.	Biph CHCH=CHCH=C Biph	12·2		2·23
24.	Phen CHCH=C Phen	13·6		2·21
25.	H-Indeno-[1,2,3-jk]fluorene	13·9		2·12
26.	BiphCHC(Ph)=CBiph	14·0		2·18
27.	Biph CHCH=CPhen	14·0		2·21
28.	Biph CHCH=CBiph	14·3		2·23
29.	Biph CHCH=C(Ph)—CH=CBiph	14·8		2·34

TABLE 5.16—*continued*

	Carbon acid	pK_a	ΔM
30.	Cyclopentadiene	15·0 (± 1·0)	2·00
31.	7-Phenyl-7H-dibenzo[c, g]-fluorene	15·9	2·06
32.	7H-Dibenzo[c, g]-fluorene	16·8	1·63
33.	BiphC=CHCH$_2$Ph	16·9	1·66
34.	BiphCHCH=CPh$_2$	17·1	2·15
35.	BiphC=CHCHPh$_2$	17·5	2·12
36.	13H-Phenyl-13H-dibenzo[a, i]fluorene	17·3	2·11
37.	13H-Dibenzo[a, i]-fluorene	17·5	1·69
38.	Indene	20·2	1·75
39.	12H-Dibenzo[b, h]-fluorene	21·4	1·45
40.	11H-Benzo[a]-fluorene	20·1	1·62
41.	11H-Benzo[b]-fluorene	23·3	1·49
42.	7H-Benz[de]-anthracene	21·0 (± 0·5)	1·50
43.	Biphenyl-4-yldiphenylmethane	30·5 (± 1·0)	1·82
44.	Triphenylmethane	31·5 (± 1·0)	1·80
45.	Diphenylmethane	33·0 (± 1·0)	1·30

Still more pronounced deviations are observed for those hydrocarbons possessing heteratoms [1, 3, 6, 7, 11, 16–20] although 9-cyano-fluorene is an exception. These results point to the need for a more sophisticated theory that will have non-zero carbon–heteroatom bond overlap integrals and where allowance for inductive effects can be made.

From the correlation of known pK_a's with ΔM values it is possible to predict acidity constants for several important carbon acids, e.g. toluene (32), methane (42) and cycloheptatriene (27). These values can be compared with previous estimates[43,63]—35 and 37 for toluene, 40 for methane and either 36 or >25 for cycloheptatriene.

5.7. ACIDITIES IN THE GAS PHASE

We have already seen how sensitive the acidities of some carbon acids are to the nature of the solvent. Because the presence of such solvent effects complicates the general problem of relating structure to reactivity there seems a clear need to determine an intrinsic scale of acidities, which can only be obtained from studies in the gas phase. In principle the energetics of acid dissociation can be considered in terms of a thermodynamic cycle made up of three fundamental processes,[42,64]

the bond dissociation energy (D) of RH	RH $\rightarrow$ R$\cdot$ + H$\cdot$	(5.9)
the electron affinity (R) of R$\cdot$	R$\cdot$ + e$^-$ $\rightarrow$ R$^-$	(5.10)
the ionisation potential (I) of H$\cdot$	H$\cdot$ $\rightarrow$ H$^+$ + e$^-$	(5.11)

The enthalpy of ionisation is then given by $\Delta H_0 = D + R + I$. Bond dissociation energies are available for many R—H bonds and the ionisation potential of the hydrogen atom is known precisely. Unfortunately electron affinities are hard to measure and are only known for a very small number of species so that this method of calculating ΔH_0 cannot be widely employed.

Recently Brauman and Blair[65,66] have used ion cyclotron resonance spectroscopy to study gas phase acidities. The principle of the method is based on the fact that an ion orbiting in a magnetic field at a frequency characteristic of its m/e ratio can absorb energy from an alternating electric field $E_1(t)$ if the frequency of $E_1(t)$ equals the cyclotron frequency of the ion. By operating at fixed observing frequency for $E_1(t)$, a mass spectrum is obtained by sweeping the magnetic field. A highly specific double-resonance technique provides a means of determining whether 2 ions of different mass, even in a complex mixture of ions and neutral species, are coupled chemically. Basically the method depends upon applying radio-frequency energy at the resonance frequency of the reactant ion, thereby increasing its kinetic energy, while at the same time the intensity of the product ion is monitored.

The single resonance negative ion spectrum of acetyl cyanide, for example, contains only one peak at m/e 26 when the ionising electron energy (2·2 eV) and the pressure ($<10^{-6}$ torr) are both low. Under these conditions the dissociative resonance capture process is probably the production of cyanide ion:

$$CH_3\overset{\overset{\displaystyle O}{\|}}{C}CN + e^- \longrightarrow CH_3\overset{\overset{\displaystyle O}{\|}}{C}\cdot + CN^- \qquad (5.12)$$

As the pressure is increased, an M-1 peak appears at m/e 68 ($\overline{CH}_2COCN$) and increases relative to the m/e 26 peak until its intensity is greater than that of the m/e 26 peak. When a pulsed double resonance experiment is carried out at a pressure where the signal intensities of the m/e 26 and 68 peaks are comparable, irradiation of the m/e 26 peak results in a decrease in the m/e 68 ion intensity. This decrease is consistent with an exothermic ion-molecule reaction whose specific rate constant decreases with increasing reactant kinetic energy.

The relative intensity behaviour of the m/e 26 and 68 peaks with changes in pressure and the double resonance experiment give direct evidence for the proton transfer reaction,

$$CH_3\overset{\overset{\displaystyle O}{\|}}{C}CN + CN^- \longrightarrow C\bar{H}_2\overset{\overset{\displaystyle O}{\|}}{C}CN + HCN \tag{5.13}$$

A 1:1 mixture of acetyl cyanide and HCN under similar conditions gave identical results. In addition no proton transfer could be observed from HCN to $C\bar{H}_2COCN$, so that the reverse reaction is probably endothermic. Acetyl cyanide is therefore a stronger acid than HCN in the gas phase.

Subsequent studies[67] have shown that the order of acidities for a series of simple aliphatic alcohols (neopentyl $>$ t-butyl $>$ isopropyl $>$ ethyl $>$ methyl $>$ water) is "reversed" from the "normal" inductive order observed in solution. The butoxide ion is now less basic than the methoxide ion so that in solution there must be a considerable shielding of the $-ve$ charge from the bulk solvent by the alkyl groups. In fact intrinsic acidities can be expected to differ drastically from solution acidities in which specific solvation, dispersion forces and steric effects can be important factors. The relative acidities of the amines[66] bear a striking parallelism to those of the alcohols (t-butylamine $>$ isopropylamine $>$ ethylamine $>$ methylamine), the primary amine with the largest alkyl group being the more acidic. This order could be anticipated on the basis of a model of a localised anion (charge largely restricted to nitrogen) and essentially identical bond dissociation energies within the series.

The application of the flowing afterglow technique[68] to the determination of acidities in the gas phase has also been reported.[69] The flow system consists of a stainless steel tube in which a fast gas flow is established using helium as the carrier gas. Negative ions are produced either directly in the excitation region by ionising the parent gas with 100 eV electrons or indirectly by secondary reaction. Thus the O^- ion is produced by the dissociative ionisation reaction

$$O_2 + e^- \rightarrow O^- + O^+ + e^- \tag{5.14}$$

and the hydroxide ion from the interaction of O^- with NH_3:

$$O^- + NH_3 \rightarrow OH^- + NH_2^- \tag{5.15}$$

The carbanions are generated by the addition of the hydrocarbon to a helium afterglow containing O^-:

$$RH + O^- \rightarrow R^- + OH \tag{5.16}$$

The decline of the primary ion signal and the variation of the secondary ion signals as a function of reactant gas addition allows the determination of the appropriate rate constants and hence the acidity. The order of acid strengths determined by Bohme, Ruff and Young[70] (n-C_4H_9SH > CH_3NO_2 > C_5H_6 ⪆ $CHCl_3$ > CH_3COCH_3 > CH_3CN > CH_2Cl_2, CH_3SOCH_3 ⪆ C_2H_2, t-C_4H_9OH, i-C_3H_7OH > C_2H_5OH > CH_3OH > C_3H_4, $C_6H_5CH(CH_3)_2$ > $C_6H_5CH_3$ > C_3H_6 > H_2O > C_6H_6 > H_2 > NH_3 > C_2H_4, C_6H_{12}, $(CH_2)_3$, CH_4) is in agreement with the sequence first established by Brauman and Blair, with the sole exception of the position assigned to toluene.

REFERENCES

1. Boyd, R. H. (1963). *J. Phys. Chem.* **67**, 737.
2. Boyd, R. H. (1961). *J. Amer. Chem. Soc.* **83**, 4288.
3. Pearson, R. G. & Dillon, R. L. (1953). *J. Amer. Chem. Soc.* **75**, 2439.
4. Walters, E. A. & Long, F. A. (1969). *J. Amer. Chem. Soc.* **91**, 3733.
5. Hibbert, F., Long, F. A. & Walters, E. A. (1969). *J. Amer. Chem. Soc.* **91**, 2381.
6. Boyd, R. H. & Wang, C. H. (1965). *J. Amer. Chem. Soc.* **87**, 430.
7. Webster, O. W. (1966). *J. Amer. Chem. Soc.* **88**, 3046.
8. Webster, O. W. (1965). *J. Amer. Chem. Soc.* **87**, 1820.
9. Bell, R. P. (1959). *The Proton in Chemistry*, p. 87. Cornell Univ. Press, New York.
10. Wheland, G. W. & Farr, J. (1943). *J. Amer. Chem. Soc.* **65**, 1433.
11. Fukuyama, M., Flanagan, P. W. K., Williams, F. T. Jr., Frainier, L., Miller, S. A. & Shechter, H. (1970). *J. Amer. Chem. Soc.* **92**, 4689.
12. Bordwell, F. G., Boyle, W. J. Jr. & Yee, K. C. (1970). *J. Amer. Chem. Soc.* **92**, 5926.
13. Bordwell, F. G. & Boyle, W. J. Jr. (1972). *J. Amer. Chem. Soc.* **94**, 3907.
14. Bell, R. P. & Higginson, W. C. E. (1949). *Proc. Roy. Soc. Ser. A* **197**, 141.
15. Bell, R. P., Gelles, E. & Möller, E. (1949). *Proc. Roy. Soc. Ser. A* **198**, 310.
16. Eigen, M. (1964). *Angew. Chem. Int. Ed. Engl.* **3**, 1.
17. Adolph, H. G. & Kamlet, M. J. (1966). *J. Amer. Chem. Soc.* **88**, 20.
18. Hine, J., Burske, N. W., Hine, M. & Langford, P. B. (1957). *J. Amer. Chem. Soc.* **79**, 1406.
19. Andreades, S. (1964). *J. Amer. Chem. Soc.* **86**, 2003.
20. Hine, J. & Langford, P. B. (1956). *J. Amer. Chem. Soc.* **78**, 5003.
21. Hine, J. (1963). *J. Amer. Chem. Soc.* **85**, 3239.
22. Slovetskii, V. I., Shevelev, S. A., Erashko, V. I., Biryukova, L. I., Fainzil'berg, A. A. & Novikov, S. S. (1966). *Izv. Akad. Nauk. SSSR, Ser. Khim.* 655.
23. Sitzmann, M. E., Adolph, H. G. & Kamlet, M. J. (1968). *J. Amer. Chem. Soc.* **90**, 2815.
24. Tselenskii, I. V., Kosmynina, A. S., Dronov, V. N. & Shokhor, I. N. (1970). *Org. React.* **7**, 20.
25. Kamlet, M. J. & Glover, D. J. (1962). *J. Org. Chem.* **27**, 537.

26. Bordwell, F. G., Imes, R. H. & Steiner, E. C. (1967). *J. Amer. Chem. Soc.* **89**, 3905.
27. Bell, R. P. & Cox, B. G. (1971). *J. Chem. Soc. (B)* 652.
28. Bell, R. P. & Smith, P. W. (1966). *J. Chem. Soc. (B)* 241.
29. Cox, M. & Darken, J. (1971). *Coord. Chem. Rev.* **7**, 29.
30. Livingstone, S. (1971). *Coord. Chem. Rev.* **7**, 59.
31. Koshimura, H. & Okubo, T. (1970). *Anal. Chim. Acta* **49**, 67.
32. Rydberg, J. (1953). *Sv. Kem. Tidskr.* **65**, 37.
33. Guter, G. A. & Hammond, G. S. (1956). *J. Amer. Chem. Soc.* **78**, 5166.
34. Koshimura, H. & Okubo, T. (1971). *Anal. Chim. Acta* **55**, 163.
35. Laloi-Diard, M. & Rubinstein, M. (1965). *Bull. Soc. Chim. Fr.* 310.
36. Eidinoff, M. L. (1945). *J. Amer. Chem. Soc.* **67**, 2072.
37. Jones, J. R. & Patel, S. P. (1973) unpublished results.
38. Truce, W. E., Bannister, W. W. & Knospe, R. H. (1962). *J. Org. Chem.* **27**, 2821.
39. Corey, E. J., König, H. & Lowry, T. H. (1962). *Tetrahedron Lett.* 515.
40. Van Uitert, Le G., Haas, C. G., Fernelius, W. C. & Douglas, B. E. (1953). *J. Amer. Chem. Soc.* **75**, 455.
41. Livingstone, S. E. & Sullivan, E. A. (1969). *Aust. J. Chem.* **22**, 1363.
42. Streitwieser, A. Jr. & Hammons, J. H. (1965). *Progr. Phys. Org. Chem.* (Cohen, S. G., Streitwieser, A. & Taft, R. W. eds.), **3**, 41.
43. Fischer, H. & Rewicki, D. (1967). *Progr. Org. Chem.* (Cook, J. & Carruthers, W. eds.) **7**, 116.
44. Bowden, K. & Stewart, R. (1966). *Tetrahedron* **20**, 511.
45. Langford, C. H. & Burwell, R. L. (1960). *J. Amer. Chem. Soc.* **82**, 1503.
46. Steiner, E. C. & Starkey, J. D. (1967). *J. Amer. Chem. Soc.* **89**, 2751.
47. Ritchie, C. D. & Uschold, R. E. (1967). *J. Amer. Chem. Soc.* **89**, 1721, 2752.
48. Ritchie, C. D. & Uschold, R. E. (1968). *J. Amer. Chem. Soc.* **90**, 2821.
49. Bowden, K. & Cockerill, A. F. (1970). *J. Chem. Soc. (B)* 173.
50. Bowden, K., Cockerill, A. F. & Gilbert, J. R. (1970). *Chem. Soc. (B)* 179.
51. Biggs, A. I. & Robinson, R. A. (1961). *J. Chem. Soc.* 388.
52. Dolman, D. & Stewart, R. (1967). *Can. J. Chem.* **45**, 911.
53. Barlin, G. B. & Perrin, D. D. (1966). *Quart. Rev. Chem. Soc.* **20**, 75.
54. Streitwieser, A. Jr., Chang, C. J. & Reuben, D. M. E. (1972). *J. Amer. Chem. Soc.* **94**, 5730.
55. Cockerill, A. F. & Lamper, J. E. (1971). *J. Chem. Soc. (B)* 503.
56. Ritchie, C. D. & Sager, W. F. (1964). *Progr. Phys. Org. Chem.* (Cohen, S. G., Streitwieser, A. & Taft, R. W., eds.) **2**, 323.
57. Streitwieser, A. Jr., Hammons, J. H., Ciuffarin, E. & Brauman, J. I. (1967). *J. Amer. Chem. Soc.* **89**, 59.
58. Streitwieser, A. Jr., Ciuffarin, E. & Hammons, J. H. (1967). *J. Amer. Chem. Soc.* **89**, 63.
59. Streitwieser, A. Jr., Chang, C. J., Hollyhead, W. B. & Murdoch, J. R. (1972). *J. Amer. Chem. Soc.* **94**, 5288.
60. Ritchie, C. D. (1969). *J. Amer. Chem. Soc.* **91**, 6749.
61. Streitwieser, A. Jr., Chang, C. J. & Young, A. T. (1972). *J. Amer. Chem. Soc.* **94**, 4888.
62. Streitwieser, A. Jr. (1960). *Tetrahedron Lett.* **6**, 23.
63. Streitwieser, A. Jr. (1961). *Molecular Orbital Theory for Organic Chemists*, p. 414. Wiley, New York.
64. Brauman, J. I. & Blair, L. K. (1970). *J. Amer. Chem. Soc.* **92**, 5986.
65. Brauman, J. I. & Blair, L. K. (1968). *J. Amer. Chem. Soc.* **90**, 5636.

66. Brauman, J. I. & Blair, L. K. (1971). *J. Amer. Chem. Soc.* **93**, 3911.
67. Brauman, J. I. & Blair, L. K. (1968). *J. Amer. Chem. Soc.* **90**, 6561.
68. Ferguson, E. E. (1968). *Adv. Electron. Electron. Phys.* (Martin, L. ed.) **24**, 1.
69. Bohme, D. K. & Young, L. B. (1970). *J. Amer. Chem. Soc.* **92**, 3301.
70. Bohme, D. K., Lee-Ruff, E. & Young, L. B. (1972). *J. Amer. Chem. Soc.* **93**, 5153.

6. Highly Basic Media

A highly basic medium may be defined[1] as a solution which is able to ionise an acid with an ability equal to or greater than 0.1M aqueous alkali metal hydroxide. To express the basicity of such a solution it is necessary to consider the equilibrium which is set up when an uncharged indicator, RH is dissolved in that medium:

$$RH \rightleftharpoons R^- + H^+ \tag{6.1}$$

The thermodynamic equilibrium constant for (6.1) is given by

$$K_{RH} = a_{H^+} a_{R^-}/a_{RH} = \frac{[R^-]}{[RH]} \frac{f_{R^-}}{f_{RH}} a_{H^+} \tag{6.2}$$

where a denotes activity, f activity coefficient and [ ] concentration. In logarithmic form Eqn (6.2) can be rearranged to

$$\log_{10}([R^-]/[RH]) = \log_{10}K_{RH} - \log_{10}a_{H^+}f_{R^-}/f_{RH} \tag{6.3}$$

In very dilute aqueous solution where the activity coefficients approach unity Eqn (6.3) reduces to

$$\log_{10}([R^-]/[RH]) = \log_{10}K_{RH} - \log_{10}[H^+] \tag{6.4}$$

Since the simple term $-\log_{10}[H^+]$ measures the ability of the dilute solution to abstract a proton the equivalent term in Eqn (6.3) can be used in more concentrated media. The acidity function H_- which is a measure of the ability of a basic solution to abstract a proton from a neutral acid is then defined by

$$H_- = -\log_{10}a_{H^+}f_{R^-}/f_{RH} = pK_{RH} + \log_{10}([R^-]/[RH]) \tag{6.5}$$

H_- then becomes equal to the pH of the solution at low concentrations of base.

For the successful operation of the acidity function approach it is necessary to satisfy a number of conditions. Thus, to establish an H_- scale referred to a standard state of infinite dilution in water the acid RH should have a pK_a that can be determined in aqueous buffers and an ionisation range which spans the upper end of the pH scale and the beginning of the H_- scale. This acid can be used to determine the H_- values for several different solutions. It is then possible to measure in the same solutions the fraction of a somewhat weaker acid SH that is ionised in these media and hence its pK_a provided the last term in Eqn (6.6) is zero:

$$pK_{RH} - pK_{SH} = \log_{10}([RH]/[R^-]) - \log_{10}([SH]/[S^-]) + \log_{10}(f_{RH}f_{S^-}/f_{SH}f_{R^-})$$

(6.6)

The procedure, known as the Hammett stepwise technique,[2,3] can be applied repeatedly to calculate individual pK_a and H_- values for a series of solutions. In practice the pK_a's for consecutive indicators should preferably be less than 1·0 unit and never greater than 2·0 units apart. That this difference remains constant as the composition of the medium is altered can best be examined by parallelism of $\log_{10}[R^-]/[RH]$ versus solvent composition plots for different indicator acids. The acids should have closely similar structures, be stable to hydrolysis and sufficiently soluble in the relevant media. The main difficulty in fact is establishing an aqueous H_- scale based on carbon acids is that many indicators such as hydrocarbons are insoluble even at spectroscopic concentrations ($10^{-4} - 10^{-5}$ M).

The process of ionisation should be both straightforward with equilibrium rapidly attained, and completely reversible. Where this is not so it may be useful to partially ionise the acid in a medium containing D_2O when the acidic hydrogen should exchange rapidly with the deuterium. However a compound could still be exchanging quite rapidly when the observed anionic species is not the simple anion.[4] If identical pK_a values are found for an indicator using different solvent systems it tends to confirm that simple ionisation by proton loss is occurring. In these circumstances it is an advantage to supplement the information already obtained by using a second analytical technique. N.m.r. spectroscopy is extremely useful in this respect as it then becomes possible to distinguish between ionisation by proton loss and ionisation by base addition as well as being able to detect the presence of radicals and/or radical anions in solution.[5] It also makes possible the use of indicators the absorption spectra of which do not show appreciable change on ionisation.

6.1. ACIDITY FUNCTIONS IN AQUEOUS HYDROXIDE SOLUTIONS

The basicities of concentrated aqueous sodium hydroxide solutions were first determined by Schwarzenbach[6] who found it necessary to use a two phase system because of the low solubility of the indigo derivatives employed as indicators. These results together with those obtained more recently by Edward and Wang[7] using thioacetamide as indicator, and Yagil[8] using a series of substituted indoles, (Fig. 6.1 and Table 6.1), are in good agreement up to 10 M. This suggests that in the method of Schwarzenbach the activity coefficients of the acid and anion forms of the indicators must vary as a function of hydroxide ion concentration in the same way in both phases and that the Hammett concept is valid in such media even though the indicators are of widely different structures. Only further measurements on additional classes of indicators will show whether the divergence at the higher concentrations, amounting to nearly a single H_- unit at 16 M, is due to differences in indicator structure.

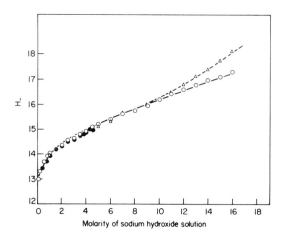

Fig. 6.1. Relation between molar concentration and H_- for NaOH. ○ Data of Yagil (1971). *J. Phys. Chem.* 71, 1034; △ data of Schwarzenbach & Sulzberger (1944). *Helv. Chim. Acta* 27, 348; ● data of Edward & Wang (1962). *Can. J. Chem.* 42, 399.

For concentrated aqueous potassium hydroxide solutions the results of both Schwarzenbach and Yagil again agree very well up to 10M but then gradually diverge until at 15M there is a difference of one H_- unit (Table 6.2). For LiOH solutions in the concentration range 0·5–5·0M the values of Stewart and O'Donnell[9] are consistently about 0·5 units lower than those of Yagil (Table 6.3) and may reflect the experimental difficulties (low indicator solubilities with consequent low optical densities even in 10 cm cells) encountered in the work.

To account for these high basicities Yagil[10] suggested that the problem is analogous to that encountered in concentrated acid solutions where the strong hydration of the proton is the main factor contributing to the high acidities. The theoretical treatment of Bell

TABLE 6.1

H_ Data for aqueous sodium hydroxide solutions

[MOH]	H_		[MOH]	H_
M	a	b	M	c
0·1	12·99		0·0097	12·03
0·2	13·30		0·075	12·17
0·5	13·71		0·033	12·53
0·8	13·92		0·058	12·75
1·0	14·02	14·00	0·095	13·01
1·5	14·20		0·147	13·12
2·0	14·37		0·184	13·27
2·5	14·54		0·252	13·40
3·0	14·65	14·70	0·556	13·69
3·5	14·81		0·761	13·90
4·0	14·95	14·92	1·01	13·97
4·5	15·08		1·57	14·22
5·0	15·20	15·18	1·83	14·34
6·0	15·40	15·38	1·97	14·37
7·0	15·62	15·60	2·49	14·55
8·0	15·75	15·80	3·04	14·65
9·0	15·97	16·00	3·44	14·73
10·0	16·20	16·20	3·75	14·79
11·0	16·42	16·50	3·98	14·85
12·0	16·58	16·80	4·32	15·04
13·0	16·76	17·10	4·59	14·95
14·0	16·93	17·40		
15·0	17·10	17·75		
16·0	17·30	18·12		

a, Data of Yagil (1967). *J. Phys. Chem.* 71, 1034, at 25° using substituted indoles; b, data of Schwarzenbach & Sulzberger (1944). *Helv. Chim. Acta* 27, 348, at 20° using indigo derivatives; c, data of Edward & Wang (1962). *Can. J. Chem.* 40, 399, at 25° using thioacetamide.

and Bascombe[11] assumes that the equilibrium between indicator acid and solvated hydroxide ion is expressed not by

$$RH + OH^- \rightleftharpoons R^- + H_2O \tag{6.7}$$

but rather by

$$RH + OH^-(H_2O)_n \rightleftharpoons R^- + (n + 1)H_2O \tag{6.8}$$

n being the hydration number of the hydroxide ion. The equilibrium constant is given by

$$K = a_{R^-} a_{H_2O}^{n+1} / a_{RH} a_{OH^-} \tag{6.9}$$

TABLE 6.2

H_ Data for aqueous potassium hydroxide solutions

[MOH] M	H_	
	a	b
0·1	13·00	
0·2	13·22	
0·5	13·75	
0·8	14·00	
1·0	14·11	14·00*
1·5	14·33	
2·0	14·51	14·50
2·5	14·69	
3·0	14·85	14·82
3·5	15·00	
4·0	15·15	15·13
4·5	15·28	
5·0	15·44	15·46
6·0	15·72	15·76
7·0	16·00	16·10
8·0	16·33	16·45
9·0	16·58	16·80
10·0	16·90	17·22
11·0	17·14	17·70
12·0	17·39	18·12
13·0	17·66	18·60
14·0	17·95	18·90
15·0	18·23	19·25

a, Data of Yagil (1967). *J. Phys. Chem.* 71, 1034, at 25° using substituted indoles; b, data of Schwarzenbach & Sulzberger (1944). *Helv. Chim. Acta* 27, 348, at 20° using indigo derivatives; * assumed value when [MOH] = 1 Molar.

Assuming that the ratio of activity coefficients is equal to unity a molar equilibrium constant can be defined by

$$K_c = [R^-][H_2O]^{n+1}/[RH][OH^-] \qquad (6.10)$$

where $[H_2O]$ denotes the molar concentration of free water. As

$$H_- = \log_{10} \frac{[R^-]}{[RH]} \frac{1}{K_{RH}}$$

it follows that

$$H_- = pK_W + \log_{10}[OH^-] - (n+1)\log_{10}[H_2O] \qquad (6.11)$$

TABLE 6.3

H_ Data for aqueous lithium hydroxide solutions at 25°

| [MOH] | H_ | |
M	a	b
0·5	13·68	
1·0	13·96	13·43
1·5	14·11	
2·0	14·26	13·53
2·5	14·36	
3·0	14·45	13·93
3·5	14·53	
4·0	14·58	14·04
4·5	14·65	
5·0		14·31

a, Data of Yagil (1967). *J. Phys. Chem.* **71**, 1034, at 25° using substituted indoles; b, data of Stewart & O'Donnell (1964). *Can. J. Chem.* **42**, 1681, using substituted anilines and diphenylamines.

The concentrations of free water for different values of hydroxide concentrations can be determined and calculations by Yagil[10] based on a hydration number of three show that both experimental and theoretical values of H_ for NaOH agree up to 7 M. Several studies lend support to the existence of a trihydrated hydroxide ion. A possible structure is similar to that of $H^+(H_2O)_4$ less two protons which is thought to exist in concentrated solutions of acid. It is interesting that calculations based on a hydration number of either 2 or 4 give far poorer agreement with experiment.

The above theory may be an oversimplification in at least two respects. Firstly, it is unlikely that the hydroxide ion can be adequately expressed in terms of a single hydration number over a wide range of concentration. Secondly, although the acidity function values of some concentrated mineral acid solutions are independent of the nature of the anion for aqueous alkali-metal hydroxides H_- values are dependent on the nature of the cation[12] and for a given concentration decrease in the order KOH > NaOH > LiOH.

The reason for this is that the hydroxides are incompletely dissociated at these high concentrations. Using the values of the dissociation constants (K_d) which have been obtained from kinetic investigations[13] (see p. 111)—5·1 for KOH, 3·4 for NaOH and 1·5 for LiOH, one can calculate the fraction of dissociated molecules at each concentration. The concentration of ion-pairs in the more concentrated media is a substantial fraction of the total base concentration and for LiOH solutions in excess of 4 molar is sufficiently high as to make an accurate calculation of the free hydroxide ion concentration difficult.

The effect of allowing for ion association is to bring the H_- values for the sodium and potassium hydroxides closer together so that they lie on the same H_- vs. concentration plot. The results for LiOH are also much closer if Yagil's more recent results[8] are used. Calculations by the same worker[10] suggest that the dissociated ions associate with 9–11 water molecules so that if the hydration number for Li^+ is 5, the hydroxide ion is solvated by between 4 and 6 water molecules.

6.2. ACIDITY FUNCTIONS IN ALCOHOL ALKOXIDE SOLUTIONS

Media of high basicity may be obtained by using solutions of alkali metal alkoxides in the corresponding alcohols.[1,14] For a 10^{-3} M concentration of base there is an order of basicity rising gradually from methanol (10·69), ethanol (12·62), isopropyl alcohol (15·00), t-pentyl alcohol (15·98) to t-butyl alcohol (17.16). The basicity of the methanolic solution is comparable to that of an aqueous solution of the same hydroxide ion concentration.[15]

Because of the low dielectric constants of the alcohols ion association is important even at low concentrations of base. Not surprisingly therefore the trend in basicity as a function of the metal cation (Fig. 6.2) is more pronounced than in the water–hydroxide media although the order is once again the same viz. H_-^M (KOMe) > H_-^M (NaOMe) > H_-^M (LiOMe); H_-^M is used as methanol rather than water is the standard state.

Much of the early data on methanol–methoxide solutions has been supplemented by the work of Terrier[16,17] (Table 6.4). H_-^M values have been obtained using both substituted indoles and anilines and it appears as if the scales are dependent on indicator structure.

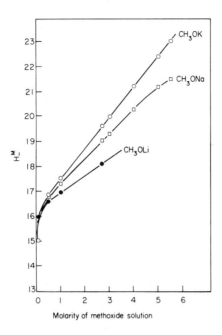

Fig. 6.2. Variation of H_-^M for sodium, potassium and lithium methoxides with concentration. ○, □, ●, data of Terrier, Millot & Schaal (1969). *Bull. Soc. Chim. Fr.* 3002.

TABLE 6.4

H_-^M Data for alkali-metal methoxides in methanol at 20°

[MOR] M	H_-^M					
	KOMe		NaOMe		LiOMe	
	a	b	a	b	a	b
0·01	14·92	14·92	14·92	14·92	14·92	14·92
0·10	15·92	15·99	15·92	15·94	15·92	15·92
0·50	16·62	16·87	16·62	16·78	16·62	16·61
1·0	17·02	17·52	16·95	17·30	16·92	16·95
2·7	17·98	19·62	17·83	19·03	17·69	18·10
3·0	18·15	20·00	17·98	19·31		
4·0	18·70	21·23	18·50	20·32		
5·0	19·26	22·42	19·00	21·20		
5·5	19·54	23·05		21·52		

a, Data of Terrier, Millott, & Schaal (1969). *Bull. Soc. Chim. Fr.* 3002, using substituted indoles as indicators; b, data of Terrier (1969). *Ann. Chim.* 4, 153, using substituted anilines and diphenylamines.

However, in solutions where ion association is important as, for example, potassium methoxide (> 0.1M) in methanol, equilibria other than that represented in (6.12) have to be considered.

$$RH + OMe^- \rightleftharpoons R^- + MeOH \tag{6.12}$$

These solutions will contain potassium ions, solvated methoxide ions and ion-pairs in equilibrium:

$$K^+, OMe^- \rightleftharpoons K^+ + OMe^- \tag{6.13}$$

Weak indicator acids react with potassium methoxide to yield the potassium salt of the conjugate base which can exist as either an ion-pair or the free ions:

$$R^- K^+ \rightleftharpoons R^- + K^+ \tag{6.14}$$

Only when due allowance has been made for these different equilibria can it be safely stated that the basicities are dependent on the structure of the indicators employed.

Although there is general agreement as to the importance of ion association in concentrated solutions of hydroxides and alkoxides the structure of the ion pairs is not firmly established. In order to account for the activity coefficient data of the hydroxides Robinson and Harned[18] suggested that sodium hydroxide in concentrated solutions exists as water bridged ion pairs with the oxygen of the water attached to the sodium ion and the hydrogen to the hydroxide ion. The smaller the cation

$$Na^+ \ldots \bar{O}H \ldots H^+ \ldots \bar{O}H$$

the more polarised the solvent molecules so that the effect tends to decrease in going from Li to Cs. Davies[19] however has argued that the associated nature of the hydroxides may be due to the absence of a water molecule from between the two ions. He suggests that a structure such as $M^{n+}(H_2O)OH^-$ would pass over into $M^{n+}OH^-(H_2O)$ by proton transfer. In such a case the coulombic interaction energy between M^{n+} and OH^- should be related to the pK of the hydroxide and the good linear relationship which is obtained in the case of Li, Na, Ba, Sr and Ca argues in favour of a purely electrostatic type of binding. As far as the alkoxides are concerned no evidence on this point is as yet available.

A slightly different medium also capable of high basicity may be obtained by using a solution of an alkali metal glycoxide in anhydrous ethylene glycol (Table 6.5). In their work Aiyar and

TABLE 6.5

H_-^{EtG} for lithium, sodium and potassium glycoxides
in ethylene glycol at 25°

[Glycoxide] M	NaOG	H_-^{EtG}* LiOG	KOG
0·10	14·75	14·71	14·82
0·25	15·17	15·10	15·33
0·50	16·52	15·40	15·82
0·75	15·74	15·57	16·07
1·00	15·94	15·73	16·30
1·25	16·11		16 49
1·50	16·26		16 67
1·75	16·40		
2·00	16·56		
2·25	16·72		
2·50	16·89		
2·75	17·06		
3·00	17·25		

* Ethylene glycol is the standard state: anilines and diphenylamines were used as indicators, Kundu & Aiyar (1971). *J. Chem.
Soc. (B)* 40.

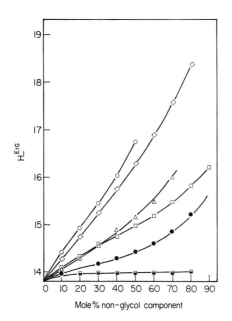

Fig. 6.3. Effect of various solvents on the basicity of a 0.01M solution of sodium
2-hydroxyethoxide (NaO . C_2H_4 . OH) in ethylene glycol. Data of Kundu & Aiyar (1972). *J.
Chem. Soc. (Perkin II)* 715. ○, Me_2SO; ◇, $Me_2N.CHO$; □, Me_2CO; ●, MeCN; △, *t*-BuOH;
▣, MeOH.

Kundu[20] used various nitro-substituted anilines and diphenylamines as indicators but differences in the pK values in ethylene glycol and water are such that the basicities of solutions of glycoxide in glycol can not be related to the basicity of aqueous media without reference to the indicator used. The H_-^{EtG} scale in ethylene glycol has therefore been defined with respect to glycol as the standard state.

The basicity of glycol–glycoxide solutions can be further enhanced[21] by addition of various solvents (Fig. 6.3), the effectiveness decreasing in the order $Me_2SO > Me_2N.CHO > t\text{-BuOH} > Me_2CO > MeCN > MeOH$. With the exception of t-butyl alcohol the H_-^{EtG} curves for the glycol–dipolar aprotic solvent systems lie above those of the corresponding protic solvent systems. Whilst dimethylformamide and acetone have the same dielectric constant they enhance the H_-^{EtG} scale quite differently.

6.3. ACIDITY FUNCTIONS IN MEDIA CONTAINING DIPOLAR APROTIC SOLVENTS

The fact that the hydroxide ion in aqueous media is so extensively hydrated must inhibit its ability as a base and this can be clearly seen in media to which a dipolar aprotic solvent is added. Such a solvent is usually defined as one having a dielectric constant greater than 15 and which, although containing hydrogen atoms, is unable to donate suitably labile hydrogen atoms to form strong hydrogen bonds with the appropriate species. Dimethyl sulphoxide, dimethylformamide, tetrahydrothiophene-1,1-dioxide (sulpholane) and hexamethylphosphoramide are examples. When dimethyl sulphoxide is added to a 0·1 M solution of tetramethylammonium hydroxide in water the H_- of the medium gradually increases[22] from a value of 12 in purely aqueous conditions to 26 in 99·5 mole % Me_2SO, corresponding to an increase of 14 powers of 10 in basicity (Fig. 6.4). When the mole % Me_2SO exceeds 85 the basicity begins to rise very steeply and it increases by a whole H_- unit on going from 97·5 to 99 mole % Me_2SO. Dimethyl sulphoxide and hexamethylphosphoramide are more effective than either sulpholane or pyridine in increasing the basicity of aqueous solutions of hydroxide ion.

A qualitative explanation of the tremendous increase in the basicity of the hydroxide ion in media containing dimethyl sulphoxide (or other aprotic solvents) has been given by Stewart[23] in terms of the effect of aprotic solvent on the equilibrium described in Eqn (6.8). Anions, especially those of small size and localised charge, are much stronger bases in these solvents because they have no general hydrogen bonding interaction with the solvent and so are much less solvated than in aqueous media. The hydroxide ion activity will therefore be raised and this effect will be considerably greater than for large delocalised anions which are frequently the products of an ionisation process. The equilibrium will then be

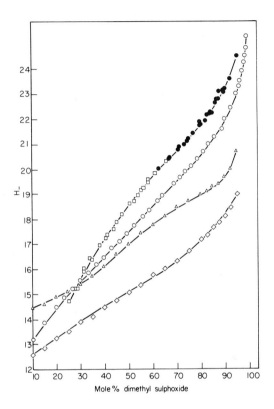

Fig. 6.4. Variation of H_- for hydroxide, methoxide and ethoxide solutions as a function of dimethyl sulphoxide concentration. ●, Data of Bowden & Cockerill (1970). *J. Chem. Soc. (B)* 173; OH$^-$–H$_2$O–Me$_2$SO; ▫, data of Cockerill & Lamper (1971). *J. Chem. Soc. (B)* 503; OH$^-$–H$_2$O–Me$_2$SO; ○, data of Dolman & Stewart (1967). *Can. J. Chem.* 45, 911: OH$^-$–H$_2$O–Me$_2$SO; △, data of Bowden & Stewart (1965); *Tetrahedron* 21, 261: OEt$^-$– EtOH–Me$_2$SO; ◇, data of Stewart, O'Donnell, Cram & Rickborn (1962). *Tetrahedron* 18, 917: OMe$^-$–MeOH–Me$_2$SO.

shifted to the right corresponding to an increase in hydroxide ion basicity.

The addition of increasing amounts of Me$_2$SO will also result in a decrease in water activity brought about not only by a dilution effect but also by the ability of Me$_2$SO to form complexes with the water. Yagil,[24] by applying the same hydration model that was used for concentrated solutions of alkali metal hydroxides to non-electrolyte mixtures such as Me_2SO-H_2O, suggests that up to 52% Me_2SO each dimethyl sulphoxide molecule co-ordinates with two water molecules. This value seems reasonable as Me_2SO has two electron pairs on the oxygen which are available for hydrogen bonding.

Experimental results for the activity of water[25] and methanol[26] in Me_2SO-H_2O and $Me_2SO-MeOH$ mixtures respectively (Table 6.7) show that as the water (or methanol) content decreases so also do the activity coefficients. If the hydration number of the hydroxide ion is three the position of equilibrium and hence the basicity of the solution depends at least on the fourth power of the water activity. Even so the major factor in the increased basicity is the greatly enhanced activity of the hydroxide ion.

The indicators employed in setting up the H_- scale—usually amines or hydrocarbons—are generally more soluble in media containing Me_2SO so that their activity coefficients tend to decrease with increasing Me_2SO concentration. In fact all the changes are consistent with the definition of H_- given in equation (6.5), which can be rearranged in the form

$$H_- = -\log_{10}(K_W a_{H_2O} f_{R^-}/a_{OH^-} f_{RH})\qquad(6.15)$$

In addition to the H_- scale set up by Dolman and Stewart[22] for the $Me_2SO-OH^--H_2O$ system using a series of amine indicators (both primary and secondary describe the same scale in contrast to H_0 scales in sulphuric acid media) Bowden and Cockerill[27,28] have covered the 40–95 mole % Me_2SO range using a series of substituted fluorenes. The results (Fig. 6.4 and Table 6.6) show that whilst the carbon acid scale lacks the rigour of the aniline based acidity function and is not anchored in aqueous solution, the acidity function increases only slightly more rapidly with increasing mole % Me_2SO than does that established by Dolman and Stewart. Part of the discrepancy at least can be attributed to the different base concentrations (0·047 M compared to 0·011 M) employed; with the higher hydroxide ion concentration the shortage of base solvating water molecules becomes important at correspondingly lower mole % Me_2SO compositions. Recently Cockerill and Lamper[29] have covered the 25–65 mole % Me_2SO range using a series of 9-substituted fluorenes. The H_- curves based on the carbon acids merges with the amine based scale at c. 30 mole % Me_2SO and then crosses over. The most plausible explanation of this behaviour, as pointed out by the authors, seems to be that in the more polar media the activity coefficients of the carbon acids do vary in a slightly different manner to those of the nitrogen acids. The latter possess a lone pair of electrons capable of hydrogen bonding interaction with the water molecules, a property denied to the carbon acids. However as the concentration of Me_2SO increases the hydrogen bond property of the anilines becomes less important and the behaviour of both the fluorenes and anilines is closely similar. It is also possible that small

TABLE 6.6

H_- Data for aqueous-alkali and alcohol-alkoxide media containing dimethyl sulphoxide

Mole % Me_2SO	H_-			
	a	b	c	d
10	13·1		12·57	14·45
15	13·8		12·85	14·6
20	14·45		13·27	14·9
25	15·0	14·7*	13·5	15·1
30	15·55	15·6*	13·9	15·4
35	16·05	16·5*	14·1	15·7
40	16·5	17·2	14·45	16·1
45	17·0	17·95	14·75	16·6
50	17·5	18·6	15·05	17·0
55	18·0	19·1	15·35	17·4
60	18·5	19·65	15·75	17·75
65	19·0	20·1	16·0	18·1
70	19·5	20·65	16·3	18·45
75	19·95	21·2	16·7	18·7
80	20·5	21·8	17·15	19·0
82·5	20·8	22·1	17·35	19·1
85·0	21·1	22·45	17·65	19·3
87·5	21·5	22·8	17·85	19·4
90·0	22·0	23·3	18·1	19·7
92·5	22·5	23·8	18·45	20·0
95·0	23·1	24·5	19·0	20·7
97·5	24·1			

a, $Me_2SO-H_2O-(CH_3)_4N^+OH^-$(0·011M). Dolman & Stewart (1967). *Can. J. Chem.* 45, 911, anilines and diphenylamine type indicators; b, $Me_2SO-H_2O-(CH_3)_4N^+OH^-$(0·0471M), Bowden & Cockerill (1970). *J. Chem. Soc. (B)* 173, and * Cockerill & Lamper (1971). *J. Chem. Soc. (B)* 503, fluorene type indicators; c, $Me_2SO-MeOH-OMe^-$(0·01M), Stewart, O'Donnell, Cram & Rickborn (1962). *Tetrahedron,* 18, 917, substituted anilines and diphenylamines; d, $Me_2SO-EtOH-OEt^-$(0·01M), Bowden & Stewart (1965). *Tetrahedron* 21, 261, carbon acid indicators.

differences in the activity coefficients of the anions contribute to the above disparity.

Dimethyl sulphoxide has also been used in setting up H_- scales for methanol-methoxide[30] and ethanol-ethoxide[31] solutions (Table 6.6) and the results show (Fig. 6.4) than the H_- values parallel one another over a mole % Me_2SO range from 0–90 although nitrogen acids were employed in the first system and carbon acids in the second. H_- values for the system $Me_2SO-OEt^--EtOH$ have been redetermined[32] using nitrogen acids and found to be virtually the same as when carbon acid indicators were employed. The ratio of indicator activity coefficients f_{R^-}/f_{RH} for both types of acid must therefore be approximately equal for the same solution, suggesting that their solvation patterns must also be somewhat similar.

The effectiveness of other solvents in increasing the basicity of solutions containing tetramethylammonium hydroxide has been investigated[33,34] and found to decrease in the order $Me_2SO >$

TABLE 6.7

Activity coefficients of water and methanol
in dimethyl sulphoxide–water and dimethyl
sulphoxide–methanol mixtures at 25°
and 20° respectively

Mole fraction Me_2SO	f_{H_2O}	f_{MeOH}
0	1·000	1·000
0·1	0·944	0·990
0·2	0·847	0·940
0·3	0·711	0·900
0·4	0·590	0·835
0·5	0·496	0·749
0·6	0·423	0·638
0·7	0·367	0·527
0·8	0·322	0·426
0·9	0·280	0·346

Me_2SO-H_2O, data of Cox & McTigue (1967). *Aust. J. Chem.* **20**, 1815.
$Me_2SO-MeOH$, data of Quitzsch, Ulbrecht & Geiseler (1967). *Z. Phys. Chem. (Leipzig)* **33**, 234.

dimethylformamide $>$ sulpholane $>$ pyridine. The dielectric constant of sulpholane is greater than that of dimethylformamide (44 against 36·7) so that the dielectric constant is, once again, not a main factor in determining solution basicity.

Because of the wide use being made of aqueous hydroxide solutions containing dimethylformamide in the study of proton transfer reactions from aromatic nitro-compounds[35,36] H_- values have recently been reported for this system.[34] Unfortunately the relatively facile reaction[37] of hydroxide ions with dimethylformamide liberating dimethylamine and formate ion is likely to affect its general utility.

6.4. OTHER MEDIA OF HIGH BASICITY

There are at least two other methods which have been used to obtain highly basic media. Firstly, a binary solvent system in which one of the constituents is itself basic has been employed. The first attempt at constructing an acidity function scale for such a system was made by Deno[38] employing various concentrations of hydrazine in water. Not only does hydrazine have a low acidity and high dielectric constant but it also has suitable optical transparency. Unfortunately it is frequently difficult to find indicators for this system as many nitro-substituted compounds which are useful indicators in other systems react rapidly with hydrazine. H_- values for mixtures of various amines and water have also been reported—these include ethylenediamine-water[39] and ethanolamine-water[40] but the low dielectric constant ($12 \cdot 9$ at $25°$ in the case of ethylenediamine) makes the interpretation of spectrophotometric measurements of indicator equilibria difficult.

The second method is based on a careful consideration of the acid strengths of suitable solvents. Liquid ammonia has a pK_a $c.$ 35 and a solution of the amide ion in this solvent is able to ionise some of the least acidic of hydrocarbons as shown by the work of Shatenshtein and co-workers.[41] Liquid ammonia has good solvent properties and kinetic measurements in it can be carried out over a wide temperature range (-40 to $+120°C$). The only disadvantages are the well known sensitivity to moisture and oxygen, making necessary the use of special experimental techniques, and the low dielectric constant.

In view of its higher basicity methylamine is sometimes preferred to liquid ammonia as a solvent. A similar system in many ways is lithium (or cesium) cyclohexylamide in cyclohexylamine, which has been used extensively by Streitwieser's group.[42] A system of comparable basicity[43] (H_- ~ 30) is obtained when the sodium salt of dimethyl sulphoxide, prepared by dissolving sodium hydride in Me_2SO at $65-70°$ under nitrogen with stirring for 45 min, is dissolved in Me_2SO (pK_a ~ 32). In the absence of air the solution is stable over long periods and can be prepared in high concentration (2 molar). A solution of potassium t-butoxide in Me_2SO is also sometimes used as a medium of high basicity.[44]

REFERENCES

1. Bowden, K. (1966). *Chem. Rev.* **66**, 119.
2. Hammett, L. P. & Deyrup, A. J. (1932). *J. Amer. Chem. Soc.* **54**, 2721.
3. Hammett, L. P. (1940). *Physical Organic Chemistry*, Chapter 9. McGraw-Hill, New York.

4. Foster, R. & Mackie, R. K. (1963). *Tetrahedron* **19**, 691.
5. Fyfe, C. A., Albagli, A. & Stewart, R. (1970). *Can. J. Chem.* **23**, 3721.
6. Schwarzenbach, G. & Sulzberger, R. (1944). *Helv. Chim. Acta* **27**, 348.
7. Edward, J. T. & Wang, I. C. (1962). *Can. J. Chem.* **40**, 399.
8. Yagil, G. (1967). *J. Phys. Chem.* **71**, 1034.
9. Stewart, R. & O'Donnell, J. P. (1964). *Can. J. Chem.* **42**, 1681.
10. Yagil, G. (1967). *J. Phys. Chem.* **71**, 1045.
11. Bascombe, K. N. & Bell, R. P. (1957). *Discuss. Faraday Soc.* **24**, 158.
12. Jones, J. R. (1968). *Chem. Commun.* 513.
13. Jones, J. R. (1968). *Trans. Faraday Soc.* **64**, 440.
14. Rochester, C. H. (1966). *Quart. Rev. Chem. Soc.* **20**, 511.
15. Jones, J. R. & Stewart, R. (1967). *J. Chem. Soc. (B)* 1173.
16. Terrier, F. (1969). *Ann. Chim.* **4**, 153.
17. Terrier, F., Millot, F. & Schaal, R. (1969). *Bull. Soc. Chim. Fr.* 3002.
18. Robinson, R. A. & Harned, H. S. (1941). *Chem. Rev.* **28**, 419.
19. Davies, C. W. (1962). *Ion Association*, p. 85. Butterworths, London.
20. Kundu, K. K. & Aiyar, L. (1971). *J. Chem. Soc. (B)* 40.
21. Kundu, K. K. & Aiyar, L. (1972). *J. Chem. Soc. (Perkin II)* 715.
22. Dolman, D. & Stewart, R. (1967). *Can. J. Chem.* **45**, 911.
23. Stewart, R. (1968). *Quart. Rep. Sulphur Chem.* **3**, 99.
24. Yagil, G. (1969). *J. Phys. Chem.* **73**, 1610.
25. Cox, B. G. & McTigue, P. T. (1967). *Aust. J. Chem.* **20**, 1815.
26. Quitzsch, K., Ulbrecht, H. & Geiseler, G. (1967). *Z. Phys. Chem. (Leipzig)* **33**, 234.
27. Bowden, K. & Cockerill, A. F. (1967). *Chem. Commun.* 989.
28. Bowden, K. & Cockerill, A. F. (1970). *J. Chem. Soc. (B)* 173.
29. Cockerill, A. F. & Lamper, J. D. (1971). *J. Chem. Soc. (B)* 503.
30. Stewart, R., O'Donnell, J. P., Cram, D. J. & Rickborn, B. (1962). *Tetrahedron* **18**, 917.
31. Bowden, K. & Stewart, R. (1965). *Tetrahedron* **21**, 261.
32. Albagli, A. & Stewart, R., unpublished work.
33. Stewart, R. & O'Donnell, J. P. (1962). *J. Amer. Chem. Soc.* **84**, 493.
34. Buncel, E., Symons, E. A., Dolman, D. & Stewart, R. (1970). *Can. J. Chem.* **48**, 3354.
35. Buncel, E. & Zabel, A. W. (1967). *J. Amer. Chem. Soc.* **89**, 3082.
36. Buncel, E., Russell, K. E. & Wood, J. (1968). *Chem. Commun.* 252.
37. Buncel, E. & Symons, E. A. (1970). *Chem. Commun.* 164.
38. Deno, N. C. (1952). *J. Amer. Chem. Soc.* **74**, 2039.
39. Vermesse-Jacquinot, C. (1965). *J. Chim. Phys.* **62**, 235.
40. Masure, F. & Schaal, R. (1956). *Bull. Soc. Chim. Fr.* 1138.
41. Shatenshtein, A. I. (1963). *Adv. in. Phys. Org. Chem.* (Gold, V. ed.) **1**, 156.
42. Streitwieser, A. Jr. & Hammons, J. H. (1965). *Progr. Phys. Org. Chem.* (Cohen, S. G., Streitwieser, A. & Taft, R. W. eds.) **3**, 41.
43. Price, G. G. & Whiting, M. C. (1963). *Chemy Ind. (London)* 775.
44. Hofmann, J. E., Muller, R. E. & Schriesheim, A. (1963). *J. Amer. Chem. Soc.* **85**, 3000.

7. Ion Association

If the ionisation of a carbon acid (AH), catalysed by a base (B) is allowed to proceed in a solvent like water with a high dielectric constant, and at a low ionic strength, the interionic effects will be entirely long range and non-specific. Furthermore the rate under these conditions can be quantitatively predicted by means of the Brönsted equation:

$$k = k_0 \frac{f_{AH} f_B}{f^{\ddagger}} \tag{7.1}$$

f_{AH}, f_B are the activity coefficients of AH and B respectively and $f^{\ddagger}$ that of the transition state.

If the solvent is changed to one of lower dielectric constant or if the ionic strength of the medium is increased, deviations from the Brönsted equation occur; these arise from the increasing importance of short range and specific interactions. If the medium is of sufficiently low dielectric or if the ionic strength is sufficiently high, the fraction of reaction proceeding through the free ions could be so low that their contribution to the overall rate is negligible.

TABLE 7.1

Dielectric constants of some solvents at 25°

Solvent	Dielectric constant
Water	78·4
Methanol	32·6
Ethanol	21·5[a]
t-Butanol	11·2[b]
Ammonia	17
Cyclohexylamine	5·4[c]
Dimethyl sulphoxide	49
Acetonitrile	36
Dimethyoxyethane	7·2
Chlorobenzene	5·6
1,4-Dioxan	2·2
Tetrahydrofuran	7·4

[a] at 33·4; [b] at 30°; [c] at −21°.

The rates of ionisation of some carbon acids have been studied in a number of solvents, the dielectric constants of which vary over a wide range (Table 7.1), and also in the presence of different salts. Such studies therefore form a good basis for the detailed analysis of these specific interactions. In this way they also serve to illustrate the important role which the solvent plays in reaction kinetics.

7.1. ION PAIRS

The difficulty that arises when Eqn (7.1) breaks down can be overcome by postulating the existence of a new species, namely the ion pair, which is formed from the interactions between oppositely charged ions. The formation of the new species comes about when the energy of mutual electrostatic attraction is greater than the thermal energy which strives to maintain a random distribution of ions. The ion pairs so formed may be separated by one or more solvent molecules or they may be formed from two oppositely charged ions in contact with one another—this distinction leads to the description "solvent-separated" and "contact" ion pairs.

For those concerned with both electrolyte solutions and the rates of chemical reactions the exact definition of an ion pair has been the source of some difficulty. Bjerrum,[1] for example, classified all oppositely charged ions within a certain distance of one another as ion pairs. This critical distance q, given by

$$q = \frac{|z_1 z_2| e^2}{2 \epsilon k T} \tag{7.2}$$

is that at which the mutual electrical potential energy of the two ions, $|z_1 z_2| e^2 / \epsilon q$ is equal to $2\,kT$. This definition has been criticised on the grounds that if considered rigorously it may be interpreted to mean an abrupt transition from bound to free ions at a specific distance. This objection is absent in Fuoss's[2] definition where the term ion pair is retained for those ions actually in contact. Prue[3] has recently shown how these two approaches can be inter-related.

7.2. AQUEOUS MEDIA

Because of the high dielectric constant of water it is frequently assumed that so far as reaction kinetics are concerned ion association effects are unimportant. This is not necessarily so as can be seen for the following reactions, one being an example of specific hydroxide ion catalysis and the other of general-base catalysis.

The decomposition of diacetone alcohol lends itself to accurate study and the results of various workers[4-6] (Fig. 7.1) show that the second-order rate constant may be either decreased or increased as the concentration of the particular base is increased. The first effect can be ascribed to the formation of unreactive associated species such as TlOH and the results fitted quantitatively by introducing association constants. The good agreement between association constants determined in this way and those found by other methods suggests that any interaction between the activated complex and the cations is unimportant. A closely similar pattern of specific cation effects has been found for the reaction of p-trimethylsilylmethyl-benzoate with hydroxide ions[7] and the neutralisation of nitro-ethane[8] using the same base. The effect of the tetraalkylammonium

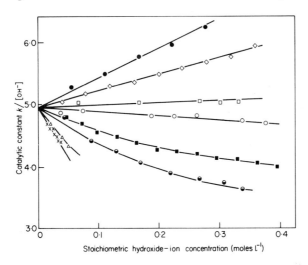

Fig. 7.1. Plot of the catalytic constant $k/[\text{OH}^-]$ $(\text{M}^{-1}\ \text{s}^{-1})$ for the decomposition of diacetone alcohol against the stoichiometric hydroxide-ion concentration.[4-6] ○, KOH; □, RbOH; ◇, $(\text{CH}_3)_4\text{N}^+\text{OH}^-$; ●, $(n\text{-}\text{C}_3\text{H}_7)_4\text{N}^+\text{OH}^-$; x, Ca(OH)_2; ■, Ba(OH)_2; ◓, TlOH; △, $\text{Co(NH}_3)_6^{+}$.

hydroxides in causing an increase in the second-order rate constant is entirely consistent with the abnormal conductance and viscosity results obtained for these compounds and interpreted in terms of an unusual activity coefficient behaviour.[5]

The decomposition of nitramide is catalysed by bases in general and Bell and Waind[9] have studied catalysis by the anions of acetic, mandelic, salicylic, malic and fumaric acids in the presence of sodium, calcium, barium and zinc ions. The results for the divalent cations show that the decrease in rate caused by their addition is somewhat smaller than the decrease of anion concentration due to association. In other words the associated anion possesses a catalytic power although this is considerably less than that of the free anion.

Consequently the derived dissociation constants are all higher than the values obtained by non-kinetic methods although they follow the same trend. Thus for each acid the zinc salts are much weaker than the calcium salts, and the calcium salts weaker than the barium salts, while for a given cation the dissociation constants follow the series: acetate > salicylate > mandelate; fumarate > malate.

In order to be able to measure the rates of ionisation of carbon acids in aqueous media at temperatures below the freezing point of water large concentrations of various salts may be added. This was done for the hydroxide catalysed ionisation of acetophenone[10] and

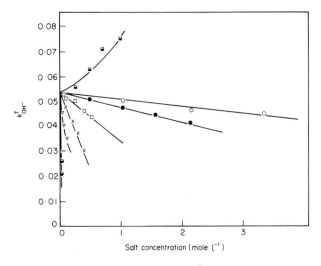

Fig. 7.2. Plot of the detritiation rate constant $k_{OH^-}^T$ (M^{-1} s^{-1}) for the detritiation of [α-^{3}H]-acetophenone against the concentration of salt.[10] o, K^+; •, Na^+; □, Li^+; x, Ba^{2+}; ▽, Ca^{2+}; ʘ, Mg^{2+}; ◘, R_4N^+.

led to large specific rate retardations (Fig. 7.2), the order being $K < Na < Li < Ba < Ca < Mg$. As for the diacetone alcohol study the results were interpreted in terms of ion association between the hydroxide ion and the various cations, with the ion pair showing no signs of being an active catalyst. Once again tetraalkylammonium salts led to a rate acceleration.

Addition of salts in the base catalysed mutarotation of tetra-methyl- and tetraacetylglucose in solvents such as pyridine and nitromethane result in spectacular and specific rate enhancements.[11,12] These results have been interpreted in terms of stabilisation of highly polar activated complexes by interaction with ion pairs.

For reactions which exhibit general acid-base catalysis in carboxylate buffers the rate, at least in dilute solution, conforms to the equation

$$\text{rate} = k_{H_2O}[H_2O] + k_{H_3O^+}[H_3O^+] + k_{OH^-}[OH^-] + k_{HA}[HA]$$
$$+ k_{A^-}[A^-] \tag{7.3}$$

As early as 1930 Dawson and Spivey[13] reported on the need, in the acetate catalysed iodination of acetone, to take into account additional cross terms such as $k_x[HA][A^-]$ and results in support of this proposal were subsequently obtained.[14] At that time these were considered to be the sole evidence for the occurrence in aqueous solution of a catalysed mechanism requiring the simultaneous presence of an acid and a base in the transition state complex.

The kinetic data are, however, consistent with the formation of the hydrogen diacetate ion HA_2^- and Rosotti[15] has shown that not only does this species exist in appreciable concentrations in concentrated buffers but that it is a more effective catalyst than the monomeric acids and carboxylate ions in enolising acetone. Furthermore it is necessary not only to take into account the association

$$A^- + HA \rightleftharpoons HA_2^- \tag{7.4}$$

but also the dimerisation equilibrium

$$HA_2^- + H^+ \rightleftharpoons H_2A_2 \tag{7.5}$$

the association constant for which is such that the concentrations of the dimeric monocarboxylic acids H_2A_2 in concentrated buffers are of comparable magnitude to the concentrations of HA_2^- in 1:1 buffers. Equation (7.3) is therefore strictly valid only for very dilute buffers and at higher concentrations has to be modified to contain a further term $k_D[HA]^2$.

Similar findings have been observed in the hydrolysis of cyanoketen dimethyl acetal[16] with the difference that in that study the associated products are assumed to be catalytically inactive. As long as the concentration-dependence of the rate is calculated for low concentrations, at which association is negligible, the occurrence of these complications does not affect the validity of the general method of determining catalytic coefficients from experiments in carboxylate buffers.

7.3. METHANOL, ETHANOL AND t-BUTANOL

Of the various alcohols these three have been the most frequently used for the study of rate processes in solution. Because of the

different dielectric constants (Table 7.1) the effects of ion association should increase in the order MeOH < EtOH < t-BuOH. Despite
the attraction of being able to study reactions at low temperatures
where, for example, quantum mechanical effects may be important,
relatively few studies on the ionisation of carbon acids in alcohol-
alkoxide solutions have been made and details of the extent of ion
association have usually come from other investigations.

Acidity function measurements[17] of concentrated methanol-
methoxide solutions show that for a given concentration
H_-^M (KOMe) > H_-^M (NaOMe) > H_-^M (LiOMe), the order being the same
as for the corresponding hydroxides (Chapter 6) and attributable to
ion association.[18]

In the aromatic nucleophilic substitution reaction between
methoxide ion and 2,4-dinitrochlorobenzene in methanol the change
in rate constant on the addition of various potassium, sodium and
lithium salts was qualitatively explained[19] in terms of ion association
effects with the ion pairs being active catalysts:

$$k_{obs} = k_1 [\bar{O}CH_3] + k_2 [M^+\bar{O}CH_3] = \alpha k_1 + (1 - \alpha)k_2 \qquad (7.6)$$

Extension of the studies to a medium of lower dielectric (50%
methanol–benzene mixture) showed the effects to be more pronounced.[20]

Recently two separate studies[21,22] have been made of the
detritiation of [9-³H]-fluorene in methanolic sodium methoxide
solutions. The results are in good agreement, showing that the
second-order rate constant (k_2) increases with increasing sodium
methoxide concentration. Both More O'Ferrall and Streitwieser
make no allowance for ion association although at the high concentrations employed it must be extensive. At low methoxide concentrations (<1 M) the dependence of rate on concentration is approximately linear and Streitwieser presents his results in terms of a "salt
effect" according to Eqn (7.7):

$$k_2 = k_2^0 [1 + b(\text{NaOMe})] \qquad (7.7)$$

The second-order rate constant at zero base concentration (k_2^0) can
then be calculated. At higher base concentrations the strongly curved
dependence on NaOMe concentration is reminiscent of an H_-
behaviour.

In the base catalysed racemisation of (+)-2-methyl-3-phenylpro-
pionitrile[23] the reaction order becomes nearly two in NaOMe and
KOMe at high concentration but falls below one for LiOMe,
suggesting that ion pairs catalyse the reaction with Li⁺O⁻Me less and

$\overset{+}{K}\overset{-}{O}Me$ more reactive than the free methoxide ion. This explanation may, however, be an oversimplification.

In the case of ethanol–ethoxide solutions dissociation constants have been obtained from conductivity measurements[24] (Table 7.2). For potassium ethoxide the K_d value is very close to an estimate previously made[25] for potassium methoxide ($K_d \sim 0.01$–0.02), as expected from the relatively small difference in dielectric constant of methanol and ethanol (Table 7.1).

TABLE 7.2

Dissociation constants of ethanol–ethoxide
solutions[24] at 25°

Base	K_d
KOEt	0.028
LiOEt	0.0057
NaOEt	0.020
RbOEt	0.0257
CsOEt	0.0154

TABLE 7.3

Kinetic data for the detritiation of [α-³H] p-dimethylaminoacetophenone
in various ethanol–ethoxide solutions[26] at 33.4°

[KOEt][a]	$10^3 k^T/[KOEt]$	[NaOEt]	$10^3 k^T/[NaOEt]$	[LiOEt]	$10^3 k^T/[LiOEt]$
0.0170	14.4	0.0304	14.0	0.0052	13.8
0.0505	14.4	0.0569	13.9	0.0115	13.9
0.108	14.8	0.0600	13.9	0.0229	13.4
0.210	15.1	0.110	14.3	0.0454	13.0
0.329	15.2	0.228	14.3	0.0896	12.7
0.406	15.2	0.341	14.8	0.136	12.4
0.524	15.6	0.570	14.7	0.276	12.6
				0.546	11.8

[a] In moles l^{-1}.

The results of a study on the detritiation of [α-³H]-p-dimethyl-aminoacetophenone in various ethanol–ethoxide solutions[26] (Table 7.3) show that with increasing base concentration the second-order rate constant increases in the case of potassium and sodium and decreases for lithium, although the changes in each case are relatively small. At low concentrations there is good agreement between the various rate constants.

In the reaction between 2,4,6-trinitrotoluene (TNT) and sodium ethoxide[27] the rate-determining step is proton transfer from the methyl group. The second-order rate constant decreases by just over 20% as the base concentration is increased from 0·0039 to 0·036 M but the authors prefer to assume that this effect arises not from ion association but because of the formation of a second species (probably a σ complex of TNT and ethoxide ion).

The dissociation constant of potassium t-butoxide in t-butanol[23] (K_d = 0·0016 at 25°) is lower by more than a factor of 10 than that of the corresponding salt in ethanol. Several qualitative observations lend support to the idea that ion association is important in this medium even at very low concentrations of base. Thus the conductance of t-butanol is only slightly increased by the addition of sodium t-butoxide whereas the addition of benzyltrimethyl ammonium chloride and 2-phenylethyltrimethylammonium bromide markedly increases the conductance.[28] These findings are consistent with the observation[29] that benzyltrimethylammonium t-butoxide in t-butanol at concentrations as low as 10^{-3} M is about 1000 times more basic than a solution of potassium t-butoxide of the same concentration. It has also been reported[29] that these latter solutions are approximately twice as basic as sodium t-butoxide solutions of the same concentration in the range 5×10^{-4} M < $[\overset{+}{M}\overset{-}{O}Bu\text{-}t]$ < 0·06M. Raising the temperature from 30° to 50° approximately halves the basicity of potassium t-butoxide solutions since the dielectric constant of t-butanol decreases with increasing temperature. Mention should also be made of the fact that in addition to ion association in these solutions there is also some evidence for the existence of ion aggregates.[30]

The results of a study[26] on the detritiation of methyldeoxybenzoin (Fig. 7.3) in various t-butoxide-t-butanol solutions show that ion association is important at low concentrations of base and increases in the order Li > Na > K, as for the methanol–methoxide and water–hydroxide solutions. The extreme behaviour of lithium is very much in line with earlier observations on the nature of lithium t-butoxide. Kamienski and Lewis[30] found that the solubility of this salt in solvents such as tetrahydrofuran and n-heptane was considerably higher than its solubility in t-butanol, indicating a tendency to covalency in the compound. This finding is reinforced by spectroscopic studies of the solid, the vapour and solutions of the compound in non-polar solvents.[31]

A solution of potassium t-butoxide in dimethyl sulphoxide constitutes a very highly basic medium suitable for studying the rates of ionisation of very weak carbon acids. In fact the detritiation of $[\alpha\text{-}^{3}H]$ toluene was studied in this medium[32]—below a base concentration of 0·3 M the reaction is close to being first-order in base but at higher concentrations becomes virtually independent of base

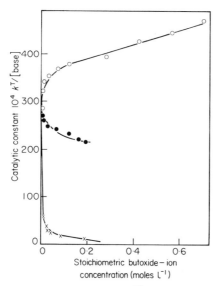

Fig. 7.3. Plot of the detritiation rate constant $k^T/[MOBu-t]$ $(M^{-1} s^{-1})$ for methyldeoxy-benzoin[26] in various t-butanol–t-butoxide solutions at $33.4°$. o, KOBu-t; •, NaOBu-t; x, LiOBu-t.

concentration. The same general type of behaviour has been noted for other base-catalysed reactions in dimethyl sulphoxide.[33]

7.4. CYCLOHEXYLAMINE AND LIQUID AMMONIA

Cyclohexylamine as solvent with either lithium or cesium cyclohexylamide as the base is the system chosen by Streitwieser and co-workers for their extensive studies on both the rates of ionisation and acidity determinations of carbon acids. Conductivity measurements show[34] that the dissociation constant of lithium cyclohexylamide in cyclohexylamine is between 10^{-10}–10^{-12} mole l^{-1}, and similar to that for lithium perchlorate and lithium fluorenyl in the same solvent. For cesium cyclohexylamide the equivalent conductance is $c.$ 10^5 less than would be expected if the salt were fully dissociated.[35] Clearly only at very low concentrations of base would the free anions be expected to play a significant part in any reaction.

Studies on the dedeuteriation of $[\alpha\text{-}^2H]$-toluene[36] using lithium cyclohexylamide as base show (Fig. 7.4) that the kinetic order in catalyst varies from close to unity at low concentrations to zero at high concentrations. Such behaviour is similar to that observed for potassium t-butoxide in dimethyl sulphoxide[32] and lithium alkyls (e.g. n-butyl lithium) in benzene or toluene solution.[37] The results can be accounted for by assuming that above a certain concentration only part of the lithium cyclohexylamide (or alkyl) is reactive, the other part being in the form of aggregates which do not make any significant contribution to the overall rate. In the case of lithium cyclohexylamide the equilibrium

$$2 \text{ LiCHA} \rightleftharpoons (\text{LiCHA})_2 \tag{7.8}$$

has a K of 60 mole l^{-1}, and the calculated dependence of rate on catalyst concentration is in the good agreement with the experimentally determined values. Further evidence that amide ions are not important in this medium comes from a study of salt effects. Lithium perchlorate, for example, should be at least as dissociated as lithium cyclohexylamide in cyclohexylamine and should therefore

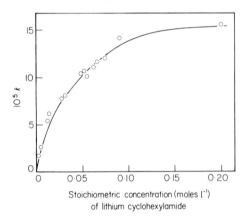

Stoichiometric concentration (moles l^{-1})
of lithium cyclohexylamide

Fig. 7.4. Effect of stoichiometric concentration of lithium cyclohexylamide on pseudo first-order rate constant $k(s^{-1})$ for the de-deuteriation of $[\alpha\text{-}^2\text{H}]$ toluene.[36] ———, represents the theoretical curve.

suppress the ionisation of the latter. The observed change in rate is however much less than would be the case if the amide ion were acting as catalyst.

Extensive studies of the rates of ionisation of carbon acids in liquid ammonia containing potassium amide have been made, particularly by Shatenshtein's group.[38] However no detailed study of the possible contribution of ion association to the rates has been made and the only kinetic investigation where this has been done refers to the isotopic exchange between hydrogen and liquid ammonia.[39]

$$\text{NH}_3 + \text{HD} \rightleftharpoons \text{NH}_2\text{D} + \text{H}_2 \tag{7.9}$$

The results (Fig. 7.5) show a familiar pattern—at a given concentration of base the second-order rate constant decreases in the order

$CsNH_2 > KNH_2 > NaNH_2$. When due allowance is made for ion association it is clear that only the free amide ion acts as a catalytic species, as was also found to be the case in the polymerisation of styrene.[40] Experiments on common ion and secondary salt effects confirm this interpretation.

Conductance measurements on alkali-metal amides in liquid ammonia have shed considerable light on the nature of these solutions.[39] In the concentration range 0–0·005 M potassium and cesium amides are dissociated to the same extent ($K_d = 2·23 \times 10^{-5}$

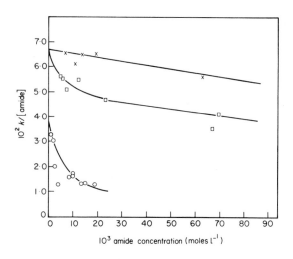

Fig. 7.5. Plot of the catalytic constant $k/[amide]$ (M^{-1} s^{-1}) against the stoichiometric amide ion concentration for the isotopic exchange of hydrogen in liquid ammonia[39] at −45·2°. ○, $NaNH_2$; □, KNH_2; ×, $CsNH_2$.

at −33·5°); the values reported for $NaNH_2$ at the same temperature vary from $0·73 \times 10^{-5}$ to $1·02 \times 10^{-4}$. At still higher concentrations triple ions of the form $(K_2NH_2)^+$ and $[K(NH_2)_2]^-$ are formed.

7.5. STRUCTURE OF CARBANIONS IN VARIOUS SOLVENTS

Up until now we have been concerned with the effect of altering the nature of the base and/or the solvent on the rates of ionisation of carbon acids. This reaction leads to the formation of a carbanion which itself is able to act as a base in the reverse reaction, that of ion-recombination. Only recently and mainly through the work of Szwarc, Smid and co-workers[41–43] has attention been drawn to the possible structures of carbanions in different solvents and the effect such variables as temperature and pressure might have on their structures.

The results of a study[44] on the temperature dependence of the electronic spectrum of the sodium salt of fluorene in tetrahydrofuran show that as the temperature decreases the sharp absorption at 355 nm decreases and a new peak at 373 nm appears until at below $-50°$ only the latter remains. The process is reversible and similar changes are observed in the visible part of the spectrum. The new entity cannot be the free fluorenyl anion as the dissociation constant for $F^-Na^+(7 \times 10^{-7}M$ at $25°$, $4 \times 10^{-5}M$ at $-70°)$ is very low. Rather does it represent an equilibrium between solvent separated ion pairs $(F^- \parallel Na^+)$ and contact ion pairs (F^-, Na^+) with the latter favoured at lower temperatures:

$$F^-, M^+ + nS \rightleftharpoons F^- \parallel M^+ \tag{7.10}$$

n representing the number of solvent molecules reacting with the contact ion-pair. Increasing the radius of the metal ion is usually associated with a decrease in the fraction of solvent separated ion pairs.

Changing the polarity and structure of the solvent can have a marked effect on the equilibrium (7.10). For a series of polyglycol dimethyl ethers, for example, the solvating power is at a maximum when 4 or 5 co-ordination sites are available for solvation.[45] In the case of unsubstituted cyclic ethers the order of increasing solvating power is largely determined by the basicity of the ether oxygen atom.[46] Steric factors are also important as when substituted tetrahydrofurans are used as solvents.

Ion pair equilibria of this kind have been observed for several other carbanions[43] —these include benzofluorene, phenanthrene and 1,3-diphenylpropene,[47] as well as for aromatic radical anion salts such as triphenylene–sodium, coronene–sodium and perylene–sodium.[41] The results of such studies show that charge delocalisation facilitates ion pair separation whilst the presence of large substituents on the anion tend to lower the stability of the contact ion pair.

A recent study[48] of the effect of temperature on the absorption spectrum of fluorenyl–lithium in cyclohexylamine–diethylamine (2:1 molar ratio) shows that 95% of the ion pairs exist as the solvent separated variety. For the indenyl anion the proportion falls to 65% as the negative charge is more concentrated in this case. The corresponding cesium salts as well as triphenylmethyl–cesium all exist primarily as contact ion pairs in this medium.

Although few kinetic studies have been made in relation to the use of carbanion ion pairs the results of Hogen-Esch and Smid[49] for the reaction between either 1,2- or 3,4-benzofluorene and various alkali-metal fluorenyls illustrate a number of important points (Table 7.4). The data for fluorenyl–lithium (as well as fluorenyl–sodium in dioxan) show a strong dependence of the rate constants on the carbanion concentration, suggesting the presence of unreactive aggregates $[F^-M^+]_n$ with a value of 5 or more for n. Both the planar structure of the carbanion and the tendency of the counterion to complex with the highly polarisable π cloud of the fluorenyl ring favour association and this could well be the reason for the large discrepancies observed for proton-transfer rate constants in solutions of fluorenyl–lithium in dimethyl sulphoxide,[50,51] in which different techniques and different carbanion concentrations were used.

At low concentrations, where aggregation is unimportant, fluorenyl–sodium is slightly more reactive in dioxan than in tetrahydrofuran and considerably more so in dimethoxyethane. In the

TABLE 7.4

Observed rate constants[49] for the reaction 1,2-benzofluorene + fluorenyl$^-$, M^+ at 25°

Metal-counterion	Solvent	$10^5[F^-, M^+]$	$k(M^{-1}s^{-1})$
Li^+	Tetrahydrofuran	0·67	51·6
		4·2	19·9
		4·7	12·3
		4·0	1·6
Na^+	Tetrahydrofuran	1·3	3500
		1·5	3960
		32	3800
Na^+	Dioxan	1·2	4200
		2·8	1660
		8·1	660
		20	294
		42	183
Na^+	Dimethoxyethane	0·92	$\sim 5 \times 10^4$
		24	$\sim 8 \times 10^4$

first two solvents the sodium salt exists as a contact ion pair while in dimethoxyethane it is essentially solvent separated. Hence, less energy is needed in the latter case to transfer the counterion to the new carbanion. Coulombic interaction between the carbanion and the counterion is not, however, the only rate-determining factor since fluorenyl–cesium would then be expected to have a higher reactivity than fluorenyl–sodium in both dioxan and tetrahydrofuran; in practice the reverse is observed. Hogen-Esch and Smid[49] believe that this comes about because the counterion activates the benzofluorene molecule and facilitates the abstraction of the proton.

The results for the sodium salt in tetrahydrofuran show the rate constant to be practically independent of salt concentration despite the increased free ion formation at low concentration. This result suggests that the free ion is less reactive than the contact ion pair in agreement with the finding that addition of the strongly dissociable salt $NaB(C_6H_5)_4$ leads not to a rate decrease but to a slight increase in rate.

The solvent separated ion pair is expected to be very reactive as long as the counterion can activate the benzofluorene nucleus. However, when the solvating entity prevents a close approach between the benzofluorene molecule and the counterion, the solvent-separated ion pair reactivity is expected to be less than that of the contact ion pair and may approach that of the free ion. This seems to be the case in the system fluorenyl–sodium–tetrahydrofuran to which small quantities of tetraethylene glycol dimethyl ether were added. Although the spectrum in the presence of this powerful solvating agent shows complete solvent-separated ion pair formation the rate of proton abstraction is slower than in the absence of this reagent.

In the reaction between the divalent fluorenyl ion pair (Ba^{2+}, F^{2-}) and 3,4-benzofluorene in tetrahydrofuran[52] the free ion rate constant is c. 75 M^{-1} s^{-1}, compared with a value of less than $0.1M^{-1}$ s^{-1} for the reaction between Ba^{2+}, F_2^-, present as the contact ion pair, and the hydrocarbon. Whereas the high rate constant for the F^-, Na^+ ion pair (3500 M^{-1} s^{-1}) owed something to the catalysing role of the Na^+ this is not possible for the Ba^{2+}, F^{2-} ion pair because the Ba^{2+} ion is shielded by two fluorenyl moieties.

REFERENCES

1. Bjerrum, N. (1926). *Kgl. Dan. Vidensk. Selsk. Mat. Fys. Medd.* 7, No. 9.
2. Fuoss, R. M. (1958). *J. Amer. Chem. Soc.* **80**, 5059.
3. Prue, J. E. (1969). *J. Chem. Educ.* **46**, 12.
4. Bell, R. P. & Prue, J. E. (1949). *J. Chem. Soc.* 362.
5. Halberstadt, E. S. & Prue, J. E. (1952). *J. Chem. Soc.* 2234.
6. Caton, J. A. & Prue, J. E. (1956). *J. Chem. Soc.* 671.
7. Eaborn, C. & Parker, S. H. (1957). *J. Chem. Soc.* 955.
8. Bell, R. P. & Panckhurst, M. H. (1956). *J. Chem. Soc.* 2836.
9. Bell, R. P. & Waind, G. M. (1951). *J. Chem. Soc.* 2357.
10. Jones, J. R. (1968). *Trans. Faraday Soc.* **64**, 440.
11. Eastham, A. M., Blackall, E. L. & Latremouille, G. A. (1955). *J. Amer. Chem. Soc.* **77**, 2182.
12. Blackall, E. L. & Eastham, A. M. (1955). *J. Amer. Chem. Soc.* **77**, 2184.
13. Dawson, H. M. & Spivey, E. (1930). *J. Chem. Soc.* 2180.
14. Bell, R. P. & Jones, P. (1953). *J. Chem. Soc.* 88.
15. Rossotti, F. J. C. (1960). *Nature (London)* **188**, 936.
16. Gold, V. & Waterman, D. C. A. (1968). *J. Chem. Soc. (B)* 839.
17. Terrier, F., Millot, F. & Schaal, R. (1969). *Bull. Soc. Chim. Fr.* 3002.

18. Jones, J. R. (1968). *Chem. Commun.* 513.
19. Reinheimer, J. D., Kieffer, W. F., Frey, S. W., Cochran, J. C. & Barr, E. W. (1958). *J. Amer. Chem. Soc.* 80, 164.
20. Reinheimer, J. D., Gerig, J. T. & Cochran, J. C. (1961). *J. Amer. Chem. Soc.* 83, 2873.
21. More O'Ferrall, R. A. (1972). *J. Chem. Soc. (Perkin II)* 976.
22. Streitwieser, A. Jr., Chang, C. J. & Young, A. T. (1972). *J. Amer. Chem. Soc.* 94, 4888.
23. Cram, D. J., Rickborn, B., Kingsbury, C. A. & Haberfield, P. (1961). *J. Amer. Chem. Soc.* 83, 3678.
24. Barthel, J., Schwitzgebel, G. & Wachter, R. (1967). *Z. Phys. Chem.* 55, 33.
25. Ogston, A. G. (1936). *Trans. Faraday Soc.* 32, 1679.
26. Earls, D. W. & Jones, J. R. (1973). Unpublished results..
27. Buncel, E., Norris, A. R., Russell, K. E. & Tucker, R. (1972). *J. Amer. Chem. Soc.* 94, 1646.
28. Saunders, W. H. Jr., Bushman, D. G. & Cockerill, A. F. (1968). *J. Amer. Chem. Soc.* 70, 1775.
29. Bethell, D. & Cockerill, A. F. (1966). *J. Chem. Soc. (B)* 913.
30. Kamienski, C. W. & Lewis, D. H. (1965). *J. Org. Chem.* 30, 3498.
31. Simonov, A. P., Shigorin, D. N., Talalaeva, T. V. & Kocheshkov, K. A. (1961). *Dokl. Akad. Nauk. SSSR* 136, 634.
32. Hofmann, J. E., Muller, R. J. & Schriesheim, A. (1963). *J. Amer. Chem. Soc.* 85, 3000.
33. Schriesheim, A. & Rowe, C. A. (1962). *J. Amer. Chem. Soc.* 84, 3160.
34. Streitwieser, A. Jr., Padgett, W. M. & Schwager, I. (1964). *J. Phys. Chem.* 68, 2922.
35. Streitwieser, A. Jr. & Caldwell, R. A. (1965). *J. Amer. Chem. Soc.* 87, 5398.
36. Streitwieser, A. Jr., Van Sickle, D. E. & Langworthy, W. C. (1962). *J. Amer. Chem. Soc.* 84, 244.
37. Welch, F. J. (1959). *J. Amer. Chem. Soc.* 81, 1345.
38. Shatenshtein, A. I. (1963). *Adv. Phys. Org. Chem.* (Gold, V. ed.) 1, 156.
39. Delmas, R., Courvoisier, P. & Ravoire, J. (1969). *Isotope Effects in Chemical Processes.* Adv. Chem. Series, 89, 25.
40. Higginson, W. C. E. & Wooding, N. S. (1952). *J. Chem. Soc.* 760.
41. Szwarc, M. (1968). *Carbanions, Living Polymers and Electron Transfer Processes.* Interscience Publishers, New York.
42. Szwarc, M. (1969). *Acc. Chem. Research* 2, 87.
43. Smid, J. (1972). *Angew. Chem. Int. Ed. Engl.* 11, 112.
44. Hogen-Esch, T. E. & Smid, J. (1965). *J. Amer. Chem. Soc.* 87, 669.
45. Chan, L. L. & Smid, J. (1967). *J. Amer. Chem. Soc.* 89, 4547.
46. Chan, L. L. Smid, J. (1968). *J. Amer. Chem. Soc.* 90, 4654.
47. Burley, J. W. & Young, R. N. (1971). *J. Chem. Soc. (B)* 1018.
48. Streitwieser, A. Jr., Chang, C. J., Hollyhead, W. B. & Murdoch, J. R. (1972). *J. Amer. Chem. Soc.* 94, 5288.
49. Hogen-Esch, T. E. & Smid, J. (1967). *J. Amer. Chem. Soc.* 89, 2764.
50. Brauman, J. I., McMillen, D. F. & Kanazawa, Y. (1967). *J. Amer. Chem. Soc.* 89, 1728.
51. Ritchie, C. D. & Uschold, R. E. (1967). *J. Amer. Chem. Soc.* 89, 1730.
52. Hogen-Esch, T. E. & Smid, J. (1969). *J. Amer. Chem. Soc.* 91, 4580.

8. Rate–Equilibria Correlations

The success of the transition state theory of reaction rates should not be allowed to obscure the fact that as it stands at present it does not allow of the *a priori* calculation of reaction rates. Under these circumstances the structure of the transition state for a particular reaction can only be inferred and Chapters 9 and 10 on primary and solvent isotope effects respectively show how such studies can help. In addition several other approaches each characterised by the fact that whilst the properties of the reactants and products are subject to

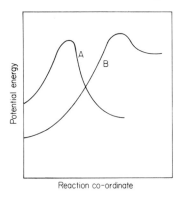

Fig. 8.1. Potential energy barriers for different kinds of reaction.[1] A, Exothermic, $\Delta pK - ve$, transition state resembles reactants; B, endothermic, $\Delta pK + ve$, transition state resembles products.

experimental observation those of the transition state are not, are available. The hope must therefore be that these methods either singly or combined can define the transition state structure so well that calculation of reaction rates becomes possible.

In 1955 Hammond[1] drew attention to the fact that in highly exothermic (downhill) reactions the transition state is expected to occur at a very early stage along the reaction co-ordinate and thereby resembles the reactants more so than the products. Similarly for a highly endothermic reaction (uphill) the transition state is product-like. These two somewhat extreme cases can be represented schematically by a potential energy diagram (Fig. 8.1). Curve A represents the destruction of a highly reactive species and curve B describes a process in which the conversion of the transition state to products is easy. If such curves refer to proton transfer reactions of the general form

$$AH + B^- \rightarrow A^- + HB \qquad (8.1)$$

then $\Delta pK = pK_{AH} - pK_{HB}$ will be negative for case A and positive for case B. It also follows that the transition state bears the greater resemblance to the less stable of the species (reactants or products) of a chemical equilibrium.[2]

Although the entropies of activation for reactions in solution are complicated by problems of solvent participation and electrostatic interactions their magnitude often provide information concerning the nature of a transition state not available by other methods.[2] In

TABLE 8.1

Thermodynamic data for the base catalysed ionisation of nitroethane[3]

Base	ΔS^0	$\Delta S_i^{\ddagger}$
NH_3	-32.4	-17.9
CH_3NH_2	-27.9	-12.0
$(CH_3)_2NH$	-21.5	-6.6
$(CH_3)_3N$	-14.1	-7.3
OH^-	-18.3	-15.5

the base catalysed ionisation of nitroethane comparison of the $\Delta S_i^{\ddagger}$ values can be made with the standard entropy ΔS^0 of the reaction (Table 8.1). The similarity between the two values for the case of hydroxide ion catalysis, for example, can be taken to indicate that the transition state closely resembles the products of the reaction.[4]

A more recent approach[5] based on the measurement of enthalpies of transfer of transition states from one solvent to another offers the promise of being able to actually measure a property of the transition state. The method is based on the premise that if a reaction is carried out in two widely different solvents changes in the difference in their interaction with the species along the reaction coordinate are a measure of the progress of such species along the reaction coordinate. Thus for a reaction having a substantial solvent effect on its enthalpy of activation $\Delta H^{\ddagger}$ the degree of resemblance between the transition state and say the reactants is a function of the similarity between the enthalpy of transfer from one solvent to the other of the transition state, $\delta H^{\ddagger}$ and the enthalpy of transfer from one solvent to the other of the reactants, $\delta\Delta H_s$. So far results only for some S_N2 reactions have been reported.

In the ionisation of carbon acids the two parameters most amenable to experimental observation are the velocity of the reaction and the base strength of the catalyst. Not surprisingly therefore a good deal of attention has been paid to investigating in what way they are related and what information may be obtained concerning the transition state from such investigations. This chapter deals with various aspects of this relationship.

8.1. THE BRÖNSTED RELATIONSIP

From their work on the base catalysed decomposition of nitramide Brönsted and Pedersen[6] were able to relate the reaction velocity (k) to the base strength of the catalyst (K_B) by Eqn (8.2) or, in the logarithmic form, Eqn (8.3)

$$k = GK_B^\beta \tag{8.2}$$

$$\log k = \log G + \beta \log K_B \tag{8.3}$$

G was a constant for a given reaction and provided the base strength was not varied to widely so also was β, values of the latter being confined to the range 0–1. During the intervening 50 years the relationship, which has become identified with the name of the senior author, has been the subject of extensive studies, particularly by Bell and co-workers.[7]

If the catalyst in the proton transfer reaction is changed from B^- to $B^{-\prime}$ the difference in reaction velocity can be expressed by Eqn (8.4).

$$\log k - \log k' = \beta(\log K_B - \log K_{B'}) \tag{8.4}$$

which is equivalent to

$$\Delta G^\ddagger - \Delta G^{\ddagger\prime} = \beta(\Delta G^0 - \Delta G^{0\prime}) \tag{8.5}$$

$$\beta = \frac{\Delta G^\ddagger - \Delta G^{\ddagger\prime}}{\Delta G^0 - \Delta G^{0\prime}} \tag{8.6}$$

Catalyst changes are usually brought about by changing substituents in the catalyst molecule and it is convenient therefore to reformulate Eqn (8.6) in terms of the substituent stabilisation operator[8] δ_R as Eqn (8.7)

$$\beta = \frac{\delta_R \Delta G^\ddagger}{\delta_R \Delta G^0} \tag{8.7}$$

β then is the ratio of substituent effects on the free energy of activation of a proton transfer process to substituent effects on its overall free energy change. Equation (8.6) expresses in mathematical terms what is more customarily discerned from a potential energy diagram (Fig. 8.2). Only when the curves for HB and HB' have the same shape and the same position on the distance axis does it follow that Eqn (8.7) is valid.

In order that β may be employed as a parameter that measures the extent to which the transition state resembles either the products or reactants several conditions must be fulfilled and Kresge[9] has recently drawn attention to these. The extent of proton transfer at

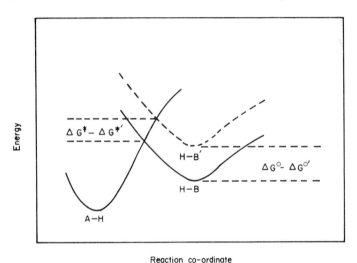

Reaction co-ordinate

Fig. 8.2. Potential energy barriers in proton transfer reactions.[7]

the transition state may be represented by z, the order of the bond being formed between the base catalyst and the transferring proton; z is also the fractional negative charged acquired by the carbon acid and lost by the catalyst. For β to measure the extent of proton transfer it must be equal to z; this requires that

$$\delta_R \Delta G^{\ddagger} = z \, \delta_R \Delta G^0 \qquad (8.8)$$

Since $\Delta G^{\ddagger}$ and ΔG^0 have the same initial limit and since z must be less than unity it follows that a substituent change in the catalyst must alter the free energy of the transition state by an amount intermediate between its effects on the free energies of initial and final states. In view of the fact that the structure of the transition state is intermediate between the structures of the initial and final states this does not seem unreasonable. Substituent effects on the transition state should therefore also be intermediate between those on initial and final states.

Exact correspondence between $\delta_R \Delta G^{\ddagger}$ and $z \delta_R \Delta G^0$ also requires that the effect of the substituent on the free energy of the system be linear in z, a condition unlikely to be quantitatively obeyed. Furthermore the requirement makes no provision for the presence in the transition state of intermolecular interactions between the carbon acid and the base abstracting the proton. Clearly further insight into the significance of β values can only be obtained after a discussion of the detailed mechanism of proton transfer.

According to Eigen[10-14] the mechanism of proton transfer consists essentially of three steps:

$$AH + B \rightleftharpoons [AH, B] \rightleftharpoons [A, HB] \rightleftharpoons A + HB \qquad (8.9)$$

(1) The diffusion of the reactants towards one another to a distance close enough to facilitate hydrogen bridge formation between the donor and the acceptor. The rate coefficient for a diffusion controlled reaction assuming both AH and B are uncharged is given by the Smoluchowski equation.

$$k = 4\pi N (r_{AH} + r_B)(D_{AH} + D_B) \qquad (8.10)$$

where $r_{AH} + r_B$ is the encounter distance and D represents the $D_{AH} + D_B$ to be 2×10^{-5} cm^2 s^{-1} $k \simeq 7 \times 10^9$ M^{-1} s^{-1}. When both AH and B are charged or have strong dipole moments Eqn (8.10) must be modified to include an electrostatic term, $(\Delta G_{es}/kT)/(e^{\Delta G_{es}/kT} - 1)$

(2) The formation of the hydrogen bridge and the transfer of the proton. The tendency to form hydrogen bonds is in the order

$$\text{OH...O} > \text{OH...N, NH...O} > \text{NH...N}, \gg \text{CH...O, OH...C}$$

and this parallels the rates of proton transfer. In some cases solvent water molecules may be involved in the process of hydrogen bridge formation. Albery,[15] for example, has shown that for diffusion controlled proton transfers to oxygen and nitrogen that the rate determining step is formation of a hydrogen bonded complex between an $H_9O_4^+$ species and the anion followed by fast translations of protons in a Grotthus-type mechanism to protonate the anion. For proton transfer to carbon on the other hand the reaction occurs via the H_3O^+ species.

(3) The separation of the products.

In the event of the formation of an efficient hydrogen bridge the activation energy barrier is likely to be low and the rate of proton transfer fast and diffusion controlled. Structural changes can increase or decrease equilibrium constants practically without limit but a bimolecular reaction can not proceed faster than bimolecular collisions. Under these circumstances the pK values of the bases are of little account and the rate is independent of ΔpK, the Brönsted plot yields a coefficient of zero with a slight scatter due to the varying diffusion coefficients. As long as the reaction remains diffusion controlled no information about the proton transfer step is obtainable—solvation or desolvation are rate-determining.

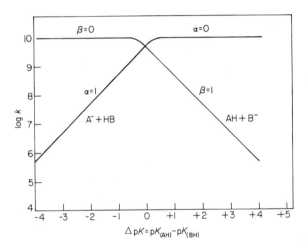

Fig. 8.3. Idealised plot[12] of log k as a function of ΔpK for the reaction AH + B$^-$ ⇌ A$^-$ + BH.

For the reverse reaction the rate is directly proportional to the equilibrium constant of the reaction and the Brönsted coefficient is unity. At Δp$K = 0$ the rate for the ionisation process is reduced at least by a factor of two as the proton has only a 50% chance of going in either direction. Figure 8.3 illustrates the situation for this ideal case.

The work of Eigen and his collaborators shows that most oxygen acids come close to the ideal behaviour so that results for different substrates and catalysts can be combined in a single curve with a Brönsted exponent varying continuously from zero to unity. Many nitrogen acids fall on the same curve but for proton transfers of the type N–H...N deviations become perceptible around $\Delta p K = 0$. Extension of the work[16] to S–H...N and S–H...S transfers shows the general trend of Brönsted plot curvature is still present but that at large ΔpK values rates for S—H...S transfer level off below the diffusion controlled limit.

The behaviour of carbon acids deviates still further from ideality and no single curve can describe the results obtained for various acids although they are of the same general shape and the slopes usually reach the limiting values at large ΔpK values. Such differences provide a possible source for understanding the detailed mechanisms of acid-base catalysis. Experience shows that, in general, the smaller the value of the rate constant at $\Delta pK = 0$ the larger the range to which a linear approximation applies. The combination of limited time range accessible to experimental studies and the slow rates observed explain why the Brönsted plot appears as a linear relationship (over more than 14 pK units in some cases) in so many studies. The first factor has been recently extended by the development of methods that enable very fast reactions to be measured (Chapter 2) and the detection of curvature is therefore made much easier.

Several reasons have been proposed for the much slower rates of ionisation of carbon acids as compared to oxygen or nitrogen acids of comparable strength and although we are still somewhat short of being able to formulate a quantitative explanation the problems are capable of at least qualitative analysis. Mention has already been made of the importance of hydrogen bonding in the process of proton transfer. It is well known that C—H bonds do not in general from hydrogen bonds with the solvent and the hydrogen is therefore more difficult to remove as compared to a hydrogen atom partially bonded to the solvent. In the case of the anions the charge is usually dispersed on activating groups such as carbonyl or nitro and the solvent is hydrogen bonded to the oxygen and not the carbon atom. For proton transfer to the carbanion to occur it may be necessary for the proton to approach very close to the carbon atom, a process for which the energy of activation is likely to be considerable.

Secondly, carbanions are frequently stabilised by charge delocalisation so that the formation of the anion is accompanied by changes in several bond distances and bond angles. Hine,[17,18] in particular, has emphasised the importance of the principle of least motion which states "that elementary reactions that involve the least change in atomic position and electronic configuration will be favoured". A reaction will then occur in such a way as to involve the least expenditure of energy in changing the relative positions of atoms. In, for example, the protonation of the cyclohexadienyl anion the necessity for greater changes in internal geometry may cause the activation energy for the formation of 1,3-cyclohexadiene to be larger than that for the formation of 1,4-cyclohexadiene by 0·5– 1·0 kcal mol^{-1}. This difference would be enough to explain the more rapid formation of the less stable isomer. Similarly the fact that phenylacetylene, although a much weaker acid than nitroethane (factor of $\sim 10^{11}$), undergoes hydroxide catalysed ionisation at a rate that is between 50 and 500 times faster (depending on the primary isotope effect) can be explained by the fact that the process of ionisation in the first case requires little change in the rest of the molecule. For nitroethane however several changes occur in bond distances and bond angles as the carbon, nitrogen and oxygen atoms take up coplanar positions. A further example[19] concerns 1,1,5,5-bisbiphenylenepentadiene-1,4 which exists as a mixture of tautomers (1a, 1b). Its pK in dimethyl sulphoxide is 8·7 which compares with a

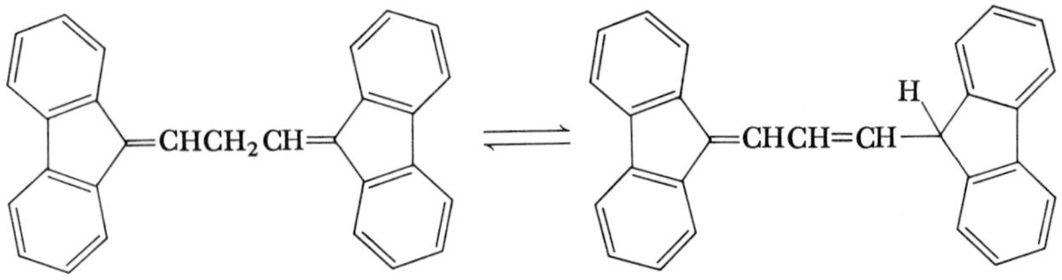

(1a)   (1b)

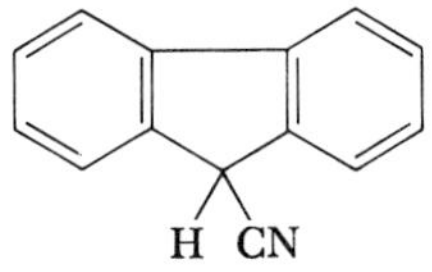

(2)

value of 8·4 for 9-cyanofluroene (2). The rate of ionisation in dimethyl sulphoxide in the presence of p-nitrobenzoate is however 1000-fold slower probably because the amount of geometric rearrangement in (1) on ionisation is much greater than for the cyano compound.

Carbon acids can be separated into different categories depending on the nature and number of the strongly electron withdrawing substituents that are normally introduced in order to confer measurable acidity. It is interesting therefore to consider in what way the Brönsted relationship differs for various carbon acids—these include β-diketones where the carbanions are capable of tautomeric reaction, cyanocarbon acids where the process of ionisation is more straightforward, ketones which have been extensively studied and nitrocompounds where ionisation is accompanied by considerable structural reorganisation.

The results in Fig. 8.4 for acetylacetone,[20] obtained by using the temperature jump method, support the view that a linear Brönsted plot represents only part of a continuous curve having slopes of 0 and 1 at its two extremities. The transition in this case occurs over a substantially wider pK range than is the case for oxygen and nitrogen acids. The rate constants for proton transfer from the ketone approach a limiting value of 10^6 M^{-1} s^{-1} at a pK difference

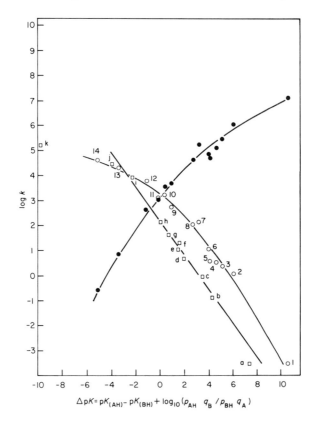

Fig. 8.4. Plot of log k against ΔpK for acetylacetone[20] (○ ●) and ethylnitroacetate[21] □. 1, water; 2, chloroacetate; 3, formate; 4, phenylacetate; 5, acetate; 6, propionate; 7, malonate; 8, cacodylate; 9, cyanophenolate; 10, o-chlorophenolate; 11, m-chlorophenolate; 12, phenolate; 13, gluconate; 14, hydroxide; a, water; b, dichloroacetate; c, chloroacetate; d, phenylacetate; e, acetate; f, trimethylacetate; g, pyridine; h, 4-methyl pyridine; i, o-chlorophenolate; j, phenolate; k, hydroxide.

$(\Delta pK = pK_{A\,H} - pK_{B\,H}) < -6$ whereas the rate constants for the reverse reaction become diffusion controlled at very high pK differences $(\Delta pK > 15)$. For the purpose of comparison the results[21,22] for the ionisation of ethylnitroacetate as catalysed by carboxylate and phenolate anions as well as neutral amines are included; the rates are slower and no curvature is discernible. As is frequently the case for reactions of this type the rate constants for OH^- and H_2O catalysis deviate from the relationship,[23-25] the former being lower by some 3 powers of 10 than the value obtained by extrapolating the straight line to the conventional pK of water (15·7). It is important to note that without the anomalously low rate for OH^- the demonstration of general base catalysis in some cases would be virtually impossible.

In the detritiation of 1,4-dicyano-2-butene[26] the anionic (phenolates) and uncharged bases (secondary and tertiary amines) generate distinctly different plots (Fig. 8.5) whilst maintaining similar slopes,

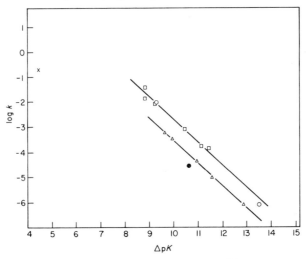

Fig. 8.5. Plot of log k against ΔpK for 1,4-dicyano-2-butene.[26] △, Phenolates; □, secondary amines; ○, tertiary amines; ●, ammonia; x, hydroxide.

0·94 in the first case and 0·98 for the amines. Such behaviour but only more so has been observed in the amine catalysed ionisation of nitroethane[27] where the results for primary, secondary and tertiary amines lie on separate lines, again of similar slopes. Similarly in the decomposition of nitramide[28,29] in anisole separate parallel lines are observed for the different classes of amines, the catalyst efficiency increasing in the order tertiary > secondary > primary. In the hydration of s-dichloroacetone[30] in 5% aqueous dioxan anion bases are $c.$ 10^3 times as effective catalysts as uncharged bases of the same strength in water but the difference in this case can be largely attributed to the fact that the equilibrium

$$RCO_2H \rightleftharpoons RCO_2^- + H^+ \tag{8.11}$$

is affected very much more than the equilibrium

$$R_3NH^+ \rightleftharpoons R_3N + H \tag{8.12}$$

by a decrease in the dielectric constant of the solvent. The fact that structural modifications in the catalyst structure lead to much larger deviations from the Brönsted plot for both nitroethane and nitramide by comparison with 1,4-dicyano-2-butene may, according to Long,[26] be because the transition state is very product-like for the latter reaction whereas for nitroethane ($\beta \simeq 0.5$) and nitramide ($\beta = 0.64$) sensitivity to base and solvent properties should be close to their maximum. It is interesting that ammonia is sufficiently different from the other amines to have a catalytic coefficient smaller than expected by a factor of 10.

For both 1,4-dicyano-2-butene and the much stronger cyanocarbon acid, t-butylmalononitrile[31] the rate coefficients in the forward direction have been combined with equilibrium data to obtain detailed information about the reverse reactions between the anions and general acids. For both compounds these rates are virtually constant ($\sim 10^8$ M^{-1} s^{-1}) and close to the diffusion controlled limits, confirming that $\alpha \simeq 0$. The behaviour of these cyanocarbon acids therefore resembles more closely that of nitrogen and oxygen acids than many other carbon acids.

The ionisation of acetone catalysed by a series of amines[32] fits the Brönsted relationship established for catalysis by carboxylate anions[24] and pyridine derivatives[33] fairly well (Fig. 8.6). Some of the amines such as glycine contain groups other than the amino which could serve as intramolecular base catalysts but the fact that they do not seriously deviate from the relationship would seem to argue against such possibilities. The large deviation of the borate ion is a well known phenomenon[34] in general base catalysis and is due to the conjugate base existing largely as the hydrated anion $H_4BO_4^-$, a much weaker base than $H_2BO_3^-$. The catalytic effect of the phosphate anion is also lower than anticipated; this is also the case in the bromination of ethyl α methylacetoacetate.[35]

Conversely there are several reactions which are distinguished by how well the Brönsted relationship is obeyed e.g. the dehydration of methylene glycol[36] and acetaldehyde[37] and the mutarotation of glucose[38] conform over an unusually wide range of velocities and types of catalyst. In these reactions neither the forward or reverse reaction velocities reach the diffusion controlled limit even with very strong acids or bases and Eigen has pointed out that such behaviour may be a characteristic of reactions in which proton transfer is coupled with the making or breaking of other bonds in the molecule. Certainly hydration–dehydration reactions are frequently concerted processes involving the participation of several water molecules. They are also reactions in which proton transfer is from and to oxygen atoms so that they resemble the equilibria used to define the acid–base strength more closely than proton transfer reactions to or from carbon.[39]

Brönsted relationships may be generated by varying either of the conjugate pairs involved in an acid–base equilibrium and the β values obtained by both methods usually agree e.g. malononitrile and

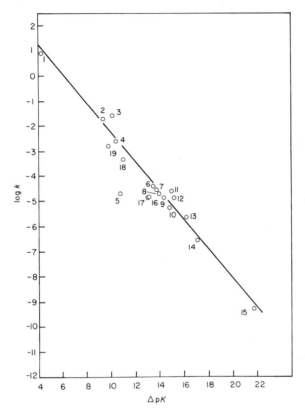

Fig. 8.6. Plot of log k against ΔpK for acetone.[24,32,33] 1, hydroxide; 2, methylamine; 3, trimethylamine; 4, ethanolamine; 5, borate; 6–10, pyridine and picoline bases; 11–14, carboxylate anions; 15, water; 16, phosphate; 17, imidazole; 18, ethylenediamine; 19, glycine.

t-butylmalononitrile considered by Long[31] as general acids in the transfer of a proton to the bases formate ion and water gave values close to unity as obtained from catalyst variations. In his studies on the rates of ionisation of ketones and keto-esters Bell[7] has used a number of catalysts for each substrate and the results (Table 8.2) show that in most cases β increases regularly with decreasing acidity. These findings imply that β is more sensitive to changes in the strength of the carbon acid than it is to changes in the strength of the base. For both nitroacetone[40] and ethylnitroacetate[21,22] the β values are larger than expected for acids of this strength.

The frequently observed deviation from the Brönsted plot of the point for water catalysis stems at least in part from the customary practice of obtaining the catalytic coefficient by dividing the spontaneous rate by 55·5, the molar concentration of water molecules in pure water. As this quantity enters into both the equilibrium and rate calculations the observed deviations are rarely as large as those observed for both the acid[41–43] and base[23,24] resulting from the self-dissociation of water. Since an appreciable fraction of the water molecules in dilute aqueous solution are associated in rather large clusters it has been suggested[44] that only the concentration of unassociated water molecules and not the stoichiometric water

TABLE 8.2

Brönsted β values in the base catalysed ionisation of some carbon acids[7,21]

Carbon acid	pK_a	β
Acetone	20	0·88
Chloroacetone	16·5	0·82
Dichloroacetone	14·9	0·82
2-Carbethoxycyclopentanone	10·2	0·60
2-Acetylcyclohexanone	9·9	0·60
Tricarboxymethane	7·8	0·72
Nitroacetone	5·0	0·65
Ethylnitroacetate	5·8	0·65

concentration should be used in calculating the basic strength of the hydroxide ion and the hydronium ion acidity constant. This interpretation is supported by the finding that protonic conduction in aqueous solutions at ordinary temperatures takes place by proton transfer to unassociated water molecules only.[45] On the basis of an estimate of the activity of unassociated water molecules in pure water Bell gave a value of 0·13 M which is considerably less than that estimated from near infra-red measurements[46] (17·4 M). An alternative approach is contained in the suggestion that the acidity constant, for example, might be evaluated by fitting hydronium ion catalytic coefficients to Brönsted correlation lines. The rather wide fluctuations observed[9] for ether hydrolysis reactions (pK_a varies from 0·7 to −0·2) suggests that other factors may be operative and that it might be better to compare the fit of the hydronium ion catalytic coefficients to Brönsted relations based on positively charged catalysts. Similarly for the hydroxide ion comparison should be made with phenolate anions.

It has long been known that an inverse relationship between the rates of proton abstraction and acidities exist in the series $MeNO_2$, $MeCH_2NO_2$ and Me_2CHNO_2. A progressive and substantial decrease in the hydroxide catalysed rates of deprotonation (relative rates $113 : 18 : 1·0$) is associated with acidity changes in the opposite manner (pK_a's $10·2 : 8·5 : 7·7$) so that the Brönsted plot has a negative slope ($-0·7$). By varying the catalyst on the other hand a value for β of $0·55$ has been obtained[47] for 2-nitropropane. It could be argued that these differences arise from the occurrence of structural variations at the acidic site but recent work by Bordwell and co-workers[48,49] on the systems $ArCHMeNO_2$ and $ArCH_2$-$CHMeNO_2$ makes this explanation less likely.

For $ArCHMeNO_2$ the plot of log k vs. log K_a gives a slope of $+1·31$ so that the Brönsted coefficient for protonation of $ArCMeNO_2^-$ by solvent must be $-0·31$. These results were rationalised on the basis that the extensive structural reorganisation accompanying the formation of the anion leads to a situation in which substituent changes affect both the forward and reverse reactions in the same manner so that the rates are more sensitive to structural changes than is the equilibrium constant. In the series $MeNO_2$, $MeCH_2NO_2$ and Me_2CHNO_2 proton abstraction by hydroxide ion is retarded by methyl substitution but proton abstraction by the nitronate ion $CH_2NO_2^-$ from the solvent is retarded to an even greater extent. These results suggest that the use of β values as a guide to the position of the transition state along the reaction co-ordinate needs modification, at least for nitro compounds, and Kresge[50] has suggested such an approach whilst retaining the essential features of the argument. This has been done by recognising that the formation of the transition state brings into play new interactions which are absent from both the initial and final states.

For the reaction for which β was found to be $1·3$,

$$\text{OH}^- + \text{H} - \overset{\overset{\displaystyle \text{Ar}}{|}}{\text{C}}\text{MeNO}_2 \rightarrow \left[\overset{\overset{\displaystyle \text{Ar}}{|}}{\underset{\delta^-}{\text{OH}}...\text{H}...\overset{\delta^-}{\underline{\text{CMe}...\text{NO}_2}}}\right]^\ddagger \rightarrow \text{H}_2\text{O} + \overset{\overset{\displaystyle \text{Ar}}{|}}{\text{C}}\text{Me}=\text{NO}_2 \tag{8.13}$$

the effect of the group Ar on ΔG^0 may be assigned to the electrical interaction of Ar with a negatively charged nitro group in the final state, $I_{\text{Ar,NO}_2^-}$ i.e. $\delta_R \Delta G^0 = I_{\text{Ar,NO}_2^-}$. There will be a corresponding interaction in the transition state the magnitude of which depends on the fraction of an electronic charge (x) transferred from the hydroxide ion i.e. the contribution to $\delta_R \Delta G^{\ddagger} = xI_{Ar,NO_2^-}$. In addition there will be another effect in the transition state contributing to $\delta_R \Delta G^{\ddagger}$, namely the interaction of Ar with the partly charged hydroxide ion. This effect will be equal to $(1-x)I_{Ar,OH^-}$ where I_{Ar,OH^-} is the interaction of Ar with a fully charged hydroxide ion situated in its transition-state position. Since this hydroxide ion is remote from Ar in the initial state and since it no longer exists in the final state the initial- and final-state limits of this effect will be zero.

The β value is given by

$$[xI_{Ar,NO_2^-} + (1 - x)I_{Ar,OH^-}]/I_{Ar,NO_2^-} \qquad (8.14)$$

and will be greater than 1 when $I_{Ar,OH^-} > I_{Ar,NO_2^-}$. Such effects are likely to be more important in carbon acids where groups capable of removing −ve charge from the vicinity of the proton transfer site are usually present than in oxygen or nitrogen acids where the charge remains on the atom from which the proton is transferred. Marcus[51] has also discussed this problem in somewhat different terms (see pp. 143–144).

Apart from studies relating to steric hindrance specific effects that could lead to deviations from the Brönsted relationship have not been the subject of much study. This probably arises at least in part from the fact that many reactions are subject to both acid and base catalysis where the difficulty of extracting accurate rate constants is at its worst. The acid catalysed hydrolysis of vinyl ethers however is a good choice as it represents a particularly simple kind of proton transfer reaction, the first step being rate determining and not subject to base catalysis. By using a homogeneous set of carboxylic acids as catalysts for the hydrolysis of 7 ethers Kresge and co-workers[9] have found small but systematic deviations from the relationship—points for cyanoacetic acid lie below the line in all cases and methoxyacetic acid is a better catalyst than it should be in most cases; less pronounced systematic deviations also occur with chloro-acetic acid. At the transition state of the hydrolysis reaction +ve charge is being generated on the oxygen and α-carbon atoms of the vinyl ether and it seems significant that the deviations occur with acids which contain strong electronegative groups capable of strong interaction with that charge. The results lead to the important conclusion that Brönsted exponents are rather imprecise measures of transition state structure—with ethyl vinyl ether and using all possible subsets of the seven available catalytic coefficients the α values range from a high of 1·21 to a low of 0·34.

The importance of steric hindrance may be reflected in deviations from the Brönsted relationship only when the effects on acid-base equilibria are different from those on reaction rates. In view of the small size of the proton the effects would be expected to be small but not necessarily the same as the equilibria refer to the addition of the proton to the base, B, and the solvation of BH^+ whereas the rates refer to the bringing together of the reactants to form a transition state which may be hindered by bulky groups in one or both of the reactants. This analysis seems to be borne out by results—methyl substituents in the pyridine nucleus increase the basic strength in a regular and additive manner but the catalytic power of these compounds is reduced in certain proton transfer reactions.[52]

Pearson and Williams[53] found steric hindrance to be important in proton transfer from nitroethane to 2 and 6-substituted pyridines in agreement with the results of Lewis and co-workers[54,55] who also found the effect to be greatly increased in the case of 2-nitropropane, the deviation from the Brönsted relationship amounting to a factor of 5 for 2,6-lutidine and nearly 30 for 2-t-butylpyridine. In the mutarotation of glucose[56] 2,6 lutidine is a poorer catalyst by a factor of 25 than expected on the basis of its base strength and by a factor of 100 in the base catalysed deuterium exchange[57] of isobutyraldehyde-2d. In the detritiation of 1,4-dicyano-2-butene[26] the deviations increase with the number of methyl groups on the carbon atoms adjacent to the basic site so that for 2,2,6,6-tetramethylpiperidine the rate is 9-fold slower than predicted. Long suggests that this modest rate retardation is possibly related to the very product-like transition state for this reaction.

The importance of steric effects in the iodination of several ketones has been the subject of detailed study.[33] The results for isopropyl methyl ketone, for example, can be represented by three separate lines denoting catalysis by pyridines lacking a 2-substituent ($\beta_0 = 0\cdot69$), by pyridines with one 2-methyl substituent ($\beta_1 = 0\cdot55$) and by 2,6 lutidine and 2,4,6, collidine ($\beta_2 = 0\cdot38$). The effect of steric hindrance therefore seems to be to induce a more reactant-like transition state. Deviations from the Brönsted law also depend on the structure of the ketone. Thus on going from acetone to methyl isopropyl ketone to pinacolone $\Delta\log k_1$, the extent of the deviation from the Brönsted line, for 2,6-lutidine increases from $0\cdot84$ to $1\cdot01$ to $1\cdot38$. On the basis of these results Feather and Gold favour a transition state (3) in which the C—H bond being broken is in the same plane as the carbonyl group and the atoms attached directly to it whereas Hine and co-workers[57] prefer a more orthodox structure in which the C—H bond is nearly perpendicular to the plane described by the carbonyl group.

Evidence for steric hindrance may also be seen in the catalytic constants for saturated amines in the de-deuteriation of [2-^{2}H] isobutyraldehyde.[57] The amount of such hindrance increases with the extent of branching of the groups attached to nitrogen, reaching a maximum with tris-2-hydroxy propylamine the reactivity of which is about 3000-fold less than predicted. It is possible with these hydroxyamines that hydrogen bonding between the amino and hydroxy groups is of importance in decreasing the reactivity.

(3)

Finally mention must be made of an instance in which steric hindrance results in an acceleration of rate. In the anion catalysed halogenation of various ketones and esters[58] when both the catalyst and substrate contain a large group such as aryl or bromine near the reaction centre the observed velocity is greater than expected by up to 300%. It has been suggested that this may be related to the degree of involvement of water molecules in the transition state.

Although the solvent plays an important role in proton transfer reactions it is rarely represented in the equation specifying the reaction. One possible method of assessing its importance is to investigate the Brönsted relationship in different solvents and this has recently been done by Ritchie and Uschold.[59] The reactions of fluoradene and of 9-carbomethoxyfluorene with benzoate ions in dimethyl sulphoxide may be compared with the isotopic exchange reactions of various fluorenes in methanol solution. The results (Fig. 8.7) show that in the latter case the rates of ionisation appear to level out considerably below the expected value for diffusion control as was found for acetylacetone in aqueous media.[20] This behaviour can be ascribed to the instability of the [AH...B] complex when AH is a poor hydrogen bond donor and B is strongly solvated by hydrogen bonding to the solvent. The rates for the reverse reaction, between methanol and the carbanions, become diffusion controlled when ΔpK is greater than 18.

In dimethyl sulphoxide solution the proton transfer reaction of hydrocarbons approach diffusion controlled limits, in both directions, at much smaller values of ΔpK than in methanol. Furthermore for negative values of ΔpK the rates do not level out at values far below diffusion control as they do in methanol. These results show that for reactions with similar equilibrium constants in the two solvents the rate of proton transfer is much faster, probably by as much as 100-fold, in dimethyl sulphoxide solution. This solvent effect cannot be ascribed to an increased basicity of the proton acceptor on going from methanol to dimethyl sulphoxide but rather reflects the

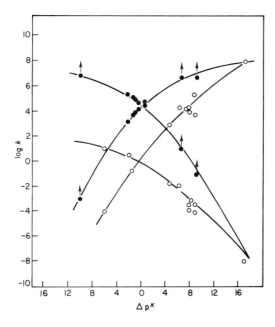

Fig. 8.7: Plot of $\log k$ against ΔpK for various hydrocarbons in dimethyl sulphoxide (●) and methanol (○).[59]

importance of solvent reorientation and in particular the reorganisation or breaking of solvent–solvent hydrogen bonds, that is necessary before proton transfer can occur in methanol (see p. 181). In dimethyl sulphoxide the anions are not hydrogen bonded to the solvent and do not need to lose the energy of solvation in order to accept a proton. The location of solvent molecules surrounding the species AH...B is probably different for A...HB and the amount of energy needed to reorganise the solvent is probably less for dimethyl sulphoxide than it is for methanol with its strongly orientated hydrogen bonds. If proton transfer entails the breaking of several of these it could account for the greater part of the observed activation energy.[60]

8.2. THE MARCUS THEORY

The electron is a unique entity being the simplest free radical, the smallest and simplest of nucleophiles and one of the most powerful of reducing agents. The hydrogen atom which is an acid comparable in strength to phenols is the conjugate acid of the solvated electron and resembles it in being a powerful reducing agent and a very simple free radical. It is not entirely surprising therefore that the successful theory for weak overlap electron transfers developed by Marcus[61,62] has been extended to cover proton and atom transfers.[51]

The model for proton transfer used by Marcus is similar to that employed by Eigen with the difference that the free energy activation barrier ΔG^* is considered in terms of an intrinsic barrier which is basically a reorganisational term and an extrinsic barrier $\Delta G^{0'}$, the free energy of reaction under the prevailing experimental conditions. The standard free energy of the first step in which the reactants are brought together is W^r, that of the actual proton transfer step is $\Delta G_R^{0'}$ and that for the separation of the products is W^p. The intrinsic contribution to the barrier $(\lambda/4)$ is equal to the average of the reorganisational barriers $(\lambda_{11}/4, \lambda_{22}/4)$ of two exchange reactions,

$$AH + A^- \rightleftharpoons A^- + HA \qquad \lambda_{11}/4 \qquad (8.15)$$
$$B^- + HB \rightleftharpoons BH + B^- \qquad \lambda_{22}/4 \qquad (8.16)$$

The relationship between ΔG^*, $\Delta G_R^{0'}$ and λ takes the form

$$\Delta G^* = W^r + \left(1 + \frac{\Delta G_R^{0'}}{\lambda}\right)^2 \frac{\lambda}{4} \qquad (8.17)$$

where

$$\Delta G_R^{0'} = \Delta G^{0'} + W^p - W^r$$

The Brönsted exponent from Eqn (8.17) is

$$\beta = (\partial \Delta G^* / \partial \Delta G^{0'})_{\lambda, W^r, W^p} = \tfrac{1}{2}\left(1 + \frac{\Delta G_R^{0'}}{\lambda}\right) \qquad (8.18)$$

For a symmetric proton transfer $\Delta G_R^{0'} = 0$ and $\beta = \frac{1}{2}$ whilst for a downhill transfer $\Delta G_R^{0'} < 0$, $\beta < \frac{1}{2}$ and the transition state is reactant-like. Similarly for an uphill transfer $\Delta G_R^{0'} > 0$, $\beta > \frac{1}{2}$ and the transition state is product-like in accordance with the Hammond postulate. W^r, W^p and λ may be expected to be constant for a series of structurally similar bases or acids.[65] Marcus has analysed the data for many proton transfer reactions in terms of Eqn (8.18) and Fig. 8.8 shows how well the relationship between ΔG^* and $\Delta G^{0'}$ is obeyed for reactions of ketones with carboxylate anions and other bases.

If the intrinsic barrier does not remain constant when the acid HA is changed the slope of the free energy plot is given by

$$\beta = 0.5(1 + x) + (1 - x^2)\beta_1 \tag{8.19}$$

where $x = \Delta G_R^{0'}/\lambda$ and $\beta_1 = (d\lambda/dA)/(d\Delta G^{0'}/dA)$.

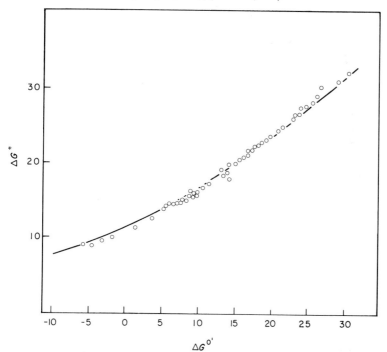

Fig. 8.8. ΔG^* vs. $\Delta G^{0'}$ for reaction of ketones with carboxylate anions and other bases.[64]

In all cases studied so far x lies within the range -1 to $+1$. Marcus has shown that $0.5(1 + x)$ represents the position of the transition state along the reaction co-ordinate and this represents the first quantitative treatment of the frequently stated view that β reflects the extent to which the transition state resembles the reaction products.

Equation (8.19) can be used[51] to account for the unusual slopes of the Brönsted plots in the ionisation of some nitro-compounds. Thus in the reaction

$$RCH_2NO_2 + B^- \rightarrow RCH{=}NO_2^- + BH \tag{8.20}$$

if the catalyst B is changed the variation in λ is related to the variation of λ_{22} in Eqn (8.16). Usually the catalysts are oxygen or nitrogen bases so that the reaction represented by this equation is usually very rapid and sometimes diffusion controlled; λ_{22} will therefore be very small and Eqn (8.19) reduces to Eqn (8.18). When however the varied group is R the exchange reaction that has to be considered is

$$RCH_2NO_2 + \bar{O}_2N=CHR \rightarrow RCH=NO_2^- + O_2NCH_2R \qquad (8.21)$$

and the free energy barrier of this reaction is not small. If the structural reorganisation is influenced by R the λ of this reaction will vary, β_1 will no longer be negligible and β does not now reflect the position of the transition state.

TABLE 8.3

Intrinsic barriers for proton transfer in solution[64]

Carbon acid	Base	$\lambda/4$ (kcal mol^{-1})
$(CH_2)_4COCHCO_2Et$	RCO_2^-	8·5
$CH_3COCHR_1R_2$	$RCO_2^-, C_6H_5O^-$	11·5
$CH_3COCHR_1R_2$	OH^-, SH^-	13·0
$NO_2CH_2CO_2Et$	RCO_2^-	13·0
$(CH_2)_5COCHCO_2Et$	RCO_2^-	14·5

The present position with regard to the experimentally obtained β values seems to be that for the cyano compounds studied by Long and co-workers, β accurately reflects the position of the transition state and it also does to a lesser degree for many ketones. The insertion of nitro groups or others capable of strong hydrogen bonding (fluorine) can lead to anomalous values.

The existing data on the magnitude of the intrinsic barriers for proton transfer reaction (Table 8.3) is rather limited. Nevertheless it is clear that the λ terms do not describe a large barrier although they are higher than those obtained for some oxygen and nitrogen acids[66] (5–8 kcal mol^{-1}). Ritchie's work provides convincing evidence for the presence of a solvation effect and a further contribution stemming from the principle of least motion can be anticipated.

8.3. HIGHLY BASIC MEDIA

Although the hydroxide ion in aqueous solution is a powerful base the fact that it is extensively hydrated must inhibit it in its role of abstracting a proton. Consequently the rates of hydroxide catalysed ionisations for many weakly acidic carbon acids, notably hydro-carbons, are inconveniently slow. Fortunately many proton transfer reactions of this kind involve the use of a small localised anion and the formation of large polarisable transition states, conditions which are ideally suited to exploit the ability of dipolar aprotic solvents to accelerate the rates of chemical reactions. This is done in the main by increasing the hydroxide ion activity and decreasing that of the water (Chapter 6).

Investigation of reactions in highly basic media has not been accorded the close scrutiny given to studies in highly acidic media where the original attempt[67] at interpreting kinetic acidity depen-dence has been found to be the subject of a number of theoretical and experimental objections.[68] The fact that experience in concen-trated acid media has shown that acidity functions may depend on the type of indicator employed in setting up the scale may be partly responsible for the difference in emphasis. The situation in highly basic media is however much simpler—the base concentration is kept low and the H_- increases as a result of solvation changes. There is a close parallelism between the H_- scales set up using both carbon and nitrogen acids[69,70] (small differences may be present in the highly aqueous region) and both primary and secondary amines generate a single H_- scale.[69]

If the behaviour of the carbon acid undergoing proton transfer is similar to that of the substrates in the equilibrium process it can be shown[71] that

$$\log k = H_- + \log_{10} a_w + \text{constant} \tag{8.22}$$

where a_w is the activity of the solvent. For investigations of reaction kinetics in solution it has been argued[72] that three conditions should be satisfied: (1) the reaction mechanism should be unambiguous; (2) the reaction should be studied over a wide H_- range at or near the temperature at which equilibrium data are available; and (3) in media where ion association is preferably absent or if present can be estimated.

The ionisation of dimethyl sulphoxide satisfies these criteria in full and seems an interesting case for study as acidity function data are available for $OH^- - H_2O - Me_2SO$,[69] $OMe^- - MeOH - Me_2SO$[73] and $OEt^- - EtOH - Me_2SO$[70] media. The fact that all the results can be described by a single $\log k$ vs. H_- line (Fig. 8.9), covering solutions that extend from the purely aqueous region to those that contain more than 90 mol % Me_2SO, indicates that the behaviour of dimethyl sulphoxide in these media is very similar to that of the indicators employed in setting up the scales.

The near unit slope is consistent with a transition state that is very product-like. The forward reaction, the loss of a proton from Me_2SO is strongly affected by the changing medium and the reverse reaction, the protonation of the dimsyl anion, occurs at a constant and probably diffusion controlled rate, consistent with the large pK difference between donor and acceptor. For such a transition state the replacement of the hydroxide ion by the marginally more powerful methoxide or ethoxide ions has little effect on the configuration of the transition state, hence the single slope.

For stronger acids ($pK_a \sim 20\text{--}25$) the rate of recombination will no longer be diffusion controlled and β for the forward reaction will be less than unity. Where results are available they usually refer to

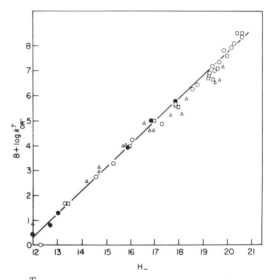

Fig. 8.9. Plot of log $k_{OR^-}^T$ against H$-$ for dimethyl sulphoxide.[72] $\bullet$, Data from ref. 74; $\circ$, OH$-H_2$O$-Me_2SO$; $\triangle$, OMe$^-$ $-MeOH-Me_2SO$; $\square$, OEt$^-$ $-EtOH-Me_2SO$.

catalysis by carboxylate anions rather than the much stronger hydroxide ion. Attention has previously been drawn to the fact that the point for OH$^-$ is usually displaced from the Brönsted relationship and some time ago Bell[44] obtained β_{OH^-} values for a number of ketones for which β_{COO^-} values had been determined. Thus in the case of acetone $\beta_{COO^-} = 0.88$, 0.34 units higher than β_{OH^-}. These results together with others based on log k vs. H$-$ plots are summarised in Table 8.4. As predicted there is a gradual increase in the β_{OH^-} values as the carbon acids become less acidic although nitroethane, once more, seems anomalous.

Log k vs. H$-$ plots with slopes considerably higher than expected can be obtained if the carbanion exists as an ion pair. In these circumstances the cation plus its sheath of solvent molecules are

TABLE 8.4

Brönsted β values from hydroxide and carboxylate ion catalysis

Carbon acid	pK_a	β_{OH^-}	β_{COO^-}	Slope log k vs. H_-	Ref.
Chloroacetone	16	0·29	0·82		44
Dichloroacetone		0·29	0·82		44
Acetone	20	0·54	0·88		44
Acetophenone	19·5–20			0·47 (avg)	76
p-Chlorophenyl methyl sulphone	~23–25			0·70	77
Menthone	~21			0·48	78
(d)-Phenylmethyl-acetophenone	~20			0·49	79
9-t-Butylfluorene	23·4			0·70	80
Nitroethane	8·6			0·72	81
Dimethyl sulphoxide	~32			0·93	72

involved in the rate of the reverse protonation so that the rate itself may be practically independent of anion structure for related series of acids. This is unlikely to be the case, however, when considerable structural reorganisation takes place. Streitwieser and co-workers[75] have considered this possibility in some detail.

REFERENCES

1. Hammond, G. S. (1955). *J. Amer. Chem. Soc.* 77, 334.
2. Leffler, J. E. (1953). *Science* 117, 340.
3. Schaleger, L. L. & Long, F. A. (1963). *Adv. Phys. Org. Chem.*, (Gold, V. ed.) 1, 1.
4. Pearson, R. G. (1948). *J. Amer. Chem. Soc.* 70, 204.
5. Haberfield, P. (1971). *J. Amer. Chem. Soc.* 93, 2091.
6. Brönsted, J. N. & Pedersen, K. J. (1924). *Z. Phys. Chem.* 108, 185.
7. Bell, R. P. (1959). *The Proton in Chemistry* Chapter 10. Cornell University Press, Ithaca, N.Y.
8. Leffler, J. E. & Grunwald, E. (1963). *Rates and Equilibria of Organic Reactions*, p. 24. Wiley, New York.
9. Kresge, A. J., Chen, H. L., Chiang, Y., Murrill, E., Payne, M. A. & Sagatys, D. S. (1971). *J. Amer. Chem. Soc.* 93, 413.
10. Eigen, M. (1964). *Angew. Chem. Int. Ed. Eng.* 3, 1.
11. Eigen, M. (1963). *Pure Appl. Chem.* 6, 97.
12. Eigen, M. (1965). *Discuss. Faraday Soc.* 39, 7.
13. Eigen, M. (1967). *Fast Reactions and Primary Processes in Chemical Kinetics*, Nobel Symposium 5, p. 245 (Claesson, S. ed.) J. Wiley, New York.
14. Eigen, M., Kruse, W., Maass, G. & De Mayer, L. (1964). *Progr. Reaction Kinetics* (Porter, G. ed.) 2, 285.

15. Albery, W. J. (1967). *Progr. Reaction Kinetics,* (Porter, G. ed.) **4**, 353.
16. Ahrens, M. L. & Maass, G. (1968). *Angew. Chem. Int. Ed. Engl.* **7**, 818.
17. Hine, J. (1966). *J. Org. Chem.* **31**, 1236.
18. Hine, J. (1966). *J. Amer. Chem. Soc.* **88**, 5525.
19. Ritchie, C. D. (1969). *J. Amer. Chem. Soc.* **91**, 6749.
20. Ahrens, M. L., Eigen, M., Kruse, W. & Maass, G. (1970). *Ber. Bunsenges. Phys. Chem.* **74**, 380.
21. Barnes, D. J. & Bell, R. P. (1970). *Proc. Roy. Soc. Ser. A* **318**, 421.
22. Bell, R. P. & Spencer, T. (1959). *Proc. Roy. Soc. Ser. A* **251**, 41.
23. Bell, R. P., Smith, R. D. & Woodward, L. A. (1948). *Proc. Roy. Soc. Ser. A* **192**, 479.
24. Bell, R. P. & Lidwell, O. M. (1940). *Proc. Roy. Soc. Ser. A* **176**, 88.
25. Hine, J. & Kaplan, L. A. (1960). *J. Amer. Chem. Soc.* **82**, 2915.
26. Walters, E. A. & Long, F. A. (1969). *J. Amer. Chem. Soc.* **91**, 3733.
27. Gregory, M. J. & Bruice, T. C. (1967). *J. Amer. Chem. Soc.* **89**, 2327.
28. Bell, R. P. & Wilson, G. L. (1950). *Trans. Faraday Soc.* **46**, 407.
29. Bell, R. P. & Trotman-Dickensen, A. F. (1949). *J. Chem. Soc.* 1288.
30. Bell, R. P. & Jensen, M. B. (1961). *Proc. Roy. Soc. Ser. A* **261**, 38.
31. Hibbert, F., Long, F. A. & Walters, E. A. (1971). *J. Amer. Chem. Soc.* **93**, 2829.
32. Bender, M. L. & Williams, A. (1966). *J. Amer. Chem. Soc.* **88**, 2502.
33. Feather, J. A. & Gold, V. (1965). *J. Chem. Soc.* 1752.
34. Bell, R. P. (1959). *The Proton in Chemistry,* p. 179. Cornell University Press, Ithaca, N. Y.
35. Bell, R. P. & Crooks, J. E. (1965). *Proc. Roy. Soc. Ser. A* **286**, 285.
36. Bell, R. P. & Evans, P. G. (1966). *Proc. Roy. Soc. Ser A* **291**, 297.
37. Bell, R. P. & Higginson, W. C. E. (1949). *Proc. Roy. Soc. Ser. A* **197**, 141.
38. Brönsted, J. N. & Guggenheim, E. A. (1927). *J. Amer. Chem. Soc.* **49**, 2554.
39. Bell, R. P. (1966). *Adv. Phys. Org. Chem.* (Gold, V. ed.) **4**, 1.
40. Bell, R. P. & Robinson, R. R. (1962). *Proc. Roy. Soc. Ser. A* **270**, 411.
41. Kresge, A. J. & Chiang, Y. (1967). *J. Chem. Soc. (B)* **53**, 58.
42. Kresge, A. J., Chiang, Y. & Sato, Y. (1967). *J. Amer. Chem. Soc.* **89**, 4418.
43. Gold, V. & Waterman, D. C. A. (1968). *J. Chem. Soc. (B)* 839, 849.
44. Bell, R. P. (1943). *Trans. Faraday Soc.* **39**, 253.
45. Horne, R. A. & Courant, R. A. (1965). *J. Phys. Chem.* **69**, 2224.
46. Buijs, K. & Choppin, G. R. (1963). *J. Chem. Phys.* **39**, 2035.
47. Bell, R. P. & Goodall, D. M. (1966). *Proc. Roy. Soc. Ser. A* **294**, 273.
48. Bordwell, F. G., Boyle, W. J. Jr., Hautala, J. A. & Yee, K. C. (1969). *J. Amer. Chem. Soc.* **91**, 4002.
49. Bordwell, F. G., Boyle, W. J. Jr. & Yee, K. C. (1970). *J. Amer. Chem. Soc.* **92**, 5926.
50. Kresge, A. J. (1970). *J. Amer. Chem. Soc.* **92**, 3210.
51. Marcus, R. A. (1969). *J. Amer. Chem. Soc.* **91**, 7224.
52. Gold, V. (1962). *Progr. Stereochem.* (de la Mare, P. B. D. & Klyne, W. eds.) **3**, 169.
53. Pearson, R. G. & Williams, F. V. (1953). *J. Amer. Chem. Soc.* **75**, 3073; (1954) **76**, 258.
54. Lewis, E. S. & Allen, J. D. (1964). *J. Amer. Chem. Soc.* **86**, 2022.
55. Lewis, E. S. & Funderburk, L. H. (1967). *J. Amer. Chem. Soc.* **89**, 2322.
56. Westheimer, F. H. & Covitz, F. (1963). *J. Amer. Chem. Soc.* **85**, 1773.
57. Hine, J., Houston, J. G., Jensen, J. H. & Mulders, J. (1965). *J. Amer. Chem. Soc.* **87**, 5050.
58. Bell, R. P., Gelles, E. & Möller, E. (1949). *Proc. Roy. Soc. Ser. A* **198**, 308.

59. Ritchie, C. D. & Uschold, R. E. (1968). *J. Amer. Chem. Soc.* **90**, 3415.
60. Caldin, E. F. (1959). *J. Chem. Soc.* 3345.
61. Marcus, R. A. (1956). *J. Chem. Phys.* **24**, 966.
62. Marcus, R. A. (1960). *Discuss. Faraday Soc.* **29**, 21.
63. Marcus, R. A. (1968). *J. Phys. Chem.* **72**, 891.
64. Cohen, A. C. & Marcus, R. A. (1968). *J. Phys. Chem.* **72**, 4249.
65. Kreevoy, M. M. & Konasewich, D. E. (1971). In *Chemical Dynamics*, p. 243 (Hirschfelder, J. & Henderson, D. eds.). John Wiley, New York.
66. Rose, M. C. & Stuehr, J. (1971). *J. Amer. Chem. Soc.* **93**, 4350.
67. Hammett, L. P. (1940). *Physical Organic Chemistry*, p. 273. McGraw-Hill, New York.
68. Long, F. A. & Paul, M. A. (1957). *Chem. Rev.* **57**, 935.
69. Dolman, D. & Stewart, R. (1967). *Can. J. Chem.* **45**, 911.
70. Bowden, K. & Stewart, R. (1965). *Tetrahedron* **21**, 261.
71. Jones, J. R. (1972). *Prog. Phys. Org. Chem.* (Streitwieser, A. & Taft, R. W. eds.) **9**, 241.
72. Albagli, A., Stewart, R. & Jones, J. R. (1960). *J. Chem. Soc. (B)* 1509.
73. Stewart, R., O'Donnell, J. P., Cram, D. J. & Rickborn, B. (1962). *Tetrahedron* **18**, 917.
74. Stewart, R. & Jones, J. R. (1967). *J. Amer. Chem. Soc.* **87**, 5069.
75. Streitwieser, A. Jr., Hudson, J. A. & Mares, F. (1968). *J. Amer. Chem. Soc.* **90**, 648.
76. Jones, J. R. & Stewart, R. (1967). *J. Chem. Soc. (B)* 1173.
77. Bordwell, F. G. & Jones, J. R., unpublished work.
78. Bell, R. P. & Cox, B. G. (1970). *J. Chem. Soc. (B)* 194.
79. Earls, D. W., Jones, J. R. & Rumney, T. G. (1972). *J. Chem. Soc. (Faraday Trans. 1)* **68**, 925.
80. Earls, D. W., Jones, J. R. & Rumney, T. G. (1973). Unpublished results.
81. Bell, R. P. & Cox, B. G. (1971). *J. Chem. Soc. (B)* 783.

9. Kinetic Hydrogen Isotope Effects

Most of the values of k_H/k_D measured for the ionisation of carbon acids at or near room temperature lie within the range 1–10 although there are several notable exceptions e.g. k_H/k_D = 24 and 19·5 for the abstraction of a proton from 2-nitropropane by 2,4,6-trimethyl-pyridine and 2,6,-dimethylpyridine respectively.[1] In order that the determined isotope effect be of most benefit it is of the utmost importance that the reaction investigated be of known and pre-ferably simple mechanism. Ideally the rate determining step should be the cleavage of the carbon–hydrogen bond, isotopic substitution should be confined to the reaction centre so as not to introduce secondary isotope effects, and the reaction carried out in the same medium for both isotopes. The first and last requirements usually provide no difficulty and where the second makes a contribution its effect can either be determined or allowed for. Thus from the hydroxide catalysed rates of ionisation of $CH_3CH_2NO_2$, CH_3CHDNO_2 and $CH_3CD_2NO_2$ at 25° a secondary isotope effect of 1·18 was obtained[2] in close agreement to the value of the 1·14 determined for the corresponding reaction[3] with $PhCH_2NO_2$, $PhCHDNO_2$ and $PhCD_2NO_2$ and 1·15 for the reaction between toluene and cesium cyclohexylamide in cyclohexylamine.[4]

The various methods employed to measure primary hydrogen isotope effects are a combination of those discussed in Chapter 2. The following are currently the most widely used: (1) the rates of halogenation of the carbon acid and its deuteriated analogue are measured;[5] (2) the rates of racemisation of an optically active carbon acid are measured and compared with the rates of detritiation under the same conditions;[6] (3) a carbon acid is labelled with both deuterium and tritium and both k_D and k_T obtained from the same experiment.[7] A similar method also capable of providing precise values for the isotope effect, is illustrated by Pocker's work[8] on proton transfer from carbon acids to organometallic compounds. A large excess of an equimolar mixture of AH and AD is allowed to react with the organometallic compound RM:

$$
\begin{array}{ccc}
A-H & \xrightarrow{k_H} & RH \\
+\,RM & & +\,AM \\
A-D & \xrightarrow{k_D} & RD
\end{array}
\qquad (9.1)
$$

Provided the process is irreversible the ratio of the product composition [RH]/[RD] is equivalent to the isotope effect k_H/k_D. In this competitive method precise temperature control is not as important as in the other methods and isotope effects for relatively fast reactions may be determined.

9.1. THEORY OF KINETIC HYDROGEN ISOTOPE EFFECTS[9-16]

Kinetic isotope effects can best be considered within the framework of absolute reaction rate theory. This is based on the assumption that the reactants come together to form a transition state which is located at the top of an energy barrier. The transition state is in equilibrium with the reactants and can be considered as a separate entity although it can be distinguished from ordinary molecules by virtue of the fact that one of its vibrations has been replaced by an internal translation.

Although it is not currently possible to calculate the potential energy surface along which a reaction occurs for the case

$$AH + B \rightleftharpoons [A...H...B]^{\ddagger} \rightarrow A + HB \tag{9.2}$$

the variation of potential energy along the reaction coordinate can be represented by Fig. 9.1. To a good approximation the electronic distributions for bonds involving other isotopes are identical so that the same potential energy curve can be used for the reaction

$$AD + B \rightleftharpoons [A...D...B]^{\ddagger} \rightarrow A + DB \tag{9.3}$$

The energy E of a molecule can be expressed as the sum of different contributions, $E = E_{transl} + E_{rotn} + E_{vibrn} + E_{elect}$. To a very good approximation there is no difference between the E_{elect} terms for AH and AD and as E_{vibrn} is much greater than either E_{transl} or E_{rotn} the major contribution to the kinetic isotope effect stems from the differences in the zero point vibrational energies of the reactants and transition states. Assuming a negligible isotope effect on the pre-exponential terms A_H, A_D of the Arrhenius equation the isotope effect k_H/k_D is given by

$$k_H/k_D = e^{\Delta E/RT}$$

where $\Delta E = \frac{1}{2}h(\nu^{\ddagger}_{AD} - \nu_{AD} - \nu^{\ddagger}_{AH} + \nu_{AH})$

ν_{AH}, ν_{AD} are the stretching frequencies of AH and AD and $\nu^{\ddagger}_{AH}$, $\nu^{\ddagger}_{AD}$ the corresponding terms in the transition state. The magnitude of the isotope effect is governed by what fraction of the energy term ΔE is utilised in getting over the energy barrier. Stretching frequencies are available for the reactants; for many carbon acids ν_{AH} is

c. 2900 cm^{-1} corresponding to a zero point energy of 4150 cal/mole
and ν_{AD} 2100 cm^{-1} (3000 cal/mole). Unfortunately none are
available for the transition state. The simplest calculation assumes a
situation in which all the energy of stretching is consumed in the
process of forming the transition state. The stretching vibration in the
transition state then becomes a degree of translational motion and
$\frac{1}{2}h\nu^{\ddagger}_{AD} - \frac{1}{2}h\nu^{\ddagger}_{AH} = 0$. The isotope effect under these circumstances
at 25° should be close to 7. At the other extreme if $(\nu^{\ddagger}_{AH} - \nu^{\ddagger}_{AD}) >$

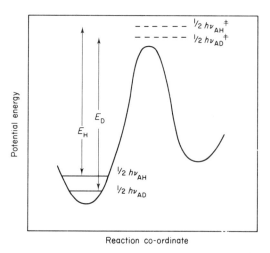

Fig. 9.1. Variation of potential energy for proton (deuteron) transfer reaction.

$(\nu_{AH} - \nu_{AD})$ an inverse isotope effect will be observed. Isotope
effects can therefore be considered as probes for force constant
changes at the position of isotopic substitution.

This simple picture predicts k_H/k_D to be both independent of *B*
and approximately constant for carbon acids of similar structure in
sharp contrast to what is found experimentally. Isotopic substitution
must therefore affect the transition states of proton transfer reactions. When the hydrogen undergoing transfer is no longer bound
to carbon the isotope effects, assuming a 3 centre model in which the
stretching vibration changes into motion along the reaction co-
ordinate, differ considerably (Table 9.1). Unfortunately it has not as

TABLE 9.1

Variation of kinetic hydrogen isotope effect k_H/k_D with type of bond[17]

Bond	N≡C—H	O—H	S—H	F—H	Cl—H	I—H
k_H/k_D	10·2	10·2	5·8	14·9	7·2	5·8

yet been possible to measure isotope effects from compounds containing some of these groups. The emphasis on stretching frequencies may be unjustified in some cases as the configuration of the transition state may dictate that bending rather than stretching vibrations are important. In general vibrational frequencies for bending are much lower than for stretching and for a carbon acid values of C–H bending of 1300 cm^{-1} and C–D bending of 930 cm^{-1} are common. If all the bending energy is lost the isotope effect at 25° is 2·4. As the stretching and bending modes are orthogonal to one another it would seem most unlikely that the energy of both stretching and bending could be lost in forming the products. If, however, this were the case the isotope effect would be very large and Bigeleisen[18] has tabulated the maximum values that could be

TABLE 9.2

Maximum kinetic isotope effects[18] at 25°

Stable isotope	Tracer isotope	Isotope effect
^{1}H	^{2}H	18
^{1}H	^{3}H	60
^{12}C	^{13}C	1·25
^{12}C	^{14}C	1·50
^{14}N	^{15}N	1·14
^{14}N	^{16}N	1·25
^{16}O	^{18}O	1·19
^{32}S	^{35}S	1·05

expected under such circumstances for different isotopes (Table 9.2). On the other hand negligible isotope effects could be observed, as in electrophilic aromatic substitution reactions, where although the overall reaction involves cleavage of a C–H bond this is not the rate determining step.

There can be little doubt that the above picture of isotope effects is grossly oversimplified. In particular the 3 centre model may be inadequate for many proton transfer reactions particularly when the transfer of the proton is concerted with the making or breaking of another bond as, for example, in some base catalysed β elimination reactions. Secondly no mention is made of the solvent although it is known to have an important effect on the rates of some proton transfer reactions. Finally it must be remembered that the proton like other particles has a dual character being both a particle and a wave. Because of its low mass the wavelength of the proton is comparable to the width of the energy barrier for proton transfer reactions. Quantum mechanics shows that there is a finite probability of systems with less energy than the potential barrier appearing on the other side. In other words quantum mechanical tunnelling through the barrier is possible. Because of its much greater mass the probability of deuteron tunnelling is considerably less—a factor of 10^{-4} has been mentioned.[19]

A satisfactory theory of isotope effects is possible only when the vibrational frequencies of the transition state are known. The experimental approach is based on the fact that the frequencies of the reactants and the isotope effects can be measured and subsequently employed to infer something about the vibrational frequencies of the transition state. The second or theoretical approach assumes some kind of model and calculates these frequencies. Despite the fact that different theoretical treatments differ in their predictions of the extent to which an isotope effect is altered for a specific transition state there can be no doubt that both methods have an important role to play in the further development of such a theory. Before dealing in some detail with the two methods it is necessary to discuss the absolute rate treatment of isotope effects.

Let us assume that reactions (9.2) and 9.3) take place in the gas phase and that tunnelling is unimportant. We shall also assume that the vibrations are simple harmonic. The rates of formation of products are given by

$$k_H = \kappa_H (kT/h) K_H, \; k_D = \kappa_D (kT/h) K_D \qquad (9.5)$$

k is the Boltzmann constant, T the temperature in $°K$, h Planck's constant and K the equilibrium constant between reactants and transition state. The transmission coefficients κ_H, κ_D express the fraction of transition state species that form products and are usually assumed to be equal. The isotope effect is then given by

$$k_H/k_D = K_H/K_D = \frac{Q_H^{\ddagger}}{Q_D^{\ddagger}} \cdot \frac{Q_{AD}}{Q_{AH}} \qquad (9.6)$$

where Q's refer to the partition functions of the transition state and reactants. Each Q term can be expressed as the product of the various contributions that make up the energy of a molecule:

$$Q_i = Q_{i(transl)} Q_{i(rotn)} Q_{i(vibrn)} \qquad (9.7)$$

Because Eqn (9.6) contains ratios of partition functions only those contributions that change on isotopic substitution need be considered:

$$Q_{i(\text{transl})} = (2\pi MkT)^{3/2} v/h^3, \quad (Q_{AD}/Q_{AH})_{\text{transl}} = (M_{AD}/M_{AH})^{3/2} \quad (9.8)$$

$$Q_{i(\text{rotn})} = \frac{8\pi^2 (8\pi^3 I_X I_Y I_Z)^{1/2} (kT)^{3/2}}{Sh^3},$$

$$(Q_{AD}/Q_{AH})_{\text{rotn}} = \frac{(I_X I_Y I_Z)_{AD}^{1/2} S_{AH}}{(I_X I_Y I_Z)_{AH}^{1/2} S_{AD}} \quad (9.9)$$

$$Q_{i(\text{vibrn})} = \sum_i^{\substack{\text{vibrn} \\ \text{modes}}} e^{u_i/2}(1 - e^{-u_i})^{-1},$$

$$(Q_{AD}/Q_{AH})_{\text{vibrn}} = \sum^{3n-6} \frac{1 - e^{-u_{i(AH)}}}{1 - e^{-u_{i(AD)}}} \exp \sum^{3n-6} (u_{i(AH)} - u_{i(AD)})/2 \quad (9.10)$$

$u_i = h\nu_i/kT$, M's are molecular weights, I's the moments of inertia along x, Y and z directions and S's are symmetry numbers.

The isotope effect k_H/k_D is then given by

$$k_H/k_D = \frac{\left(\dfrac{M_{AD}}{M_{AH}}\right)^{3/2} \dfrac{(I_X I_Y I_Z)_{AD}^{1/2}}{(I_X I_Y I_Z)_{AH}^{1/2}} \cdot \dfrac{S_{AH}}{S_{AD}} \displaystyle\sum^{3n-6} \dfrac{1 - e^{-u_{i(AH)}}}{1 - e^{-u_{i(AD)}}}}{\left(\dfrac{M_D^{\ddagger}}{M_H^{\ddagger}}\right)^{3/2} \dfrac{(I_X^{\ddagger} I_Y^{\ddagger} I_Z^{\ddagger})_D^{1/2}}{(I_X^{\ddagger} I_Y^{\ddagger} I_Z^{\ddagger})_H^{1/2}} \dfrac{S_H^{\ddagger}}{S_D^{\ddagger}} \displaystyle\sum^{3n-7} \dfrac{1 - e^{-u_{i(H)}^{\ddagger}}}{1 - e^{-u_{i(D)}^{\ddagger}}}}$$

$$\times \frac{\exp \displaystyle\sum^{3n-6} (u_{i(AH)} - u_{i(AD)})/2}{\exp \displaystyle\sum^{3n-7} (u_{i(H)}^{\ddagger} - u_{i(D)}^{\ddagger})/2} \quad (9.11)$$

The Teller–Redlich product rule (a derivation of the expression for a simple case is given by Pitzer[20]) relates the products of the frequencies in a molecule to those in an isotopically substituted molecule. For the reactants

$$\left(\frac{M_{AD}}{M_{AH}}\right)^{3/2} \frac{(I_X I_Y I_Z)_{AD}^{1/2}}{(I_X I_Y I_Z)_{AH}^{1/2}} = \sum_j^n \frac{M_{j(AD)}}{M_{j(AH)}} \sum_i^{3n-6} \frac{u_{i(AD)}}{u_{i(AH)}} \quad (9.12)$$

For the transition state

$$\left(\frac{M_D^{\ddagger}}{M_H^{\ddagger}}\right)^{3/2} \frac{(I_X^{\ddagger} I_Y^{\ddagger} I_Z^{\ddagger})_D^{1/2}}{(I_X^{\ddagger} I_Y^{\ddagger} I_Z^{\ddagger})_H^{1/2}} = \frac{\nu_{L(D)}^{\ddagger}}{\nu_{L(H)}^{\ddagger}} \sum_j^{n^{\ddagger}} \frac{M_{j(D)}^{\ddagger}}{M_{j(H)}^{\ddagger}} \sum_i^{3n^{\ddagger}-7} \frac{u_{i(D)}^{\ddagger}}{u_{i(H)}^{\ddagger}} \quad (9.13)$$

$\nu^{\ddagger}_{L(D)}$, $\nu^{\ddagger}_{L(H)}$ being the imaginary frequencies corresponding to motion along the reaction co-ordinate. Assuming the symmetry terms cancel substitution of Eqns (9.12) and (9.13) in (9.11) gives

$$k_H/k_D = \frac{\nu^{\ddagger}_{L(H)}}{\nu^{\ddagger}_{L(D)}} \frac{\sum\limits^{3n-6} \frac{u_{i(AD)}}{u_{i(AH)}}}{\sum\limits^{3n-7} \frac{u^{\ddagger}_{i(D)}}{u^{\ddagger}_{i(H)}}} \frac{\sum\limits^{3n-6} \frac{1 - e^{-u_{i(AH)}}}{1 - e^{-u_{i(AD)}}}}{\sum\limits^{3n-7} \frac{1 - e^{-u^{\ddagger}_{i(H)}}}{1 - e^{-u^{\ddagger}_{i(D)}}}}$$

$$\times \frac{\exp \sum\limits^{3n-6} (u_{i(AH)} - u_{i(AD)})/2}{\exp \sum\limits^{3n^{\ddagger}-7} (u^{\ddagger}_{i(H)} - u^{\ddagger}_{i(D)})/2} \qquad (9.14)$$

Eqn (9.14) can be considerably simplified if we assume the isotopic atoms are essentially free in the transition state. The total product term of the transition state becomes unity as all the $u^{\ddagger}_i$ terms approach zero. Equation (9.14) reduces to

$$k_H/k_D = \frac{\nu^{\ddagger}_{L(H)}}{\nu^{\ddagger}_{L(D)}} \sum\limits^{3n-6} \frac{u_{i(AD)}}{u_{i(AH)}} \sum\limits^{3n-6} \frac{1 - e^{-u_{i(AH)}}}{1 - e^{-u_{i(AD)}}} \exp \sum\limits^{3n-6} \Delta u_i/2 \qquad (9.15)$$

If the temperature is low u_i becomes large and $1 - e^{-u_i} \to 1$ and to a good approximation

$$k_H/k_D = \sum\limits^{3n-6} e^{h(\nu_{i(AH)} - \nu_{i(AD)})/2\,kT} \qquad (9.16)$$

Equation (9.16) forms a basis for comparing the different hydrogen isotope effects[21] k_H/k_D and k_H/k_T. The cleavage of the A–H bond is pictured in Fig. 9.2. In the transition state the spring between the hydrogen and the rest of the molecule A has been broken and the remaining two springs have altered in strength. When using deuterium or tritium the force constants F_x, F_y, F_z, f_y and f_z for vibrations in the directions indicated are unchanged. Assuming that $m_A \gg m_H$ and vibrations are simple harmonic Eqn (9.16) gives

$$k_H/k_D = E^{[(1/\sqrt{m_H}) - (1/\sqrt{m_D})]} \qquad (9.17)$$

where $E = e^{[\sqrt{F_x} + \sqrt{F_y} + \sqrt{F_z} - \sqrt{f_y} - \sqrt{f_z}]/4\pi\,kT}$

Similarly for tritium the isotope effect is

$$k_H/k_T = E^{[(1/\sqrt{m_H}) - (1/\sqrt{m_T})]} \qquad (9.18)$$

Since $m_H = 1 \cdot 0081$, $m_D = 2 \cdot 0147$, $m_T = 3 \cdot 0170$

$$k_H/k_T = (k_H/k_D) \left[\frac{(1/\sqrt{m_H}) - (1/\sqrt{m_T})}{(1/\sqrt{m_H}) - (1/\sqrt{m_D})} \right] = (k_H/k_D)^{1 \cdot 442} \qquad (9.19)$$

This relationship is known as the Swain–Schaad equation.[21]

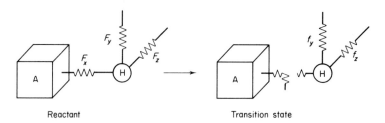

Reactant   Transition state

Fig. 9.2. Model for comparison of isotope effects with different hydrogen isotopes.[21]

9.2. RESULTS OF MODEL CALCULATIONS

Calculations of isotope effects based on Eqns (9.11) and (9.14) can be done in several different ways and as they have recently been discussed[16] they are only considered briefly here. Of the normal vibrational frequencies ν_{AH}, ν_{AD}, $\nu_H^{\ddagger}$ and $\nu_D^{\ddagger}$ the first two are usually available and $\nu_H^{\ddagger}$, $\nu_D^{\ddagger}$ can be obtained by assuming a set of harmonic force constants (i.e. assuming a potential surface). Calculations are then performed with a number of different sets of force constant changes. Without a computer these tend to be long and tedious and the first methods used involved certain approximation procedures consisting of expansions about u_i or Δu_i. One of the most successful is due to Bigeleisen and Mayer.[22] Taking the logarithms of Eqn (9.14) and expressing $u_{i(AH)} - u_{i(AD)} = \Delta u_i$, and $u_{i(H)}^{\ddagger} - u_{i(D)}^{\ddagger} = \Delta u_i^{\ddagger}$ we get

$$\ln k_H/k_D = \ln \frac{\nu_{L(H)}^{\ddagger}}{\nu_{L(D)}^{\ddagger}} + \sum^{3n-7} \left[\ln \left(1 + \frac{\Delta u_i^{\ddagger}}{u_{i(D)}^{\ddagger}} \right) - \frac{\Delta u_i^{\ddagger}}{2} \right.$$

$$\left. + \ln \frac{1 - e^{-u_{i(D)}^{\ddagger}}}{1 - e^{-(u_{i(D)}^{\ddagger} + \Delta u_i^{\ddagger})}} \right] - \sum^{3n-6} \left[\ln \left(1 + \frac{\Delta u_i}{u_{i(D)}} \right) \right.$$

$$\left. - \frac{\Delta u_i}{2} + \ln \frac{1 - e^{-u_{i(D)}}}{1 - e^{-(u_{i(D)} + \Delta u_i)}} \right] \qquad (9.20)$$

It can be shown[23] that

$$\ln \left(1 + \frac{\Delta u_i}{u_{i(D)}}\right) - \frac{\Delta u_i}{2} + \ln \frac{1 - e^{-u_{i(D)}}}{1 - e^{-(u_{i(D)} + \Delta u_i)}}$$

$$\equiv - G(u_i)_D (\Delta u_i) \qquad (9.21)$$

when $\Delta u_i \ll u_i$ (i.e. at high temperatures) so that

$$\ln k_H/k_D = \ln \left(\frac{\nu^{\ddagger}_{L(H)}}{\nu^{\ddagger}_{L(D)}}\right) - \sum^{3n-7} G(u^{\ddagger}_{i(D)} \Delta u^{\ddagger}_i) + \sum^{3n-6} G(u_{i(D)} \Delta u_i) \qquad (9.22)$$

$G(u)$ values have been tabulated[22] and this equation is a very convenient one for calculation of hydrogen isotope effects at high temperatures. It is interesting to note that the limiting isotope effect is not unity as in equilibrium isotope effects but $\nu^{\ddagger}_{L(H)}/\nu^{\ddagger}_{L(D)}$. Attempts have been made to extend the use of the equation to lower temperatures. Other types of expansions including the Bernoulli and Chebyshev polynomials have also been investigated by Bigeleisen and colleagues.[24]

The availability of large digital computers has made the calculation of isotope effects considerably easier than previously. A programme for calculating the normal harmonic vibrational frequencies using the FG matrix method of Wilson has been developed by Schacht-schneider[25] and widely use, notably by Wolfsberg and Stern.[26-28] From these studies a number of important conclusions can be drawn. Firstly, all terms in Eqn (9.14) make a significant contribution to the isotope effect unless the temperature is either very low or very high. Calculations made to test the various expansion methods show that some, at least, are very accurate.

Wolfsberg and Stern[26] have shown that changes in parts of the molecule well removed from the point of isotopic substitution have no effect on the calculated isotope effect. They suggest it is valid to "cut-off" the parts of the molecule more than two atoms away from the point of isotopic substitution. This conclusion may not be generally true, however, as it is well known that substituents far removed from the reaction centre e.g. the para position of a benzene ring, can alter the symmetry of the transition state.

The temperature dependence of isotope effects may under certain circumstances be more complicated than usual and exhibit maxima, minima, points of inflexion, single or double crossovers.[29] These anomalies are most likely to occur when (a) the force constant and geometry changes, between reactant and transition state, at the isotopic position(s) are very small; (b) when concomitant force constant increases and decreases occur at an isotopic position; (c) when quantum mechanical tunnelling is operative in an otherwise inverse isotope effect; and (d) in cases of multiple isotopic substitution when the individual substitutions produce effects in opposite directions. Situations (b), (c) and (d) can each be rationalised in terms of additive isotope effects. That such findings have not been reported may be because the anomalous region is not easily accessible to experimental work. Temperature dependent anomalies for normal magnitude pure primary hydrogen isotope effects should however not be common.

Finally, in the absence of large tunnelling factors the value of r in the Swain–Schaad equation (1·442) should be restricted[30] to the range $1\cdot33 \leqslant r \leqslant 1\cdot58$ within the temperature interval 20–1000°K. This assumes that the individual isotope effects, k_H/k_T, k_H/k_D are reasonably large in the normal direction ($k_H > k_D$) and exhibit regular temperature dependencies at all temperatures. These limits to r are the same as those previously specified by Bigeleisen.[31]

To account for the observed variation of kinetic hydrogen isotope effects in the base catalysed ionisation of various carbon acids (see pp. 167–168) the model proposed should ideally approximate to the real situation and be able to relate the calculated values to some experimentally obtainable properties of the reactants or products. In addition such details of the transition state as the frequencies of the stretching and bending vibrations, internuclear distances and the curvature of the reaction co-ordinate should be obtainable. That many calculations fall short of this high aim only goes to show the difficulties involved.

If it is possible to assume a linear 3 atomic transition state [A...H...B], A being a carbanion and B a base of variable strength the $3n - 5$ fundamental modes of vibration will be made up of (a) an unsymmetrical stretching vibration, $i\nu_3$ $\overleftarrow{A}...\overrightarrow{H}...\overleftarrow{B}$ which corresponds to the reaction co-ordinate; its frequency must either be zero or imaginary. It is this vibration that defines the curvature of the energy barrier, and determines the extent of tunnelling; (b) a "symmetrical" stretching vibration ν_1 $\overleftarrow{A}...H...\overrightarrow{B}$ in which the motion of the hydrogen is unspecified; (c) bending frequencies ν_2 $\overset{\uparrow}{A}...\overset{\uparrow}{H}...B$, $\overset{+}{A}...\overset{-}{H}...\overset{+}{B}$ which are doubly degenerate, the + and − signs refer to motion out and into respectively the plane of the paper.

Initial attempts at explaining the small and variable isotope effects frequently obtained assumed that the A—H bond was only partly broken in the transition state so that it maintained part of its strength and hence a definite vibrational frequency. Only when the bond was completely broken would this frequency become zero. Westheimer[12] has however pointed out that such a picture is at variance with the absolute reaction rate theory—there must be one normal mode (ν_3) lacking a real vibrational frequency.

The symmetric stretching vibration ν_1 does possess a zero point energy and its sensitivity to isotopic substitution will depend on the force constants of the partial bonds to hydrogen. For a symmetric transition state in which the hydrogen is equally firmly bound to A and to B the hydrogen will remain motionless and the frequency ν_1 under these conditions becomes independent of the hydrogen isotope. There will then be no zero point energy in the transition state to offset that in the ground state and the isotope effect will be a maximum. For non-linear transition states the situation is considerably different as no balance of the forces on hydrogen can be achieved—the frequencies corresponding to ν_1 and ν_3 are

and

respectively. It is clearly no longer possible to assume as is sometimes done for linear transition states that only stretching vibrations are important.

When the transition state is no longer symmetrical the stretching frequency ν_1 contributes to the zero point energy and the question of whether its sensitivity to isotopic substitution is, on its own, sufficiently large to account for the variations in isotope effects has been considered by several workers.[12,32] If we neglect bending motions the potential energy of the transition state is given by

$$2V = f_{11}\Delta r_{AH}^2 + f_{22}\Delta r_{HB}^2 + 2f_{12}\Delta r_{AH}\Delta r_{HB} \qquad (9.23)$$

where f_{11}, f_{22} are stretching force constants and f_{12} an interaction force constant. In a series of different transition states f_{22} is taken to increase with bond making to the product value while at the same time f_{11} decreases with bond breaking from the reactant value. One can calculate the forces on A, H and B and by assuming that they move in normal vibrations with harmonic motion Westheimer[12] obtained a quadratic equation for v_1 and v_3 in terms of the masses m_A, m_B and force constants. With the simplifying assumption $f_{12}^2 - f_{11}f_{22} = 0$ which corresponds to $v_3 = 0$ (i.e. a reaction with zero energy of activation) Eqn (9.24) was obtained

$$\lambda = 4\pi^2 v_1^2 = \frac{f_{11}}{m_A} + \frac{f_{22}}{m_B} + \frac{f_{11} + f_{22} - 2(f_{11}f_{22})^{1/2}}{m_H} \qquad (9.24)$$

illustrating the influence of isotopic mass on the "symmetrical" stretching frequency v_1. When $f_{11} = f_{22} = f$ Eqn (9.24) becomes

$$\lambda = 4\pi^2 v_1^2 = f\left(\frac{m_A + m_B}{m_A m_B}\right) \qquad (9.25)$$

The frequency is unchanged on isotopic substitution as m_H does not enter the expression. For the case $f_{11} \gg f_{22}$ Eqn (9.24) reduces to

$$\lambda = 4\pi^2 v_1^2 = f_{11}\left(\frac{m_A + m_H}{m_A m_H}\right) \qquad (9.26)$$

so that since m_A is usually much larger than m_H the frequency ratio v_1^H/v_1^D will be close to the upper limit of $2^{1/2}$, illustrating the large influence of isotopic mass. The results of calculations made by Willi and Wolfsberg[33] assuming $f_{12}^2 - f_{11}f_{22} = 0$ agree well with these findings.

Bell,[32] however, has drawn attention to the fact that the assumption $v_3 = 0$ is an artificial one and unlikely to be encountered frequently. It seems more reasonable to suggest that the energy surface has curvatures $d(= f_{12}^2 - f_{11}f_{22})$ of similar magnitude in different directions. Investigations of the effect of varying f_{12} on the ratio v_1^H/v_1^D, summarised in Table 9.3, shows that increasing f_{12} reduces the sensitivity to isotopic substitution of the "symmetric" vibration. Similarly, calculations by Willi and Wolfsberg[33] and also Saunders[34] both show that with increasing curvature of the potential barrier k_H/k_D remains close to its maximum value over a wide range of f_{11}/f_{22} and only when values outside the limits $0.1 < f_{11}/f_{22} > 10$ occur does k_H/k_D fall below two. The results obtained by Albery[35] are somewhat similar and can be summarised diagrammatically (Fig. 9.3) by plotting f_{11}/f_{12} against f_{22}/f_{12}. PQ represents the limiting hyperbola $\alpha\beta = 1$ which corresponds to the case considered by Westheimer.[12] The figure is symmetrical in α and β and only the half corresponding to reactant-like transition states $(f_{11} > f_{22})$ is given. Lines radiating from the origin represent transition states with a constant ratio f_{11}/f_{22} and for the case OP it represents a symmetric transition state. Similarly transition states lying on a hyperbola of the form $\alpha\beta = C$ ($C < 1$) have the same value of $f_{11}f_{22}/f_{12}^2$ and therefore the same negative curvature of the energy surface in the transition state. Once more low values of k_H/k_D only occur for very unsymmetric transition states. It seems safe therefore to conclude that for a 3 centre model the frequently observed low isotope effects and the variation within a closely related group of compounds can not be accounted for by changes in the symmetric stretching frequency ν_1. It might also be questioned whether the extreme values of f_{11}/f_{22} are experimentally realistic in view of the narrow range of velocities encountered and the fact that the weaker of the two bonds would not even compare in strength to an ordinary hydrogen bond.

As mentioned previously if instead of the stretching frequency ν_3 it is the bending frequency ν_2 that is converted into translational motion the isotope effect would be expected to be much lower. As

TABLE 9.3

Effect of varying the interaction force constant* on the "symmetric" stretching frequency ratio ν_1^H/ν_1^D [32]

$f_{12}/(f_{11}f_{22})^{1/2}$	1·0	1·27	1·74	3·16
ν_1^H/ν_1^D	1·32	1·28	1·14	1·08

* Assuming $f_{11} = 10f_{22}$.

ν_2 is clearly dependent on the isotopic mass it is a potential source of low and variable isotope effects. The bending frequency for a carbon acid would be in the region of 1300 cm^{-1} but the corresponding value in the transition state is not known with any certainty. The closest stable analogue of the transition state is the bifluoride ion, HF_2^- which has a bending frequency of 1233 cm^{-1} close to the value calculated on the basis of an electrostatic model.[36] Results using this model suggest that under most circumstances the importance of the bending frequency either cancels or is outweighed by the importance of tunnelling.

Model calculations by Saunders[34] show that the emergence of high bending frequencies in the transition state can reduce the isotope effect considerably. It seems preferable however to consider bending frequencies in the context of 4 and 5 centred transition states where the various motions can be coupled together and this has been done for both linear and non-linear transition states.[17,37,38] In More O'Ferrall's work vibrational frequencies and

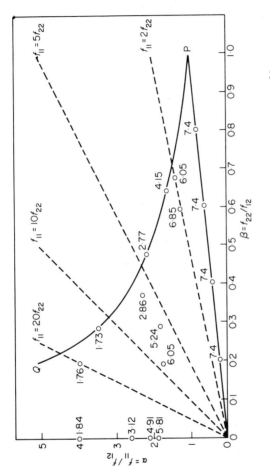

Fig. 9.3. Variation of isotope effects with transition state force constants.[35]

isotope effects were calculated from assigned molecular geometries, and force constants for transition states ranging in structure from reactant-like to product-like were employed. The structure of the transition state was expressed in terms of x, the order of the reacting hydrogen bond, and $1 - x$, the order of the partial bond to the base. The model used for proton transfer from a carbon acid to a methoxide or carboxylate ion was of the form

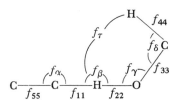

The various stretching force constants were estimated from Badger's rule and the bending force constants by some function

TABLE 9.4

Calculated isotope effects* for proton transfer from a carbon acid to various bases at 25° [17]

Bond order (x)	MeO⁻	MeS⁻	CO_2^-
1·0	1·0	1·0	1·0
0·875	3·5	2·8	3·4
0·75	5·6	3·8	5·4
0·625	7·3	5·4	7·3
0·50	6·8	7·0	7·1
0·375	4·8	7·8	5·4
0·25	3·4	7·0	3·9
0·125	2·5	5·9	3·1
0·0	0·84	2·3	1·1

* Includes tunnelling correction.

involving the bond order and the force constants in either the reactants or products e.g. $f_\alpha = x^2 F_\alpha$, $f_\gamma = (1 - x)^2 F_\gamma$. The lengths of the partial bonds to hydrogen were obtained from Pauling's relation ($r_1 = R_1 - 0·6 \log x$). All interaction force constants except f_{12} were assumed to be zero and in this case its dependence on x was arbitrarily assigned as $f_{12} = \{1 + x^2(1 - x)^2\} (f_{11}f_{22})^{1/2}$. The calculated isotope effects are given in Table 9.4 and it is seen that the incorporation of bending frequencies and tunnelling does not fundamentally alter the conclusion based on the 3 centre model that the isotope effect should pass through a maximum for a symmetrical transition state. The region of large isotope effects may however be broader than for a 3 centre model if in going to a more asymmetric transition state the decrease in the influence of the stretching vibrations is offset by an increasing contribution from the bending vibrations as their transition state frequencies reduce to zero.

It has been asserted[39] that isotope effects for non-linear transition states should be small and this is borne out by the calculations of More O'Ferrall[38] (Table 9.5) in which the angle β between the bond to hydrogen was systematically varied for the transition state

$$\overset{\displaystyle H}{\underset{\displaystyle C-C \quad O-C}{\diagup \beta \diagdown}}$$

Of course the possibility exists that geometric effects may be offset by changes in force constants but results in Table 9.5 show the

TABLE 9.5

Dependence of isotope effect* k_H/k_D on geometry of the transition state[38] (assuming $x = 0.5$)

β	At constant interaction force constant Reaction co-ordinate frequency (cm^{-1})	k_H/k_D	At constant reaction co-ordinate frequency	
			N[a]	k_H/k_D
180°	715i	7.9	1.0	7.9
175	715i	7.8	1.0	7.8
150	670i	6.2	1.39	6.4
120	532i	3.0	1.62	3.9
90	319i	1.7	2.82	2.3
60	181i	0.9	6.0	1.4

* Includes tunnelling correction.

[a] Adjustable parameter used to vary the interaction force constant.

findings to be fairly insensitive to changes in the latter. The low isotope effects are ascribed to the presence of a large isotope sensitive vibration in the transition state sufficiently large as to offset the combined zero point energy changes in the stretching and bending vibration in the reactants.

Theoretical calculations of isotope effects in elimination reactions affords the opportunity of investigating the possibility of whether there is any interdependence between the deuterium isotope effect originating in one part of the molecule and either nitrogen, carbon, or sulphur isotope effects occurring at another part. For the reaction between ethyl dimethylsulphonium ion and hydroxide ion at least the deuterium isotope effect is not strongly affected by the extent of weakening of the carbon–sulphur bond and similarly the sulphur isotope effect does not depend much on the extent of proton transfer.[37] Just as important however is the finding that k_H/k_D may be strongly influenced by the extent of coupling of the proton transfer with other atomic motions so that the value may not be a good guide of the extent of proton transfer in the transition state.

More recently Bell and co-workers[40] have used an electrostatic model to simulate the transfer of a proton from a carbon acid to basic oxygen anions of variable strength. It consists essentially of a proton (or deuteron) moving in the field of two rigid spherical electron distributions, represented by Slater atomic orbitals, and surrounding the two nuclei. To represent the electron cloud repulsions a term Ar_{AB}^{-m} (m is usually 12) is introduced. The energy of the system $A^-...H^+...B^{\delta^-}$ is represented as usual in terms of r_{AB}, r_{AH}, r_{BH}, the force constants f_{11}, f_{22}, f_{12} determined and the frequencies ν_1 and $i\nu_3$ calculated. The bending force constant and frequency

TABLE 9.6

Variation of isotope effect for the electrostatic model[40]

$R_{AB}^{\ddagger}$ (Å)	3·65	3·75	3·85	3·95	4·05	4·15	4·25
$(k_H/k_D)_S$	1·34	1·39	1·45	1·52	1·59	1·65	1·73
k_H/k_D	4·93	8·45	11·76	12·90	12·90	9·93	8·38

$R_{AB}^{\ddagger}$ is the internuclear distance in the transition state for a δ value of unity.

ν_2 can be calculated from f_{11}, f_{22} and f_{12} and the charge distribution given by the model. Values of the isotope effect were calculated in the presence of tunnelling (k_H/k_D) assuming a parabolic barrier, and in its absence ($k_H/k_D)_S$.

The results (Table 9.6) for a fixed value of δ show that $(k_H/k_D)_S$ are small in the range 1·3–1·8 whilst (k_H/k_D) values increase from nearly 5 through to 12·9 before falling to much lower values. Only when tunnelling is allowed for, can the experimental findings of variable hydrogen isotope effects be explained.

Secondly, the ratios of the force constants f_{11}/f_{22} vary within narrow limits (1·15–1·23) in contrast to the large values (~10) previously required to account for reasonable changes in isotope effects. It follows therefore that the symmetric stretching vibration contributes virtually nothing to the isotope effect, in line with previous findings. Finally the model suggests that isotope effects should be sensitive to steric hindrance.

9.3. EXPERIMENTAL ISOTOPE EFFECTS

Experimental variations in kinetic hydrogen isotope effects have usually been recorded for reactions in which (1) the substrate is kept the same and the base varied, or (2) the substrate is varied. In the former case the choice of a suitable reaction so that rates over a wide range of basic strengths can be investigated is not always easy but these difficulties have been nicely overcome in Barnes and Bell's[41] work on ethylnitroacetate which was studied over 18 pK units. The results (Table 9.7) show the isotope effect k_H/k_D to increase with the base strength of the catalyst, reaching a maximum for the pyridine-type, and then falling off quite rapidly. In view of the uncertainties concerning the configuration of the transition state no quantitative measure of its departure from symmetry can be made. It seems reasonable however to relate the property to the difference in basic strength between A and B i.e. $\Delta pK = pK_{(AH)} - pK_{(BH)}$ or if we take into account statistical factors $\Delta pK' = \Delta pK + \log_{10}(p_{AH}q_B/p_{BH}q_A)$. The isotope effect is then a maximum close to $\Delta pK' \simeq 0$ in line with theory.

TABLE 9.7

Isotope effects in the ionisation of ethylinitroacetate[41] (pK_a = 5·8)

Base (B)	$k_B^H (M^{-1}s^{-1})$	k_H/k_D	$\Delta pK'$
water	$2 \cdot 83 \times 10^{-4}$	3·6	7·7
monochloroacetate	0·92	6·6	3·5
acetate	13·5	7·7	1·6
2-methylpyridine	78	9·6	0·1
4-methylpyridine	129	9·1	0·1
2,6-lutidine	207	9·9	−0·6
2-chlorophenoxide	$8 \cdot 7 \times 10^3$	8·1	−2·3
phenoxide	$2 \cdot 9 \times 10^4$	6·7	−3·9
hydroxide	$1 \cdot 5 \times 10^5$	4·6	−10·0

For many carbon acids the observed isotope effects have been brought together by Bell and Goodall[2] and Fig. 9.4 incorporates most of their data as well as some later values. Once more the isotope effect seems to pass through a maximum in the region $\Delta pK' = 0$. However the scatter of individual points from a smooth curve is much higher than the experimental errors and there is good reason to believe that structural modifications close to the reaction site constitute such a drastic modification that it is unreasonable to expect that all the isotope effects can be correlated using a single parameter. The suspicion prevails that the absolute magnitude of the observed isotope effect varies with the type of substrate and base used.

Until very recently the experimental data in the region $\Delta pK' = -5$ to +5 relied heavily on the k_H/k_D values obtained for the hydroxide

catalysed ionisation of nitromethane, nitroethane and 2-nitro-
propane, reactions in which secondary and possibly steric factors are
important. The situation has been improved by the publication of
preliminary details[3] of isotope effects in the region $\Delta pK = -10$ to
$+0.3$ for $ArCHMeNO_2$, $ArCH_2NO_2$ and $CH_2{=}CHCH_2NO_2$ type
compounds. These show a rather broad and poorly defined
maximum suggesting that k_H/k_D may be relatively insensitive to the
symmetry of the transition state or that the symmetry does not
change over a wide range of ΔpK.

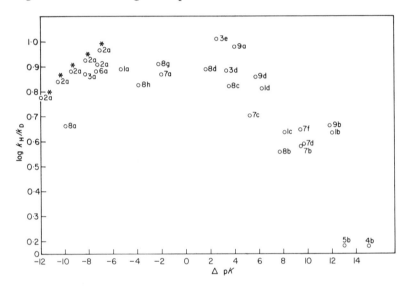

Fig. 9.4. Relation between kinetic isotope effect and pK differences of the reacting
systems. Numbers refer to the following compounds and letters to the following bases:
1, nitromethane;[2] 2, nitroethane;[2,42] 3, 2-nitropropane;[2] 4, *t*-butylmalononitrile;[43]
5, malononitrile;[43] 6, nitrocyclohexane;[3] 7, tricarbomethoxymethane;[41] 8, ethylnitroacetate;[41] 9, 2-acetylcyclohexanone;[41] a, hydroxide; b, water; c, chloroacetate; d, acetate;
e, pyridine; f, trimethylacetate; g, 2-chlorophenoxide; h, phenoxide.
* Refers to medium containing dimethyl sulphoxide.

The effects of substituents can best be illustrated by confining the
discussion to isotope effects obtained for a single catalyst such as
water (Table 9.8). For those compounds containing the $-CH_2 . CO-$
grouping there is a good relationship between the isotope effect and
relative reactivity but this is destroyed as soon as alkyl or bromine
substituents are introduced presumably because of steric and other
short range interactions. Although relative reactivities are a frequently employed measure of transition state structure it is clear that
only under certain limited circumstances is this justified. Kresge[44]
for example has shown that isotope effects k_{H_3O}/k_{D_3O} on the

hydrolysis of vinyl ethers, a reaction involving proton addition to a carbon–carbon double bond activated by a single oxygen atom, increase regularly with log k_{H_3O}. However the expected correlation breaks down when the comparison is extended to reactions that involve protonation of an aromatic ring, a triple bond or even a double bond bearing other heteroatoms.

The isotope effect k_H/k_D can however be correlated with the exponent β of the Brönsted equation. This behaviour supports the view that the magnitude of the isotope effect is a function of the extent to which the proton has moved along the reaction co-ordinate

TABLE 9.8

Isotope effects from studies of water catalysis[5,43] at 25°; k_H in s^{-1}, β = exponent in Brönsted relation for anion bases

Acid	k_H	k_H/k_D	β
$CH_2(CO_2Et)_2$	2.45×10^{-5}	2.0	0.79
$CHBr(CO_2Et)_2$	2.15×10^{-4}	2.7	0.73
CH_3NO_2	6.5×10^{-8}	3.8	0.67
$MeCOCH_2CO_2Et$	1.16×10^{-3}	3.5	0.59
$\underset{\displaystyle \lfloor (CH_2)_2 \rfloor}{CH_2COCHCO_2Et}$	2.3×10^{-3}	3.4	0.64
$MeCOCHMeCO_2Et$	1.14×10^{-5}	3.8	0.60
$(MeCO)_2CH_2$	1.32×10^{-2}	4.5	0.48
$(MeCO)_2CHBr$	3.35×10^{-2}	3.9	0.42
$MeCOCHBrCO_2Et$	1.56×10^{-2}	4.3	0.42
$CH_2(CN)_2$	2.86×10^{-2}	1.5	0.98
$CH(C_4H_9\text{-}t)(CN)_2$	5.36×10^{-4}	1.5	0.98

as β has been interpreted in such terms (see p. 143). There is no sign of a maximum isotope effect at $\beta = \frac{1}{2}$ probably because the values of β refer to carboxylate anion catalysis whereas the isotope effects refer to the weaker base water for which the relevant values of β would be higher.

The above discussions makes clear that in experimental investigations of the variation of isotope effect with transition state symmetry it is desirable on the one hand to keep changes in the substrate and base to a minimum and on the other to vary the rate, or basic strength over as wide a range as possible. These two requirements which seem to be contradictory can be achieved by using highly basic media. In Chapter 6 we have seen how very large increases in basicity may be achieved by adding variable amounts of dipolar aprotic solvents such as dimethyl sulphoxide to an aqueous hydroxide medium. Several studies bear witness to the very large rate increases that may be observed under such conditions. The possible application of highly basic media to the study of kinetic hydrogen isotope effects has been discussed[45] and the first reported example of a k_H/k_D maximum with a single substrate under changing solvent conditions referred to an elimination reaction.[46]

To further strengthen the weakness in the Bell–Goodall curve at negative ΔpK values the ionisation of nitroethane[42] was studied in

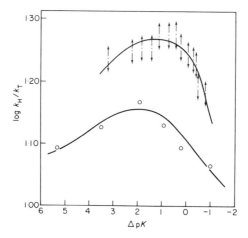

Fig. 9.5. Variation of kinetic isotope effect with basicity $o(-)$menthone,[47]   (d)-phenyl-methylacetophenone.[6] k_H/k_D data for menthone have been converted to k_H/k_T values using Swain-Schaad equation.

highly basic media and the results presented in Fig. 9.4 indicate that qualitatively at least the variation of isotope effect with ΔpK is the same as if ΔpK arises from the use of different substrates or bases; the correlation between rates and basic strength however is much better.

Two further studies, one on the inversion of $(-)$menthone[47] and the other the racemisation of (d)-phenylmethylacetophenone[6] (Fig. 9.5) show the isotope effect passing through a clearly defined maximum in the region $\Delta pK = 0$. The results also show that the slopes of the $\log k$ vs. H$_-$ plots, which can to a first approximation be interpreted in terms of a Brönsted β_{OH^-} exponent (see p. 146) are gratifyingly close to 0·5. It is, however, interesting that even for these two carbon acids which have the same carbonyl activating group and closely similar acid strengths that the isotope effects are considerably different, those for the phenylmethylacetophenone being consistently higher.

For reactions in which the transition state is considerably more asymmetric the isotope effect is less sensitive to changes in basicity.[48] Thus for the methoxide catalysed racemisation of 2-methyl-3-phenylpropionitrile ($pK_a \sim 30$) k_H/k_D only changes from 1·15 to 1·67 on going from 0 to 98·4 wt% dimethyl sulphoxide. The most probable explanation lies in the fact that the reverse reaction is probably diffusion controlled and therefore the transition state is very reactant-like so that a negligible isotope effect is observed. The isotope effect for the forward reaction must therefore be equal to the equilibrium value and the transition state resembles closely the products of the reaction.

9.4. QUANTUM MECHANICAL TUNNELLING

Although not possible according to classical theory the tunnel effect has established itself as an important concept in modern chemistry and it may turn out to be the major factor responsible for the observed variations in kinetic hydrogen isotope effects. Not only has it been invoked to explain certain anomalies in the discharge of protons at electrodes during electrolysis[49] but it is also claimed to be important in proton conductance in ice[50] and also thought to have been demonstrated experimentally in studies of the infra-red and raman spectra of imidazole.[51] Furthermore it may have major biological implications.[52]

The concept of tunnelling[53] can best be illustrated by considering a particle having a wavelength $\lambda = h/mv$, m and v being the mass and velocity respectively, incident upon a one-dimensional energy barrier (Fig. 9.6). The wave properties of the particle only become important when λ is large in relation to the process concerned, in other words, when m is small. For protons at room temperature $\lambda = 1-2$ Å which is comparable with the width of the energy barrier in a proton transfer reaction. Such reactions must therefore be treated quantum mechanically. If the energy of the particle is W and the height of the energy barrier E classical theory shows the reaction probability to rise abruptly from zero to unity at $W = E$. In terms of quantum mechanics however there is a finite probability that reaction may occur even when $W < E$.

The question now is how can the importance of tunnelling be assessed and if it is important how can it be detected. To calculate the tunnel-effect correction it is first necessary to obtain an expression for the permeability $G(W)$ of the barrier to protons of a given energy, W. This can be done by choosing a barrier of a particular shape and for which the potential energy can be clearly defined. Solution of the familiar Schrödinger equation representing wave motion in one dimension then gives $G(W)$, which is of course the reaction probability. The rate of reaction is then given by the product of reaction probability and fraction of protons possessing an

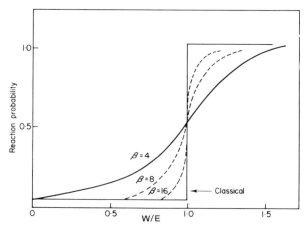

Fig. 9.6. Reaction probability against energy W of the proton, expressed as W/E, for various parabolic barriers.[53] β is related to the barrier dimensions.

energy W. Assuming a Boltzmann type distribution the rate can be expressed by Eqn (9.27)

$$k_{\text{quant}} = \int_0^\infty G(W)(1/kT) \exp(-W/kT) \, dW \tag{9.27}$$

Had the proton been treated in classical terms G would have been zero for $W < E$ and unity when $W > E$ so that Eqn (9.27) would reduce to

$$k_{\text{class}} = \exp(-E/kT) \tag{9.28}$$

The quantum correction

$$Q = k_{\text{quant}}/k_{\text{class}} = \exp(E/kT) \int_0^\infty G(W)(1/kT) \exp(-W/kT) \, dW \tag{9.29}$$

has usually been calculated by replacing the actual potential energy barrier by some simplified model (thought to approximate the former) for which $G(W)$ can be analytically determined. The model frequently takes the form of a parabola and Wigner[54] found, to a good approximation, that

$$Q = 1 + (h\nu_i/kT)^2/24 \tag{9.30}$$

for small tunnelling corrections. Similarly Eckart[55] has used an artificial barrier that may correspond quite closely to the actual potential energy barrier. Although the equation for Q lacks somewhat in computational simplicity numerical integrations have been performed[56] and convenient tables published.[57] That such a treatment in terms of a single reaction co-ordinate may be an oversimplification is suggested by the work of Mortensen and Pitzer,[57] and Johnston and Rapp,[56] on a two-dimensional analysis of the $H + H_2 \rightarrow H_2 + H$ reaction.

If the process of proton transfer has zero heat of reaction and the energy barrier can be represented by a symmetric parabola the tunnel-effect correction can be treated by the exact analytical methods developed by Bell.[58] The permeability of the barrier is obtained as a function of the energy W by using the Brillouin–Wenzel–Kramers approximation[59] of the Schrödinger equation, leading to the expression

$$G(W) = \exp\{-\beta(1 - W/E)\}, \quad (W < E) \qquad (9.31)$$
$$G = 1, \quad (W > E)$$

where $\beta = 2\pi^2 a(2mE)^{1/2}/h$, $2a$ being the width of the parabola at the base. The BWK approximation is valid only when W is considerably less than E so that the treatment will be satisfactory when the degree of tunnelling is large. The value of Q can be readily calculated and takes the form

$$Q = \beta/(\beta - \alpha) \qquad (9.32)$$

when $\alpha(= E/kT) < \beta$ as it frequently is for chemical reactions, or

$$1/Q = 1 - (\alpha/\beta) = 1 - hE^{1/2}/2\pi^2 akT(2m)^{1/2} \qquad (9.33)$$

Tunnelling will then be most important when m is small, the temperature is low and the energy barrier both tall and narrow. The curvature at the top of the barrier (C_t) can be shown to be equal to $2E/a^2$ and may be related to the frequency ν_t defined by

$$u = h\nu_t/kT = 2\pi\alpha/\beta \qquad (9.34)$$

or

$$\nu_t = E^{1/2}/\pi a(2m)^{1/2} \qquad (9.35)$$

so that

$$\nu_t = C_t^{1/2}/2\pi m^{1/2} \qquad (9.36)$$

A decrease in barrier width corresponds to an increase in C_t and therefore ν_t.

The observed energy of activation as given by the Arrhenius equation, $k = A_{obs}e^{-E_{obs}/RT}$, is related to the barrier height by

$$E_{obs}/E = 1 - [1/(\beta - \alpha)] \tag{9.37}$$

and the corresponding pre-exponential term by

$$A_{obs}/A = [\beta/(\beta - \alpha)] \exp [-E/kT(\beta - \alpha)] \tag{9.38}$$

Clearly $E_{obs} < E$ and $A_{obs} < A$.

For small degrees of tunnelling energies in the neighbourhood of $W = E$ will be important and Eqn (9.31) will be a bad approximation; in particular the assumption $G = 1$ for $W > E$ neglects the reflection of particles which takes place in this neighbourhood and the resulting expression for Q when expanded in powers of h/kT does not reduce to Wigner's Eqn (9.30). On this basis Bell[60] suggested that Eqn (9.39)

$$G(W) = [1 + \exp (\beta\gamma)]^{-1} \tag{9.39}$$

where $\gamma = 1 - (W/E)$ be preferred to Eqn (9.31). If, once again, $\alpha < \beta$ the tunnel-effect correction is given by

$$Q = (\pi\alpha/\beta)/\sin (\pi\alpha/\beta) = \tfrac{1}{2}u/\sin \tfrac{1}{2}u \tag{9.40}$$

Equations corresponding to (9.37) and (9.38) are

$$E_{obs} - E = kT(\tfrac{1}{2}u \cot \tfrac{1}{2}u - 1) \tag{9.41}$$

$$A_{obs}/A = (\tfrac{1}{2}u/\sin \tfrac{1}{2}u) \exp(\tfrac{1}{2}u \cot \tfrac{1}{2}u - 1) \tag{9.42}$$

In the one case where a direct comparison of the two treatments has been made[61] the results are in good agreement, the largest difference in barrier height being less than $0\cdot1$ kcal mol^{-1} and for the barrier width it is $0\cdot05$ Å. If the actual reactions however do have finite heats of reaction it is clear that the symmetric treatment overestimates the importance of tunnelling but the difference is not thought to be very important unless the heats of reaction become very large.

Recently, however, the validity of a good deal of tunnelling calculations has been questioned. Truhlar and Kuppermann[62] point out that the transition state theory rests on the assumption that motion along a reaction path is separable from motion in directions transverse to it and that the latter are adiabatic i.e. their quantum numbers are preserved as the reaction proceeds. This assumption requires that in calculating tunnelling corrections the zero point energy of the transverse motions be added to the potential energy along the reaction path to furnish an effective vibrationally adiabatic barrier which should be used in such calculations. The results of quantum mechanical calculations by numerical methods for the collinear exchange reactions of $H + H_2$ and $D + D_2$ are dramatically different from those in which this factor is neglected.

Despite the differences as to how the tunnel-effect correction should be computed all treatments agree that $Q_H > Q_D > Q_T$. The kinetic consequences can be summarised as follows:

(1) As the importance of tunnelling increases with decreasing temperature the observed energy of activation for proton transfer (E_{obs}^H) is reduced from its value at higher temperatures. Provided the reaction can be accurately studied over a sufficiently wide temperature range curvature of the Arrhenius plot should be observable.

(2) The measured activation energy difference $(E_{obs}^D - E_{obs}^H)$ is greater than it would be in the absence of tunnelling $(E^D - E^H)$. The maximum value of the latter corresponds to the difference of zero point energy for the stretching of C–D and C–H bonds (1150 cal/mole).

(3) The pre-exponential factor A_{obs}^H is less than that for deuteron transfer A_{obs}^D. Transition state theory permits extreme values of $\frac{1}{2}$ and $2^{1/2}$ for the ratio A_{obs}^H/A_{obs}^D in the absence of tunnelling so that only values below 0·5 can be ascribed to this effect. In theory it should be possible to measure changes in this ratio as a function of temperature.

(4) The isotope effect k_H/k_D should be higher than in the absence to tunnelling but if the abnormality in the pre-exponential factor just about cancels the abnormality in the activation energy effect the value could be lower than the permitted maximum.

(5) When both deuterium and tritium isotope effects are available the following relationships should hold:

$$A_{obs}^H/A_{obs}^D < A_{obs}^D/A_{obs}^T \text{ and } E_{obs}^D - E_{obs}^H > E_{obs}^T - E_{obs}^D. \qquad (9.43)$$

(6) The value of r in the Swain-Schaad equation could be reduced from the value of 1·44.

For several years there was only one investigation[63] which gave reliable values for the isotope effect on activation energies in a proton transfer reaction and only in 1964 was the detailed temperature dependence of two hydrogen isotope effects for a reaction recorded.[64] Since then several investigations have been reported and the importance of tunnelling has become well established.[53]

Of all the arguments for proton tunnelling it is the non-linearity of the Arrhenius equation that is probably weakest. This stems from the fact that there are several other reasons why such deviations may occur.[65] Thus the activation energy is a composite function of several terms; (a) E_b, due to stretching of bonds in the reactants and forming new ones in the transition state; (b) E_r, from repulsive forces between unbonded atoms or groups at close range; (c) E_e, representing electrostatic interactions between reactants; (d) E_s, arising from the varying degrees of solvation of the reactants and transition state, all of which may be temperature dependent. The likely contribution of each term has been discussed by Caldin.[66]

The enthalpy of activation at constant pressure $\Delta H_p^{\ddagger}$ is the customarily measured parameter and is related to the energy of activation at constant volume, $\Delta E_v^{\ddagger}$ by

$$\Delta H_p^{\ddagger} = \Delta E_v^{\ddagger} + (d\,T\,\Delta v_T^{\ddagger}/b) \tag{9.43}$$

where d and b are the coefficients of cubical expansion and compressibility respectively.

It follows that if $\Delta E_v^{\ddagger}$ is independent of temperature $\Delta H_p^{\ddagger}$ cannot be. Although the second term in Eqn (9.43) is small in aqueous solution at room temperature Hills[67] has pointed out that it can be as high as $1 \cdot 2$ kcal mol^{-1} in other solvents even for modest values of $\Delta v^{\ddagger}$.

When neutral or diffusely charged reactants, one of which is often a solvent molecule, come together to form a markedly polar transition state there will be considerable changes in solvation that may make a significant contribution to the dE/dT term and so lead to curvature of the Arrhenius equation.

An estimate of the temperature at which deviations from linearity in the Arrhenius equation, arising from quantum mechanical tunnelling, may occur can be made by considering the special case $\alpha = \beta$ for which

$$E_{obs}/E = (\beta - 2)/2\beta \tag{9.44}$$

For reactions of practical interest $\beta \gg 1$ so that $E_{obs}/E = \frac{1}{2}$ leading to

$$T = hE^{1/2}/2\pi^2 ak (2m)^{1/2} \tag{9.45}$$

In the ionisation of 2-carbethoxycyclopentanone the data gives $T = -20°$ for fluoride catalysis and $-60°$ for both the chloroacetate ion and the solvent. In order to test this prediction Hulett[61] used a $5 \cdot 2$ M aqueous solution of NaBr and followed the reaction over the temperature range -20 to $+15°$. The results obtained for fluoride catalysis are in agreement with the theoretical predictions, curvature in the right direction appearing below $-10°$ and by the time the temperature is lowered to $-20°$ the rate constant was 75% faster than the value corresponding to a linear plot. On reflection however the result is less convincing that it would appear for the corresponding solvent catalysed reaction gave curvature at low temperatures in the opposite direction. Another reaction, the bromination of acetone, when studied in a similar medium ($6·7$ M $NaClO_4$) gave signs of curvature for both proton and deuteron transfer.[68]

A study of the rates of bromination of acetone and hexadeutero-acetone in alkaline media[69] containing large concentrations of lithium, sodium and potassium bromides showed the cations to have a retarding influence on the rate, the order $Li > Na > K$ being consistent with the amount of ion association present. In fact most anions in the presence of such large concentrations of salt will be associated to some extent and as this will also be a function of

TABLE 9.9

Deviations from the Arrhenius equation[70] for the reaction
$$HF + C_6H_2(NO_2)_3CH_2^- \rightarrow C_6H_2(NO_2)_3CH_3 + F^-$$

Temp. (°C)	25·0	7·0	0·0	−49·9	−59·9	−69·9	−79·8	−89·8
$\log k_{obs} - \log k_{Arrh}$	0·0	+0·004	−0·001	+0·064	+0·106	+0·17	+0·225	+0·345

temperature deviations from the Arrhenius equation should not be uncommon and equally, should not be ascribed to quantum mechanical tunnelling unless the importance of ion association has been correctly allowed for.

Two of the most convincing examples of curved Arrhenius plots which can probably be ascribed to tunnelling stem from the work of Caldin and co-workers.[70,71] The use of ethanol as a solvent enables reactions to be studied over a very wide temperature range. The reaction between hydrofluoric acid and the 2,4,6-trinitrobenzyl anion in this solvent was studied[70] over the range $+25°$ to $-90°$, the deviations from linearity being expressed in terms of $\log k_{obs} - \log k_{Arrh}$ (Table 9.9). At the lowest temperature the difference amounts to c. 120%. Curvature was also observed for the acetic acid catalysed reaction but this became apparent only at the lower temperatures; it seems unlikely therefore that the deviations can be ascribed to changes in solvent structure.

Positive deviations also occur in the proton transfer reaction between ethoxide ion and 4-nitrobenzyl cyanide in ethanol + ether,[71] the study having covered the temperature range -60 to $-124°C$. At the lowest temperature the observed rate constant is about 100% faster than that calculated, a difference nearly 24 times the standard deviation of the observed rate. The small value of $\Delta S^{\ddagger}$ suggests that there is no great change in solvation on forming the transition state. That the probable reason for the curvature is tunnelling is strengthened by the finding that the Arrhenius plot for 4-nitrobenzylcyanide-α, α-d_2 in the range -60 to $-90°$ is linear. It seems clear from the above that curved Arrhenius plots may be ascribed to quantum mechanical tunnelling only after careful consideration has been given to the elimination of possible alternative explanations.

TABLE 9.10

Arrhenius parameters for some proton transfer reactions
ΔE in kcal mol^{-1}

Reaction	Activation energy difference		Pre-exponential ratio	
	$E^T_{obs} - E^H_{obs}$	$E^D_{obs} - E^H_{obs}$	A^H_{obs}/A^T_{obs}	A^H_{obs}/A^D_{obs}
(1) Ethoxide catalysed elimination of 1-bromo-2-phenyl-propane[64]	2·43	1·79	0·33	0·40
(2) Hydroxide catalysed[72] ionisation of acetone	2·90	2·10	0·10	0·26
(3) Ethoxide catalysed ionisation of 4-nitro-benzylcyanide[71]		1·85		0·18
(4) Fluoride catalysed ionisation of 2-carbethoxyclo-pentanone[63,73]	2·65	2·44	0·04	0·04
(5) 2,4,6-Trimethylpyridine catalysed ionisation of 2-nitropropane[1]	3·01			0·15
(6) Oxidation of leuco crystal violet by chloranil[74]	3·36			0·04

The most sensitive criteria for measuring tunnelling effects are undoubtedly the activation energy differences for the various isotopes and the corresponding ratios of the pre-exponential terms. The results collected in Table 9.10 show that there are several instances where $A^H_{obs}/A^D_{obs} < 0·5$ and $E^D_{obs} - E^H_{obs} > 1·1$ kcal mol^{-1} have been reported. The argument in favour of tunnelling being the primary cause is strengthened by the fact that the corresponding $E^T_{obs} - E^D_{obs}$ and A^D_{obs}/A^T_{obs} values are much closer to the limits set by classical theory—this is particularly striking in the work on 2-carbethoxycyclopentanone.[73]

In line with theoretical considerations the value of r in the Swain-Schaad equation (Table 9.11) seems to be relatively insensitive to the degree of quantum mechanical tunnelling. In the case of acetone and acetophenone a small secondary isotope effect is partly responsible for the low values.

It is interesting to consider in what way tunnelling can make an increasing contribution to the rate of a reaction. We mentioned previously that the activation energy is made up of several terms one of which reflects the energy required to overcome repulsions between nonbonded atoms or groups. If by suitable modification of

TABLE 9.11

Value of $\ln (k_H/k_T)/\ln (k_H/k_D)$ for different reactions

Reaction	$\ln (k_H/k_T)/\ln (k_H/k_D)$
(1) Ionisation of α-phenylisocaprophenone[21]	1·44
(2) Hydrolysis of triphenylsilane[75]	1·61
(3) Elimination of 1-bromo-2-phenylpropane[64]	1·48–1·49
(4) Hydration of ethyl vinyl ether[76]	1·46
(5) Ionisation of acetone[77]	1·10
(6) Ionisation of acetophenone[77]	1·37
(7) Hydrolysis of pyridine-diphenylborane[78]	1·38
(8) Elimination of 2,2-diphenylethyl benzene sulphonate[79]	1·47–1·50
(9) Ionisation of 2-nitropropane[74]	1·42
(10) Oxidation of 1-phenyl-2,2,2-trifluoroethanol[74]	1·45
(11) Oxidation of leuco crystal violet[74]	1·31
(12) Ionisation of 2-carbethoxycyclopentanone[73]	1·32–1·72

substrate structure the reaction can be sterically hindered the importance of the repulsive energy will be enhanced. At short interatomic distances the repulsive energy between atoms rises very rapidly as the distance decreases so that the potential energy barrier will be both narrow and high. These are exactly the conditions where significant tunnelling contributions can be expected and was first demonstrated by Lewis and Funderburk[1] in reactions of pyridine bases with 2-nitropropane. The values of k_H/k_D are about 10 for pyridine and various substituted pyridines as long as one of the hydrogen atoms adjacent to the nitrogen atom remains unsubstituted, but for 2,6,dimethyl- and 2,4,6-trimethyl pyridine the value is as high as 24, well outside the classical limits. The corresponding k_H/k_T is close to 80.[74]

The dimensions of the energy barriers may be obtained by applying Bell's equations[58,60] for tunnelling through symmetrical parabolic barriers and much of the data has been brought together in Caldin's review.[53] Despite the uncertainties involved in such a treatment two major factors, the effect of steric hindrance, and the importance of the solvent, are clearly recognisable (Table 9.12). The value of the barrier width is very small for the sterically hindered reaction between 2-nitropropane and 2,4,6-trimethylpyridine and only slightly higher than for reaction 8 which is an example of a hydride transfer where a narrow barrier is expected as an electron

TABLE 9.12

Energy barriers in hydrogen transfer reactions[53]

Reaction	Solvent	$2a$	E^H	E^D	E^T	C_t	ν_t	E^H_{obs}/E^H
(1) 2-CCP + F$^-$	D$_2$O	1·17	18·0$_1$	18·0$_7$	17·8	104	1106	0·81
(2) Acetone + OH$^-$	H$_2$O	1·26	13·6	14·7		68	894	0·91
(3) o-MAP + OH$^-$	H$_2$O	1·27	14·1		15·5	70	908	0·84
(4) Me$_2$CHNO$_2$ + B	t-BuOH—H$_2$O	1·14	16·3	17·6		100	965	0·88
(5) CH$_2$BrCMePhH + OEt$^-$	EtOH	1·59	22·1	23·0	23·4	70	908	0·95
(6) TNT anion + HF	EtOH	1·48	11·7			43	717	0·95
(7) 4-NBC + OEt$^-$	EtOH—H$_2$O	1·63	10·3	11·3		31	600	0·89
(8) (p-Me$_2$NC$_6$H$_4$)$_3$CH + CA	MeCN	0·97				52	1150	0·72

E^H, E^D, E^T = heights calculated for energy barriers for H, D and T transfer in kcal mol^{-1}; $2a$ = width of parabolic energy barrier at base in Å; C_t = curvature of parabola at apex $(2E^H/a^2)$ in kcal mol^{-1} Å^{-2}; ν_t = frequency corresponding to barrier dimensions; 2CCP = 2-carbethoxycyclopentanone; o-MAP = ortho methyl acetophenone; B = 2,4,6-trimethylpyridine; TNT = 2,4,6-trinitrotoluene; 4NBC = 4-nitrobenzyl cyanide; CA = Chloranil.

deficient atom can approach without the electron repulsion characteristic of nucleophilic substitution.

For reactions in alcoholic solutions the barrier widths are considerably higher than is the case for reactions in aqueous media. The difference also appears in the curvature and could be a result of solvent size or more probably of greater participation of the water in the process of proton transfer. The difference in barrier height $E^D - E^H$ is close to the limit of 1·15 kcal mol^{-1} except for the fluoride catalysed ionisation of 2-carbethoxycyclopentanone. This difference in behaviour could possibly be related to the strong hydrogen bonds formed by fluorine.

9.5. SOLVENT REORGANISATION

One further contribution to the primary hydrogen isotope effect not accounted for by the zero point energy differences or tunnelling considerations stems from the fact that during the process of forming the transition state the reorientation of solvent molecules cannot keep pace with the transfer of the proton.[32,6] The dielectric relaxation time for H_2O is in the region of 10^{-11} s which is probably greater than the time required for a proton transfer between two suitably orientated activated molecules, estimated as being between $10^{-12}-10^{-13}$ s. Since the deuterium and tritium transfer reactions are much slower the departure from equilibrium will be much less for these two isotopes. If this interpretation holds it would mean that E_{obs}^H would be higher than it would otherwise be and the entropy of activation enhanced by virtue of the fact that the transition state is less ordered than it would be at equilibrium. This could then lead to, instead of the expected $E_{obs}^D - E_{obs}^H > E_{obs}^T - E_{obs}^D$ and $A_{obs}^H/A_{obs}^D < A_{obs}^D/A_{obs}^T$, the finding $E_{obs}^D - E_{obs}^H \simeq E_{obs}^T - E_{obs}^D$ and $A_{obs}^H/A_{obs}^D > A_{obs}^D/A_{obs}^T$ as was observed for the D_2O and CH_2ClCOO^- catalysed ionisation of 2-carbethoxycyclopentanone.[73]

The importance of solvent reorganisation could also be responsible for the fact that in at least three reactions, involving 2-carbethoxy-cyclopentanone,[73] diethyl ketone[80] and t-butylmalononitrile[43] the solvent isotope effect depends on the nature of the hydrogen isotope being transferred. Thus for the latter $k_T(H_2O)/k_T(D_2O) = 3\cdot48$ and $k_H(H_2O)/k_H(D_2O) = 3\cdot70$. The size of the effect is small and it could be argued that a more convincing case could be made by working in a medium in which the intermolecular forces are considerably stronger. Recent data[81] both for the energy-volume coefficient and cohesive energy density of the binary liquid mixture dimethyl sulphoxide–water suggest that this is such a medium, the intermolecular forces being even higher than in the acetone–water and pyridine–water systems. The energy-volume coefficient like the excess thermodynamic functions of mixing passes through a maximum at $0\cdot3-0\cdot4$ mole fraction dimethyl sulphoxide where the intercomponent interactions are thought to be at a maximum; other work[82] consistent with this finding indicates a minimum in molecular mobility at $\sim0\cdot35$ mole fraction dimethyl sulphoxide.

Recent results[6] (Table 9.13) for the ionisation of phenylmethyl-acetophenone in dimethyl sulphoxide–water mixtures containing base are consistent with the above interpretation. The activation energy difference, which by comparison with similar work in aqueous conditions, is somewhat lower than expected, passes through a maximum in the region of 0·4 mole fraction dimethyl sulphoxide, corresponding to an H_- of 16·5 and a situation in which the difference in basicity between proton donor and acceptor is close to zero. The A_{obs}^H/A_{obs}^T values are much higher than allowed by transition state theory and if we assume that tunnelling becomes more important as the proton becomes more symmetric we see that the effect of tunnelling acts in opposition to the solvent reorganisation contributions and makes a correct assessment of the former's importance more difficult.

TABLE 9.13

Activation energy differences and pre-exponential ratios in the ionisation of (d)-phenylmethylacetophenone in dimethyl sulphoxide–water mixtures containing base[6]

Mole fraction dimethyl sulphoxide	Activation energy difference $E_{obs}^T - E_{obs}^H$ (kcal mol^{-1})	Pre-exponential ratios $\log_{10} (A_{obs}^H/A_{obs}^T)$
16·87	0·66	0·70
27·79	1·09	0·43
36·8	1·46	0·20
43·3	1·85	0·05
49·19	0·76	0·65
51·56	0·50	0·91

Finally mention should be made of the fact that dielectric relaxation studies[83] have shown that small molecules such as chlorobenzene have reorientation relaxation times in the liquid state in the range 10^{-10} to 6×10^{-13} s. On cooling this increases but crystallisation usually occurs before the relaxation time exceeds $\sim 10^{-10}$ s. However, by dissolving molecules in a solvent that can be supercooled (e.g. p-terphenyl) the reorientation times may occur at rates $10^8 - 10^{11}$ slower than in normal low viscosity solvents.

REFERENCES

1. Lewis, E. S. & Funderburk, L. H. (1967). *J. Amer. Chem. Soc.* **89**, 2322.
2. Bell, R. P. & Goodall, D. M. (1966). *Proc. Roy. Soc. Ser. A* **294**, 273.
3. Bordwell, F. G. & Boyle, W. J. Jr. (1971). *J. Amer. Chem. Soc.* **93**, 512.
4. Streitwieser, A. Jr. & Van Sickle, D. E. (1962). *J. Amer. Chem. Soc.* **84**, 254.
5. Bell, R. P. & Crooks, J. E. (1965). *Proc. Roy. Soc. Ser. A* **286**, 285.
6. Earls, D. W., Jones, J. R. & Rumney, T. G. (1972). *J. Chem. Soc. (Faraday Trans. 1)* **68**, 925.
7. Streitwieser, A. Jr. & Mares, F. (1968). *J. Amer. Chem. Soc.* **90**, 644.
8. Pocker, Y. & Exner, J. H. (1968). *J. Amer. Chem. Soc.* **90**, 6764.
9. Wiberg, K. B. (1955). *Chem. Rev.* **55**, 713.

10. Bell, R. P. (1959). *The Proton in Chemistry*, Chapter 11. Cornell University Press, Ithaca, N.Y.
11. Melander, L. (1960). *Isotope Effects on Reaction Rates.* The Ronald Press Co., New York.
12. Westheimer, F. H. (1961). *Chem. Rev.* 61, 265.
13. Saunders, W. H. Jr. (1966). *Survey. Progr. Chem.* (Scott, A. F. ed.) 3, 109.
14. Weston, R. E. Jr. (1967). *Science* 158, 332.
15. Wolfsberg, M. (1969). *Annu. Rev. Phys. Chem.* 20, 449.
16. Hook, V. (1971). *Isotope Effects in Chemical Reactions*, Chapter 1. (Collins, C. J. & Bowman, N. S. eds.) Van Nostrand, New York.
17. More O'Ferrall, R. A. & Kouba, J. (1967). *J. Chem. Soc. (B)* 985.
18. Bigeleisen, J. (1949). *Science* 110, 14.
19. Pitzer, K. S. (1953). *Quantum Chemistry*, p. 29. Prentice-Hall, New York.
20. Pitzer, K. S. (1953). *Quantum Chemistry*, p. 275. Prentice-Hall, New York.
21. Swain, C. G., Stivers, E. C., Reuwer, J. T. Jr. & Schaad, L. J. (1958). *J. Amer. Chem. Soc.* 80, 5885.
22. Bigeleisen, J. & Goeppert-Mayer, M. (1947). *J. Chem. Phys.* 15, 261.
23. Dole, M. (1954). *Introduction to Statistical Thermodynamics*, p. 240. Prentice-Hall, New York.
24. Bigeleisen, J. & Ishida, T. (1968). *J. Chem. Phys.* 48, 1311.
25. Schachtschneider, J. H. & Snyder, R. G. (1963). *Spectrochim. Acta* 19, 117.
26. Wolfsberg, M. & Stern, M. J. (1964). *Pure Appl. Chem.* 8, 225.
27. Stern, M. J. & Wolfsberg, M. (1966). *J. Chem. Phys.* 45, 4105.
28. Monse, E. U., Spindel, W. & Stern, M. (1969). *Isotope Effects in Chemical Processes* (Adv. in Chem. Series) 89, 148.
29. Vogel, P. C. & Stern, M. J. (1971). *J. Chem. Phys.* 54, 779.
30. Stern, M. & Vogel, P. C. (1971). *J. Amer. Chem. Soc.* 93, 4664.
31. Bigeleisen, J. (1962). *Tritium in the Physical and Biological Sciences*, *I.A.E.A., Vienna* 1, 161.
32. Bell, R. P. (1965). *Discuss. Faraday Soc.* 39, 16.
33. Willi, A. V. & Wolfsberg, M. (1964). *Chemy Ind. (London)* 2097.
34. Saunders, W. H. Jr. (1966). *Chemy Ind. (London)* 663.
35. Albery, W. J. (1967). *Trans. Faraday Soc.* 63, 200.
36. Bell, R. P. (1961). *Trans. Faraday Soc.* 57, 961.
37. Katz, A. M. & Saunders, W. H. Jr. (1969). *J. Amer. Chem. Soc.* 91, 4469.
38. More O'Ferrall, R. A. (1970). *J. Chem. Soc. (B)* 785.
39. Lewis, E. S. & Symons, M. C. R. (1958). *Quart. Rev. Chem. Soc.* 12, 230.
40. Bell, R. P., Sachs, W. H. & Tranter, R. L. (1971). *Trans. Faraday Soc.* 67, 1995.
41. Barnes, D. J. & Bell, R. P. (1970). *Proc. Roy. Soc. Ser. A* 318, 421.
42. Bell, R. P. & Cox, B. G. (1971). *J. Chem. Soc. (B)* 783.
43. Hibbert, F. & Long, F. A. (1971). *J. Amer. Chem. Soc.* 93, 2836.
44. Kresge, A. J., Sagatys, D. S. & Chen, H. L. (1968). *J. Amer. Chem. Soc.* 90, 4174.
45. Jones, J. R. (1972). *Progr. Phys. Org. Chem.* (Streitwieser, A. & Taft, R. W. eds.) 9, 241.
46. Cockerill, A. F. (1967). *J. Chem. Soc. (B)* 964.
47. Bell, R. P. & Cox, B. G. (1970). *J. Chem. Soc. (B)* 194.
48. Melander, L. & Bergman, N. A. (1971). *Acta Chem. Scand.* 25, 2264.
49. Conway, B. E. (1959). *Can. J. Chem.* 37, 178.
50. Conway, B. E. & Bockris, J. O'M. (1958). *J. Chem. Phys.* 28, 354.
51. Zimmermann, H. (1965). *Angew. Chem. Int. Ed. Engl.* 4, 40.
52. Löwdin, P. O. (1963). *Rev. Mod. Phys.* 35, 724.

53. Caldin, E. F. (1969). *Chem. Rev.* **69**, 135.
54. Wigner, E. P. (1932). *Z. Phyzik. Chem.* **19B**, 903.
55. Eckart, C. (1930). *Phys. Rev.* **35**, 1303.
56. Johnston, H. S. & Rapp, D. (1961). *J. Amer. Chem. Soc.* **83**, 1.
57. Mortensen, E. M. & Pitzer, K. S. (1962). *The Transition State*, p. 57. Special publication no. 16, The Chemical Society, London.
58. Bell, R. P. (1935). *Proc. Roy. Soc. Ser. A* **148**, 241.
59. Pauling, L. & Wilson, E. B. (1935). *Introduction to Quantum Mechanics*, p. 198. McGraw-Hill, New York.
60. Bell, R. P. (1959). *Trans. Faraday Soc.* **54**, 1.
61. Hulett, J. R. (1959). *Proc. Roy. Soc. Ser. A* **251**, 274.
62. Truhlar, D. G. & Kuppermann, A. (1971). *J. Amer. Chem. Soc.* **93**, 1840.
63. Bell, R. P., Fendley, J. A. & Hulett, J. R. (1956). *Proc. Roy. Soc. Ser. A* **235**, 453.
64. Shiner, V. J. & Martin, B. (1964). *Pure Appl. Chem.* **8**, 371.
65. Hulett, J. R. (1964). *Quart. Rev. Chem. Soc.* **18**, 227.
66. Caldin, E. F. (1959). *J. Chem. Soc.* 3345.
67. Hills, G. J. (1965). *Discuss. Faraday Soc.* **39**, 59.
68. Hulett, J. R. (1965). *J. Chem. Soc.* 1166.
69. Jones, J. R. & Subba Rao, S. C. (1967). *Trans. Faraday Soc.* **63**, 120.
70. Caldin, E. F. & Kasparian, M. (1965). *Discuss. Faraday Soc.* **39**, 25.
71. Caldin, E. F. & Tomalin, G. (1968). *Trans. Faraday Soc.* **64**, 2814.
72. Jones, J. R. (1969). *Trans. Faraday Soc.* **61**, 95.
73. Jones, J. R. (1969). *Trans. Faraday Soc.* **65**, 2430.
74. Lewis, E. S. & Robinson, J. K. (1968). *J. Amer. Chem. Soc.* **90**, 4337.
75. Wilzbach, K. E. & Kaplan, L. (1955). *J. Amer. Chem. Soc.* **77**, 1297.
76. Kreevoy, M. M. & Eliason, R. (1968). *J. Phys. Chem.* **72**, 1313.
77. Jones, J. R. (1969). *Trans. Faraday Soc.* **65**, 2138.
78. Lewis, E. S. & Grinstein, R. H. (1962). *J. Amer. Chem. Soc.* **84**, 1158.
79. Willi, A. V. (1966). *J. Phys. Chem.* **70**, 2705.
80. Calmon, J. P., Calmon, M. & Gold, V. (1969). *J. Chem. Soc. (B)* 659.
81. Macdonald, D. D. & Hyne, J. B. (1971). *Can. J. Chem.* **49**, 611.
82. Packer, K. J. & Tomlinson, D. J. (1971). *Trans. Faraday Soc.* **67**, 1302.
83. Williams, G. & Hains, P. J. (1971). *Chem. Phys. Lett.* **10**, 585.

10. Solvent Isotope Effects

Kinetic behaviour in solution is not fully understood at present as detailed information on solvent structure and the extent of inter-component interaction is not available. Under such circumstances minor modifications to the solvent such as the replacement of light by heavy water may help to provide some of the missing information. Although many of the physical properties of H_2O and D_2O are very similar those like melting point and temperature of maximum density which are most sensitive to structural changes are considerably different (Table 10.1) and are in line with the commonly held view that the structure of D_2O is more ordered than that of

TABLE 10.1

Some physical properties of H_2O and D_2O[1]

Property	Unit	H_2O	D_2O
Melting point	°C	0·00	3·81
Temp. of maximum density	°C	3·98	11·23
Dielectric constant at 25°C	—	78·39	78·06
Viscosity at 25°C	centipoise	0·8903	1·107
Density at 25°C	g/cm^3	0·99701	1·1044

H_2O. The much higher viscosity of D_2O only becomes important when reaction velocities are very fast and diffusion controlled.

The discovery of a second isotope of hydrogen by Urey[2] in 1932 prompted a good deal of research into deuterium chemistry. Early measurements of acidity constants in H_2O–D_2O mixtures by La Mer,[3] Gross,[4] and Butler[5] showed that the acidities changed much less at low concentrations of deuterium than at high concentrations. On the basis of these observations Gross and Butler formulated a quantitative explanation which, with the passage of time became known as the Gross–Butler theory. The corresponding variation in reaction rates was not so straightforward. In particular for reactions in which a pre-equilibrium mechanism was operative theory was well obeyed but for those in which a rate-determining proton transfer occurred it seemed to fail. It was subsequently suggested that the form of the dependence of isotope effect on solvent deuterium content could be used as a criterion of reaction mechanism—a reaction conforming to theory was assigned a pre-equilibrium proton transfer mechanism whereas if the isotope effect deviated from theory and especially if it showed a linear dependence on solvent deuterium content a rate-determining proton transfer mechanism was assigned to it. There then followed a long period of inactivity before Purlee[6] undertook a re-examination of the theory. This was soon followed by important contributions from Gold, Kreevoy, Kresge, Long, Swain and their co-workers. Most of the work referred to acid catalysed reactions and only in the last few years has theory been applied to various base catalysed reactions of carbon acids.

Addition of a solute to either H_2O or D_2O even in low concentrations results in the formation of new bonds and the breakage of old ones. The solvent isotope effect, be it either for an equilibrium or kinetic process, is caused by differences in solute–solvent interactions and in particular by changes in the frequencies and zero-point energies of hydrogen (deuterium) bonded solute and solvent molecules. For these solvents two fairly detailed physical models have been proposed. In Bunton and Shiner's[7] treatment emphasis is placed on changes in internal stretching frequencies of bonds to hydrogen in the water molecules during the activation process, whilst Swain and co-workers[8,9] favour the librational (hindered external rotational) degrees of freedom of the water molecules as the major factor contributing to the solvent isotope effect.

In practical terms two factors are now thought to be responsible for the variation of rate with changing deuterium content of the solvent. Firstly there is the exchange effect which represents the fact that hydrogen and deuterium are not randomly distributed between the various species present in a solution containing both isotopes. Secondly there is a transfer or medium effect which arises from changes in solvation in going from one solvent to another. Although this contribution is usually less than that due to exchange it can not be neglected especially in circumstances where a considerable charge difference between reactants and transition state exists.

10.1. FRACTIONATION FACTORS

The exchange equilibrium between a substrate SH containing a labile hydrogen atom and the deuterium of the solvent,

$$SH + \tfrac{1}{2}D_2O \rightleftharpoons SD + \tfrac{1}{2}H_2O \tag{10.1}$$

can be characterised by a fractionation factor ϕ where

$$\phi = \frac{[SD]}{[SH]} \times \frac{[\frac{1}{2}H_2O]}{[\frac{1}{2}D_2O]} \tag{10.2}$$

$$= \frac{(D/H)_{SL}}{(D/H)_{L_2O}} = \frac{F_{SL}}{1 - F_{SL}} \cdot \frac{1-n}{n} \tag{10.3}$$

L is a general hydrogen nucleus, F_{SL} the fractional abundance of deuterium in the substrate and n that in water.

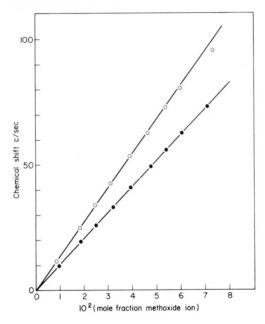

Fig. 10.1. The chemical shift of the OH group, relative to that of pure methanol, plotted against the mole fraction of added base for methanolic solutions of sodium methoxide.[12] o, deuterium mole fraction 0·903; •, deuterium mole fraction zero.

Nuclear magnetic resonance studies on isotopically mixed solutions enable fractionation factors to be obtained directly.[10,11] In principle one observes the chemical shifts in the n.m.r. absorption of the hydroxylic protons (relative to some standard) as a function of solute concentration, firstly, in an entirely light solvent and secondly in a partially deuteriated solvent. Figure 10.1 shows the results obtained by More O'Ferrall[12] for solutions containing zero and 90·3 mole % CH_3OD. For the same concentration of base the chemical shift is increased by the presence of CH_3OD indicating that (by comparison with CH_3OH) CH_3OD molecules prefer a site in the bulk of the solvent to one hydrogen bonded to a methoxide ion.

If only a single set of m equivalent hydrogens associated with each pair of solute ions differs in isotopic composition from that of the solvent it can be shown that the fractionation factor is related to the limiting slopes S_H, S_n by

$$(S_n - \delta_0)/(S_H - \delta_0) = (1 - n + n\phi_{OMe^-})^{-1} \tag{10.4}$$

δ_0 contains contributions to the chemical shift from exchangeable hydrogens not subject to fractionation and its value can be estimated by assuming that in NaOMe fractionation is confined to the solvation shell of the methoxide ion and that contributions to δ_0 arise only from the sodium ion. The fractionation factor ϕ_{OMe^-} (0·76) compares well with a more recently obtained value[13] of 0·74.

Since CH_3O^- contains no exchangeable protons the fractionation factor must stem from some specific interaction between the methoxide ion and the solvent with the creation of modified hydroxylic positions for which the deuterium abundance differs from that in the bulk solvent. The equilibrium between solvent and solute molecules can be expressed in terms of

$$CH_3O^-(CH_3OD)_m + mCH_3OH \rightleftharpoons CH_3O^-(CH_3OH)_m + mCH_3OD \tag{10.5}$$

A number of results suggest that m has a value of 3 and since the methoxide ion has three lone pairs available for hydrogen bonding this seems very reasonable.

For the aqueous hydrogen ion[10,11] the fractionation factor is denoted by l and refers to the equilibrium

$$\tfrac{1}{3}H_3O^+ + \tfrac{1}{2}D_2O \rightleftharpoons \tfrac{1}{3}D_3O^+ + \tfrac{1}{2}H_2O \tag{10.6}$$

Its value is 0·69 ± 0·01 which is not very different to the fractionation factor l_M (0·63) of the solvated hydrogen ion in methanol which was recently determined by Gold and Grist.[13]

The fractionation factor for the aqueous hydroxide ion is an important parameter in the interpretation of the rates of base catalysed reactions. Heinzinger and Weston[14] determined a value of 0·47 for ϕ_{OH^-} based on measurements of the isotopic composition of water vapour in equilibrium with concentrated aqueous solutions of potassium and sodium hydroxides. It was assumed that fractionation was restricted to a single site in the hydroxide ion.

The fractionation factor ϕ_{OH^-} may also be obtained[15] from a study of the solvent isotope effect on the ionic product of water. If the autoprotolysis can be written as

$$2H_2O \rightleftharpoons H_3O^+ + OH^- \tag{10.7}$$

the data of Gold and Lowe[16,17] give $\phi_{OH^-} = 0.42$. Gold and Grist[18] have recently suggested that the difference between the two values is too large to be accounted for by experimental error and can possibly be ascribed to the fact that Eqn (10.7) is an oversimplification in so far as the formulation of the hydroxide ion in solution is concerned—a good deal of evidence points to a trihydrated species $OH^-(H_2O)_3$ (see Chapter 6). From n.m.r. studies the chemical shift of the hydroxide ion is smaller than for the aqueous hydrogen ion but is in the same downfield direction implying strong deshielding. For the hydroxide ion this seems to be anomalous since a proton in OH^- should be more shielded than a proton in H_2O. Gold and Grist rationalise the result by assuming that the hydroxide ion shift is made up of opposing contributions from the single proton of the OH^- moiety (H_a) and from 3 protons in hydrogen bonds of attached water molecules (H_b)

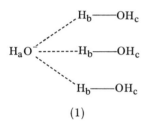

(1)

The outer hydrogen atoms of the solvating water molecules (H_c) are assumed to form part of the normal water structure and have a fractionation factor of unity. ϕ_b is found to lie in the range 0·65–0·70 and ϕ_a between 1·2 and 1·5.

Several other methods have been used to measure fractionation factors. In addition to the use of cells with and without transfer[19] it is sometimes possible to measure the D/H ratio in the products as a function of n.

10.2. THEORY OF SOLVENT ISOTOPE EFFECTS[15,20,21]

Let us initially consider the dissociation of an acid, HA in ordinary water and see in what way the dissociation constant varies as the solvent is changed in going from H_2O to D_2O. If we neglect activity coefficients the acidity constant K_{HA} in water is given by

$$K_{HA} = \frac{[A^-][H_3O^+]}{[HA][H_2O]} \tag{10.8}$$

In an H_2O–D_2O mixture of deuterium atom fraction n the equilibrium can be described by

$$LA + L_2O \rightleftharpoons A^- + L_3O^+ \tag{10.9}$$

where $L_3O^+ = H_3O^+ + D_3O^+ + DH_2O^+ + D_2HO^+$ and $L_2O = H_2O + D_2O + HOD$.

The acidity constant

$$K_n = \frac{[A^-][L_3O^+]}{[LA][L_2O]} \tag{10.10}$$

so that

$$\frac{K_{HA}}{K_n} = \frac{[H_3O^+]}{[L_3O^+]} \times \frac{[LA]}{[HA]} \times \frac{[L_2O]}{[H_2O]} \tag{10.11}$$

The concentrations of the various isotopic species can be obtained if we assume that the rule of the geometric mean[22] is obeyed. For the equilibrium

$$H_2O + D_2O \rightleftharpoons 2HOD \tag{10.12}$$

the equilibrium constant is given by a ratio of symmetry numbers

$$K = \frac{x_{HOD}^2}{x_{H_2O}x_{D_2O}} = \frac{\sigma_{H_2O}\sigma_{D_2O}}{\sigma_{HOD}^2} = \frac{2 \times 2}{1}$$

where x denotes mole fraction. Similarly for the equilibria

$$\tfrac{2}{3}H_3O^+ + \tfrac{1}{3}D_3O^+ \rightleftharpoons H_2DO^+ \tag{10.14}$$

$$\tfrac{1}{3}H_3O^+ + \tfrac{2}{3}D_3O^+ \rightleftharpoons HD_2O^+ \tag{10.15}$$

we have

$$K' = \sigma_{H_3O^+}^{2/3}\sigma_{D_3O^+}^{1/3}/\sigma_{H_2DO^+} = 3 \tag{10.16}$$

and

$$K'' = \sigma_{H_3O^+}^{1/3}\sigma_{D_3O^+}^{2/3}/\sigma_{HD_2O^+} = 3 \tag{10.17}$$

It then follows that

$$[HOD] = 2[H_2O]^{1/2}[D_2O]^{1/2} \tag{10.18}$$

$$[H_2DO^+] = 3[H_3O^+]^{2/3}[D_3O^+]^{1/3} \tag{10.19}$$

$$[HD_2O^+] = 3[H_3O^+]^{1/3}[D_3O^+]^{2/3} \tag{10.20}$$

The distribution of hydrogen and deuterium among isotopically mixed species is given by a Poisson distribution so that for a fractional abundance F of a species XD_pH_{m-p} we have

$$\frac{[XD_pH_{m-p}]}{[XL_m]} = \frac{[XD_pH_{m-p}]}{\sum_{p=0}^{m}[XD_pH_{m-p}]} = F^p(1-F)^{m-p}\frac{m!}{p!(m-p)!} \tag{10.21}$$

For the water species (for which $F = n$)

$$[H_2O] = (1 - n)^2 \qquad\qquad (10.22)$$

$$[HOD] = 2n(1 - n) \qquad\qquad (10.23)$$

$$[D_2O] = n^2 \qquad\qquad (10.24)$$

and for the hydrogen ions

$$[H_3O^+] = (1 - F_{L_3O^+})^3 [L_3O^+] \qquad\qquad (10.25)$$

$$[H_2DO^+] = 3F_{L_3O^+}(1 - F_{L_3O^+})^2 [L_3O^+] \qquad\qquad (10.26)$$

$$[HD_2O^+] = 3F_{L_3O^+}^2(1 - F_{L_3O^+})[L_3O^+] \qquad\qquad (10.27)$$

$$[D_3O^+] = F_{L_3O^+}^3[L_3O^+] \qquad\qquad (10.28)$$

If the acid contains only a single hydrogen atom the fractionation factor is given by

$$\phi_{LA} = \frac{[DA](1 - n)}{[HA]n} \qquad\qquad (10.29)$$

By setting $[LA] = [HA] + [DA]$, Eqn (10.29) can be rearranged to give

$$\frac{[LA]}{[HA]} = \frac{1 - n + n\phi_{LA}}{1 - n} \qquad\qquad (10.30)$$

For the lyonium ion the fractionation factor l is given by

$$l = \frac{F_{L_3O^+}(1 - n)}{(1 - F_{L_3O^+})n} \qquad\qquad (10.31)$$

and can be rearranged to give

$$1 - F_{L_3O^+} = \frac{1 - n}{1 - n + nl} \qquad\qquad (10.32)$$

Equation (10.11) now takes the form

$$\frac{K_{HA}}{K_n} = \left(\frac{1 - n}{1 - n + nl}\right)^3 \left(\frac{1 - n + n\phi_{LA}}{1 - n}\right)\left(\frac{1}{(1 - n)^2}\right) \qquad\qquad (10.33)$$

since $[L_2O] = 1$ for a dilute solution.
    Equation (10.33) reduces to

$$\frac{K_{HA}}{K_n} = \frac{1 - n + n\phi_{LA}}{(1 - n + nl)^3} \qquad\qquad (10.34)$$

As $n \to 1$ $K_n = K_{DA}$ and Eqn (10.34) leads to

$$\frac{K_{HA}}{K_{DA}} = \phi_{LA}/l^3 \tag{10.35}$$

Substitution of this result in Eqn (10.34) yields

$$\frac{K_{HA}}{K_n} = \frac{1 - n + nl^3 K_{HA}/K_{DA}}{(1 - n + nl)^3} \tag{10.36}$$

the usual Gross–Butler equation. This treatment, which follows on closely that given by Gold,[15] assumed not only that the aqueous hydronium ion has the formula H_3O^+ (for which there is a good deal of evidence) but also that both K_H and K_D are independent of the medium and that the free energy of transfer is negligible.

Equation (10.34) is made up of two terms of the form $(1 - n + n\phi)$, the numerator representing the reactants and the denominator the products. Each term is raised to a power which corresponds to the number of equivalent hydrogens or deuteriums in the relevant species. For any equilibrium therefore we can write

$$\frac{K_H}{K_n} = \frac{\overset{\text{Reactants}}{\prod} (1 - n + n\phi)^r}{\underset{\text{Products}}{\prod} (1 - n + n\phi)^p} \tag{10.37}$$

r and p referring to reactants and products respectively. The solvent isotope effect thus depends on the state of solvation of the hydrogen ion, the fractionation factor of this ion and K_H/K_D as well as the deuterium atom fraction of the solvent.

The theory of equilibrium solvent isotope effects can be applied to kinetic problems with the minimum of modification as the transition state is in equilibrium with the reactants. In an acid catalysed reaction with a pre-equilibrium proton transfer to substrate followed by unimolecular decomposition of the substrate conjugate acid (A-1 mechanism),

$$H_3O^+ + S \rightleftharpoons HS^+ + H_2O$$

$$HS^+ \to \text{Products} \tag{10.38}$$

the equilibrium constant between reactants and transition state, neglecting activity coefficients, is given by

$$K_H = \frac{[HS^+] [H_2O]}{[H_3O^+] [S]} \tag{10.39}$$

In an H_2O-D_2O mixture a similar reaction occurs,

$$L_3O^+ + S \rightleftharpoons LS^+ + L_2O$$
$$LS^+ \rightarrow Products \tag{10.40}$$

and the equilibrium constant in this case is

$$K_n = \frac{[LS^+][L_2O]}{[L_3O^+][S]} \tag{10.41}$$

The rate constants for both reactions are given by

$$k_H = \kappa_H \frac{kT}{h} K_H \tag{10.42}$$

$$k_n = \kappa_n \frac{kT}{h} K_n \tag{10.43}$$

so that the ratio of rate constants is equal to the ratio of the equilibrium constants,

$$\frac{k_n}{k_H} = \frac{K_n}{K_H} \tag{10.44}$$

It therefore follows that

$$\frac{k_n}{k_H} = \frac{(1 - n + n\phi_{HS^+})}{(1 - n + nl)^3} \tag{10.45}$$

As

$$n \rightarrow 1, \quad k_n \rightarrow k_D \quad and \quad \frac{k_D}{k_H} = \frac{\phi_{HS^+}}{l^3} \tag{10.46}$$

so that

$$\frac{k_n}{k_H} = \frac{(1 - n + nl^3 k_D/k_H)}{(1 - n + nl)^3} \tag{10.47}$$

This last equation is of the same form as Eqn (10.36).

At this stage it seems appropriate to discuss the autoprotolysis of water. Not only does such a study provide information on the fractionation factor of the hydroxide ion in aqueous solution and is therefore of much relevance to reaction kinetics but it also makes possible, at least in theory, a choice between various possible structures.

If the equilibrium represented by Eqn (10.7) is correct the ratio of the ionic products is given by

$$\frac{(K_W)_H}{(K_W)_n} = \frac{1}{(1 - n + nl)^3 (1 - n + n\phi_{OH^-})} \tag{10.48}$$

For the isotopically pure solvents

$$\frac{(K_W)_H}{(K_W)_D} = \frac{1}{l^3 \phi_{OH^-}} \tag{10.49}$$

so that

$$\frac{(K_W)_H}{(K_W)_n} = \frac{1}{(1 - n + nl)^3 [(1 - n + n(K_W)_D/(K_W)_H l^3)]} \tag{10.50}$$

The results of Gold and Lowe[17] for the variation of K_W as a function of the deuterium content of the medium can be expressed by

$$\Delta pK = 0.7282n + 0.0512n^2 + 0.0826n^3 \tag{10.51}$$

None of the experimental points deviate by more than 0.010 from this equation. Equation (10.50) also represents the results fairly well but this is not an unique solution. If for example the hydronium and hydroxide ion can be represented by H^+ and OH^- we have

$$\frac{(K_W)_H}{(K_W)_n} = \frac{1}{(1 - n + nl')(1 - n + n\phi_{OH^-})} \tag{10.52}$$

where

$$l' = \frac{[D^+]}{[H^+]} \frac{1 - n}{n};$$

it has possible values of $0.328_5 (l^3)$ or $0.371(K_D/K_H)^{1/2}$.
For H_2O and D_2O

$$\frac{(K_W)_H}{(K_W)_D} = \frac{1}{l' \phi_{OH^-}} \tag{10.53}$$

so that

$$\frac{(K_W)_H}{(K_W)_n} = \frac{1}{(1 - n + nl')(1 - n + n(K_W)_D/(K_W)_H l')} \tag{10.54}$$

Alternatively, if the hydroxide ion can be represented by the formula $OH^-(H_2O)_3$ the chemical equation for the autoprotolysis becomes

$$5H_2O \rightleftharpoons OH^-(H_2O)_3 + H_3O^+ \tag{10.55}$$

and the relevant equation now is

$$\frac{(K_W)_H}{(K_W)_n} = \frac{1}{(1 - n + nl)^3 (1 - n + n\phi_a)(1 - n + n\phi_b)^3} \tag{10.56}$$

where ϕ_a is the fractionation factor for the hydrogen of the hydroxide ion and ϕ_b refers to the hydrogen of the water molecule that is hydrogen bonded to it. The solvent isotope effect in this case is

$$\frac{(K_W)_H}{(K_W)_D} = \frac{1}{l^3 \phi_a \phi_b^3} \tag{10.57}$$

so that

$$\frac{(K_W)_H}{(K_W)_n} = \frac{1}{(1 - n + nl)^3 (1 - n + n\phi_b)^3 (1 - n + n(K_W)_D/(K_W)_H l^3 \phi_b^3)} \tag{10.58}$$

Further equations can also be obtained as when the hydronium ion is considered to be given by the formula $H_9O_4^+$.

From Fig. 10.2 it is clear that Eqn (10.50) represents the results much better than Eqn (10.54). In other words the monosolvated proton model is more satisfactory than that in which the solvation is unspecified. The introduction of a further constant in Eqn (10.58)

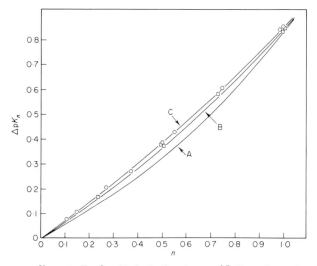

Fig. 10.2. Isotope effect ΔpK_n for H_2O–D_2O mixtures.[17] Experimental values □, ○; Curves (calc with $\Delta pK = 0.682$): A, Eqn (10.54) with $l' = 0.371$; B, Eqn (10.50) with $l = 0.69$; C, Eqn (10.52).

means that the predictions of the empirical equation can be reproduced to within 0·001 pK unit over the entire composition range. The value of ϕ_b chosen by Gold and Lowe was 0·92 but another lower value (0·70) gives an equally good fit to the data.[23]

Similarly this extra term has been used by Long and co-workers to stress the importance of the transfer contribution on going from one medium to another. It is pointed out that the fractionation factor ϕ_{HA} used here really refers to

$$HA^{H_2O} + \tfrac{1}{2}D_2O^{D_2O} \rightleftharpoons DA^{D_2O} + \tfrac{1}{2}H_2O^{H_2O} \quad \phi_{HA} \tag{10.59}$$

and a better approach would be to use Eqn (10.60):

$$HA^{H_2O} + \tfrac{1}{2}D_2O^{H_2O} \rightleftharpoons DA^{H_2O} + \tfrac{1}{2}H_2O^{H_2O} \quad \phi'_{HA} \tag{10.60}$$

ϕ'_{HA} is then a medium independent constant and is related to ϕ_{HA} via Eqn (10.61)

$$HA(\text{or } DA)^{D_2O} \rightleftharpoons HA(\text{or } DA)^{H_2O} \quad \gamma \tag{10.61}$$

$$\phi'_{HA} = \phi_{HA}\gamma \tag{10.62}$$

which clearly illustrates how both exchange and transfer effects contribute to changes in solvent. For intermediate solvent mixtures it is usually assumed that the free energy of transfer is linear in the atom fraction of deuterium so that the appropriate value of the degenerate activity is given by γ_{DA}^n.

Equation (10.52) now takes the form

$$\frac{(K_W)_H}{(K_W)_n} = \frac{1}{(1 - n + nl')(1 - n + n\phi_{OH^-})(\gamma_{H^+}\gamma_{OH^-})^{-n}} \tag{10.63}$$

$$= \frac{1}{(1 - n + nl')[1 - n + n(K_W)_D/(K_W)_H l' b^{-1}] b^{-1}} \tag{10.64}$$

where $b = \gamma_{H^+}\gamma_{OH^-}$. This equation fits the data of Gold and Lowe[17] very well. Similarly Eqn (10.48) becomes

$$\frac{(K_W)_H}{(K_W)_n} = \frac{1}{(1 - n + nl)^3(1 - n + n\phi_{OH^-}) b^{-n}} \tag{10.65}$$

where b now refers to the product $\gamma_{H_3O^+}\gamma_{OH^-}$. Walters and Long[24] find that with $b = 1·14$ and $\phi_{OH^-} = 0·45$ an excellent fit to the data is obtained. It is clear that a range of values for b and ϕ_{OH^-} could reproduce the observed $(K_W)_H/(K_W)_n$ ratio with the same accuracy. Only with the onset of further and still more accurate work will it become possible to decide amongst the various possibilities.

10.3. MODEL CALCULATIONS

At the time of writing no model calculations for solvent isotope effects in the base catalysed ionisation of carbon acids have been reported. There has, however, been one case[25] where model calculations of solvent deuterium isotope effects on acid catalysed reactions have been made and, in view of the importance of such a study and its relevance to the kind of reactions investigated here a brief outline of the procedure used seems to be in order.

Both primary and secondary isotope effects were calculated for the model proton transfer reaction

$$H_3O^+ + C{=}C \rightarrow [H_2O\text{-}\text{-}\text{-}H\text{-}\text{-}\text{-}C{=}C] \rightarrow H_2O + H{-}C{-}C^+ \qquad (10.66)$$

The substrate was a two atom "olefinic" fragment which gives a linear carbonium ion $H{-}C{-}C^+$ as product. The hydronium ion was represented by (2)

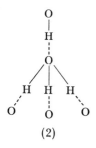

(2)

and the transition state by (3)

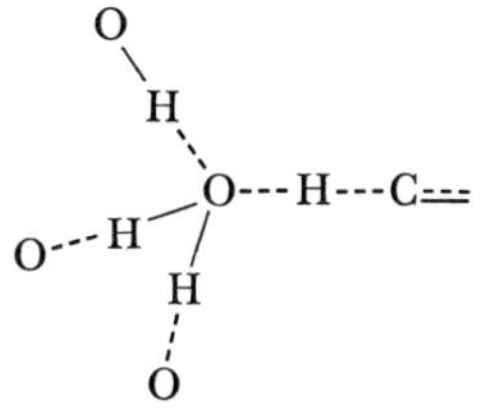

O
\
H
        O---H---C≡≡
O--H /
      H
      ⋮
      O

(3)

it being assumed that one of the H_3O^+ hydrogens is partially bonded to the substrate and that in other respects the geometry is intermediate between that of reactants and products. The water molecule (4) is tetrahedrally bonded to two oxygen atom fragments and two O–H groups.

(4)

The calculations are carried out by a method similar to that applied previously to primary isotope effects.[26] Vibrational frequencies and isotope effects are evaluated from force constants and geometries assigned to models of the reactants, products and transition state. The principal new feature of the calculations is that librational modes arising from hindered rotations of H_2O and H_3O^+ within the hydrogen-bonded water lattice have to be considered as these modes are known to contribute substantially to solvent isotope effects in H_2O and D_2O.

TABLE 10.2

Model calculations of solvent isotope effects[25]

z (Partial H---C bond order)	Primary isotope effect (k_H/k_D)	Secondary isotope effect $(k_{H_2O}^H/k_{D_2O}^H)$
0	1·0	1·0
0·125	3·1	0·946
0·25	4·7	0·864
0·375	6·3	0·788
0·50	6·1	0·733
0·625	4·4	0·681
0·75	2·8	0·634
0·875	1·75	0·566
1·0	0·68	0·470

Force constants for H_3O^+ were assigned to yield calculated frequencies which when combined with the frequencies for H_2O gave the experimentally determined value of 9·0 for the equilibrium constant for the reaction

$$2D_3O^+ + 3H_2O \rightleftharpoons 3D_2O + 2H_3O^+ \tag{10.67}$$

The results (Table 10.2) show that the solvent isotope effects decrease monotonically with the degree of proton transfer in the transition state and correlate strongly with the calculated primary isotope effects. The calculations also suggest that neglect of deviations from the rule of the mean and of transfer contributions associated with protonation by H_3O^+ do not seriously impair the simple treatment of solvent effects.

10.4. APPLICATION TO SOLVENT CATALYSED REACTIONS

Although there are many proton transfer reactions in which water acts both as solvent and catalyst there have been suprisingly few reported instances in which solvent isotope effects (Table 10.3) have been determined. The apparent dependence of k_{H_2O}/k_{D_2O} on the

TABLE 10.3

Solvent isotope effects k_{H_2O}/k_{D_2O} at $25°$

Carbon acid	$k_{H_2O}^H/k_{D_2O}^H$	$k_{H_2O}^T/k_{D_2O}^T$	Refs.
Malononitrile		3·67	23
t-Butylmalononitrile	3·70	3·48	23
2-Carbethoxycyclopentanone	2·23	1·85	27, 28
2-Acetylcyclohexanone	1·40		29
3-Methylacetylacetone	1·37		30

TABLE 10.4

Medium effects for various proton transfer reactions at $25°$

Carbon acid	Base	$k_B^{H_2O}/k_B^{D_2O}$	Refs.
t-Butylmalononitrile	Acetate	1·12	23
1,4-Dicyano-2-butene	Triethylamine	1·24	31
Acetone	Acetate	1·15	32
3-Methylacetylacetone	Acetate	1·25	30
Diethyl ketone	Pyridine	1·20	33
2-Acetylcyclohexanone	Acetate	1·20	29
2-Carbethoxycyclopentanone	Chloroacetate	1·32	27
Diethyl ketone	2,6-Lutidine	1·22	33

isotope being transferred has been commented upon previously (p. 181) in discussing solvent reorganisation contributions and will not be considered further. In all cases proton transfer is slower in D_2O than in H_2O in agreement with other findings that D_2O is slightly less basic than H_2O. Each isotope effect is made up of exchange and medium effects and the magnitude of the latter can be seen in Table 10.4 where the results of various base catalysed reactions in H_2O and D_2O (and under conditions where no exchange is possible) are summarised. In all cases but one the reactions are between 10 and 25% faster in H_2O than D_2O. The magnitude of this medium effect could well turn out to be characteristic of proton transfer reactions involving the formation of a highly polar transition state similar to an ion pair. Whether more accurate work will show it to be related to the degree of charge separation remains to be seen.

Recent contributions by Long and co-workers[2 3] have clearly shown how studies of solvent isotope effects in the ionisation of carbon acids can supplement information obtained by other means. The low primary hydrogen isotope effects and the high Brönsted β coefficient for base catalysis in the ionisation of both malononitrile and t-butylmalononitrile suggest a transition state in which the triton is almost completely transferred.

$$RCT + H_2O \rightleftharpoons \left[RC^- \text{---} T \text{--} \overset{+}{O} \overset{H}{\underset{H}{<}} \right] \rightleftharpoons RC^- + TH_2\overset{+}{O} \qquad (10.68)$$

The solvent isotope effect is given by

$$\frac{k_n}{k_H} = (1 - n + n\phi_2^{\ddagger})^2 (1 - n + n\phi_1^{\ddagger}) \frac{(\gamma_{RCT}\gamma_{H_2O})}{\gamma^{\ddagger}} \qquad (10.69)$$

where $\phi_1^{\ddagger}$ and $\phi_2^{\ddagger}$ are medium independent fractionation factors for the carbon acid and water protons in the transition state respectively. γ_{H_2O} is taken as unity and the degenerate activity coefficient of transfer (γ_{RCT}) for t-butylmalononitrile from solubility methods is $1\cdot04$. As the proton corresponding to ϕ_1 is prevented from fractionating in reactants and transition state the limiting isotope effect is given by

$$\frac{k_D}{k_H} = (\phi_2^{\ddagger})^2 \frac{1\cdot04}{\gamma^{\ddagger}} \qquad (10.70)$$

In an analogous manner to that adopted by Kresge[2 0] for proton transfer from the hydronium ion Long suggests that for proton transfer to water ϕ_2 is related to the degree of proton transfer in the transition state (β). Complete transfer implies that $\phi_2^{\ddagger} = l$ whereas the opposite $(\beta = 0)$ corresponds to $\phi_2^{\ddagger} = 1$. For an intermediate β, $\phi_2^{\ddagger} = l^{\beta}$. From studies of carboxylate anion catalysis the value of β is $0\cdot98$ so that $\phi_2^{\ddagger} = 0\cdot69^{0\cdot98} \simeq 0\cdot7$. Insertion of $\phi_2^{\ddagger} = 0\cdot7$ in Eqn (10.70) together with the measured isotope effect gives $\gamma^{\ddagger} = 1\cdot83$ so that the medium effect in the reaction accounts for almost half the isotope effect.

The overall solvent isotope effect (5.4) for t-butylmalononitrile, made up of a small primary isotope effect (1·46) and a large solvent isotope effect (3·7), suggests a useful generalisation for isotope effects in proton transfer reactions where the solvent water acts as the base catalyst. When the primary isotope effect is low because of a high degree of proton transfer the solvent isotope effect is likely to be large and the overall solvent effect will be quite large as in the example mentioned. However when the primary effect is small because of a reactant like transition state the solvent isotope effect will be low and so also will the overall solvent isotope effect.

An alternative explanation of the high medium effect would require the introduction of further water molecules with fractionation factors less than unity in the transition state. This could come about if proton transfer occurs through one or more solvent bridges. However the big difference in the medium effects for both acetate and water catalysis suggests that only for the latter can this mechanism be important. As the primary isotope effect for both water and acetate ion catalysis are the same the evidence seems to favour the more direct route. A study by Goodall and Long[34] on nitromethane favours a similar conclusion.

In principle it should be possible to obtain information about the participation of solvent bridges from a study of the dependence of rate on the deuterium composition of the solvent as the relevant equations contain a term for every proton involved in a reaction. At present very few studies have been carried out and it is doubtful whether the results are sufficiently accurate to permit a clear distinction to be made between the various possibilities.

The dependence of rate on the deuterium composition of the solvent for α-D -tetramethylglucose mutarotation and nitramide decomposition is very much the same (Fig. 10.3) and reminiscent of that found for the variation of the ionic product of water K_W with solvent composition implying that the transition states resemble the products of the ionisation of water but with less complete charge separation. Strictly speaking nitramide being a nitrogen acid falls outside the scope of this book but in view of the important role that studies of its decomposition have played in the development of modern theories of acid-base catalysis the results are worthy of some consideration.

The early results of La Mer and Greenspan[36] have been re-analysed by Batts and Gold[37] in terms of modern theory. The reaction in an H_2O-D_2O medium can be represented by

$$L_2O + NL_2^4.NO_2 \longrightarrow \left[\begin{array}{c}\overset{2}{L}\\L\end{array}\!\!>O --- \overset{1}{L} --- N.NO --- O\overset{3}{L}\right] \longrightarrow N_2O + 2L_2O$$

$$(10.71)$$

where the non-equivalent hydrogens are numbered 1–4. Applied to Eqn (10.71) the solvent isotope effect becomes

$$\frac{k_n}{k_H} = \frac{(1 - n + n\phi_1)(1 - n + n\phi_2)^2(1 - n + n\phi_3)}{(1 - n + n\phi_4)^2}$$

$$(10.72)$$

The fractionation factor for H_2O is taken as unity and that due to nitramide must be very similar. The isotope fractionation factor of the two hydrogen atoms labelled 2 should be intermediate between that of L_3O^+ (l) and L_2O (unity); if the degree of proton transfer in the transition state is β we have $\phi_2 = l^\beta$. Similarly the fractionation factor ϕ_3 is intermediate between that of OH^- and H_2O and can be

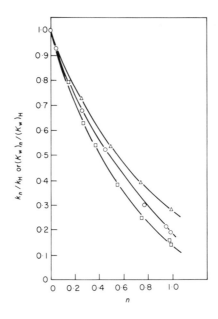

Fig. 10.3. Dependence of solvent catalysed rate on deuterium composition of the solvent. $\triangle$, Mutarotation of α-D-tetramethylglucose;[35] $\bigcirc$, decomposition of nitramide,[36,37] curve calculated using Eqn (10.74); $\square$, experimental results for $(K_W)_n/(K_W)_H$ reported by Gold and Lowe.[17]

given by $\phi_3 = \phi_{OL^-}^\beta$ if the reaction is truly concerted. The limiting solvent isotope effect is given by

$$\frac{k_D}{k_H} = \phi_1 l^{2\beta} \phi_{OL^-}^\beta \qquad (10.73)$$

so that Eqn (10.72) takes the form

$$\frac{k_n}{k_H} = \left(1 - n + n\frac{k_D}{k_H l^{2\beta} \phi_{OL^-}^\beta}\right)(1 - n + nl^\beta)^2(1 - n + n\phi_{OL^-}^\beta) \qquad (10.74)$$

By taking a value of 0·75 for β Batts and Gold[37] found good agreement between theory and experiment. However the curve is not very sensitive to the exact value of β so that almost the same results are obtained by using $\beta = 1$, a situation corresponding to complete proton transfer and ruled out by the observation of general catalysis.

10.5. APPLICATION TO HYDROXIDE CATALYSED REACTIONS

In the several cases reported (Table 10.5) the rates of proton transfer from carbon acids are faster when deuteroxide rather than hydroxide is the catalyst. The ratio $k_{OD^-}^{D_2O}/k_{OH^-}^{H_2O}$ involves contributions from an exchange isotope effect on hydroxide ion and a medium effect for transferring OH^- from H_2O to D_2O. Long[24] has recently shown in

TABLE 10.5

Solvent isotope effects for some hydroxide catalysed reactions at 25°

Carbon acid	$k_{OD^-}^{D_2O}/k_{OH^-}^{H_2O}$	Refs.
Nitroethane	1·39*, 1·40	38, 39
2-Nitropropane	1·36*, 1·35	38, 39
Acetone	1·47	32, 40
Phenylacetylene	1·33	41
t-Butylmalononitrile	1·72	24
9-Fluorenylmethanol	1·49	42
1,4-Dicyano-2-butene	1·38	24

* At 5°.

the case of 1,4-dicyano-2-butene detritiation how, by using medium independent fractionation factors, these two effects can be separated. For the reaction

$$RCT + OH^- \rightarrow [RC^- \text{---} T^+ \text{---} OH^-] \rightarrow RC^- + THO \qquad (10.75)$$

the solvent isotope effect is given by

$$\frac{k_D}{k_H} = k_{OD^-}^{D_2O}/k_{OH^-}^{H_2O} = \frac{\phi_{OH^-}}{\phi^\ddagger} \frac{\gamma_{OH^-}\gamma_{RCT}}{\gamma^\ddagger} \qquad (10.76)$$

As ϕ_{OH^-} and $\phi^\ddagger$ are medium independent and H_2O is the reference solvent the exchange effect can be identified with a fractionation factor term for the single solvent water,

$$\frac{\phi_{OH^-}}{\phi^\ddagger} = k_{OD^-}^{H_2O}/k_{OH^-}^{H_2O} \qquad (10.77)$$

and the transfer effect by the activity coefficient ratio

$$k_{OH^-}^{D_2O}/k_{OH^-}^{H_2O} = \frac{\gamma_{RCT}\gamma_{OH^-}}{\gamma^\ddagger} \qquad (10.78)$$

A value of 0·45, this being the mean of Weston's[14] (0·47) and Gold's[17] (0·42) can be used for ϕ_{OH^-} and for $\phi^{\ddagger}$ Kresge's[20] approach can be adopted once again; β for carboxylate anion catalysis is close to unity but that for the hydroxide ion will be somewhat lower (see p. 146). Long[24] suggests a value of 0·7. The calculated isotope effect is

$$k_{OD^-}^{H_2O}/k_{OH^-}^{H_2O} = 1·75$$

which by comparison with the experimental findings suggests that OD^- in H_2O is a slightly more powerful base than OD^- in D_2O.

The transfer isotope effect is then given by

$$\frac{1·38}{1·75} = \frac{\gamma_{OH^-}\gamma_{RCT}}{\gamma^{\ddagger}} \tag{10.79}$$

γ_{RCT} is usually approximated to unity. From equilibrium studies (p. 196) $\gamma_{H_3O^+}\gamma_{OH^-} = 1·14$ and if it is assumed that $\gamma_{H_3O^+} = 1$, the value of $\gamma^{\ddagger}$ is close to 1·4 which is similar to the medium effects reported in Table 10.4.

One of the interesting aspects of this work is the bearing it has on the acid-base properties of H_2O and D_2O and in particular on the reason for the large difference (factor of 7 at 25°) in their ionic products. The results show that it can not be due to differences in base strength between H_2O and D_2O or OH^- and OD^-. Similarly analysis of the rates of formation of ketones from enolate ions indicates[29] that the acids H_3O^+ and D_3O^+ are of virtually the same acid strength. The implication therefore is that the large difference in the ionic products must be almost entirely due to a difference in acid strengths of H_2O and D_2O and this seems to be borne out by Pocker's[32] finding that in 50% D_2O the rate of bromination of acetone is c. 5·5 times the rate of exchange (in 99·8% D_2O the rates of bromination and exchange are the same). Since in the absence of an isotope effect one would expect the two rates to be equal the neutralisation of the carbanion of acetone must be ~5·5 times faster by H_2O than D_2O.

Only the ionisation of two carbon acids, namely nitroethane[39] and 2-nitropropane,[18] have been studied as a function of the deuterium content of the medium. The rates of ionisation in hydroxide–water are very similar and the change in rates can be described by the same curve (Fig. 10.4). If the hydroxide ion is correctly formulated as $OH^-(H_2O)_3$ the reaction can be represented by Eqn (10.80):

$$RCH + OH^-(H_2O)_3 \rightarrow RC^- + 4H_2O \tag{10.80}$$

Gold[18] has drawn attention to the fact that direct proton transfer from RCH to OH⁻ under these circumstances cannot take place without the simultaneous expansion of the co-ordination of the hydroxide oxygen from 4 to 5. This seems unlikely and alternative schemes which involve proton transfer to one of the hydrogen bonded water molecules of the hydroxide ion and from that water molecule to the hydroxide ion have been proposed. The transition state in either case will contain hydrogen atoms whose fractionation

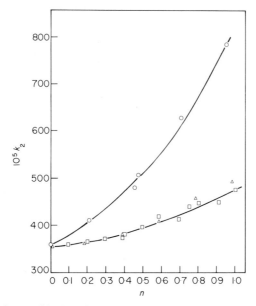

Fig. 10.4. Dependence of hydroxide and methoxide catalysed rates on deuterium composition of the medium. □, Results of Gold and Grist for 2-nitropropane[18] in H_2O-D_2O mixtures; Δ, results of Wynne-Jones et al.[39] for nitroethane in H_2O-D_2O mixtures; ○, results of Gold and Grist[43] for 2-nitropropane in MeOH–MeOD mixtures; curve is calculated on the basis of OMe⁻(MeOH)₃ and a transition state containing two methanol molecules.

can not be described in the same terms as the exchangeable hydrogen atoms which are intermediate between reactants and product states and the concept of β in terms of transition state structure becomes less useful.

10.6. APPLICATION TO METHOXIDE CATALYSED REACTIONS

The solvent isotope effects for proton transfer reactions in methanol-methoxide solutions are consistently higher than those obtained in water–hydroxide media (Table 10.6). As the methoxide ion contains no exchangeable hydrogens and the carbon bound hydrogen atoms of the carbon acids exchange with the solvent at a rate that is much slower than that induced by the methoxide ion the solvent isotope effect can not be accounted for in terms of Eqn (10.81).

$$RH + OMe^- \rightarrow [R^---H---OMe^-] \rightarrow R^- + MeOH \qquad (10.81)$$

Like the hydroxide ion there is reason to believe that the methoxide ion in methanol is firmly bound to 3 solvent molecules

TABLE 10.6

Solvent isotope effects in methanol at $25°$

Carbon acid	$k_{OMe^-}^{MeOD}/k_{OMe^-}^{MeOH}$	Refs.
2-Nitropropane	2·28	43
α-Phenylisocaprophenone	2·04	43
2-(N,N-Dimethylcarboxamido)-9-methyl fluorene	2·3	44
Pentafluorobenzene	2·3	45
2-Heptafluoropropane	1·5[a]	46

[a] At 70°.

and a more accurate representation of the reaction, as suggested by Gold,[43] is probably given by

$$RH + OMe^-(MeOH)_3 \rightarrow [R^---H---OMe^-(MeOH)_2]$$
$$+ MeOH \rightarrow R^- + 3MeOH \qquad (10.82)$$

The solvent isotope effect is then given by

$$\frac{k_n}{k_H} = \frac{(1 - n + n\phi^\ddagger)^2}{(1 - n + n\phi_{OMe^-})^3} \qquad (10.83)$$

and the limiting value by

$$\frac{k_D}{k_H} = \frac{k_{OMe^-}^{MeOD}}{k_{OMe^-}^{MeOH}} = \frac{(\phi^\ddagger)^2}{(\phi_{OMe^-})^3} \qquad (10.84)$$

During the process of proton transfer the hydrogen bonding molecules are transformed into ordinary solvent molecules. Their fractionation factor in the transition state is expected to be between that for the methoxide ion (0·74) and the solvent (unity). For a product like transition state $\phi^\ddagger$ becomes unity and the solvent isotope effect is a maximum, $k_D/k_H = (0·74)^{-3} = 2·5$; a formulation $OMe^-(MeOH)_2$ gives a maximum of only 1·8. Further support in favour of a trihydrated methoxide ion comes from a study of the variation in rate of ionisation of 2-nitropropane with the deuterium composition of the solvent (Fig. 10.4). The curve is calculated on the basis that the methoxide ion is solvated by three methanol molecules and that the transition state contains two methanol molecules.

The difference in solvent isotope effects between hydroxide and methoxide catalysed reactions is brought out most clearly by the results of Gold and Grist[43] for the ionisation of 2-nitropopane (k_D/k_H in methanol = $2 \cdot 28$, in water $1 \cdot 35$). The maximum solvent isotope effect for hydroxide catalysis is $2 \cdot 4$ close to that calculated for methoxide catalysis. The primary isotope effects for both reactions are virtually the same. The difference could arise, at least partly, from smaller transfer effects and weaker hydrogen bonding in the methanol system. Another possibility mentioned by Gold and Grist stems from the fact that the ionic mobility of methoxide ions in methanol is normal but that of the aqueous hydroxide ion is well known to be abnormally high and indicative of a chain conduction mechanism.

REFERENCES

1. Laughton, P. M. & Robertson, R. E. (1969). *Solute-Solvent Interactions*, Chapter 7. (Coetzee, J. F. & Ritchie, C. D. eds.) Dekker, New York.
2. Urey, H. C., Brickwedde, F. G. & Murphy, G. M. (1932). *Phys. Rev.* 39, 164.
3. La Mer, V. K. & Chittum, J. P. (1936). *J. Amer. Chem. Soc.* 58, 1642.
4. Gross, P., Steiner, H. & Krauss, F. (1936). *Trans. Faraday Soc.* 32, 877.
5. Orr, W. J. C. & Butler, J. A. V. (1937). *J. Chem. Soc.* 330.
6. Purlee, E. L. (1959). *J. Amer. Chem. Soc.* 81, 263.
7. Bunton, C. A. & Shiner, V. J. Jr. (1961). *J. Amer. Chem. Soc.* 83, 42, 3027, 3214.
8. Swain, C. G., Bader, R. F. W. & Thornton, E. R. (1960). *Tetrahedron* 10, 182.
9. Swain, C. G. & Thornton, E. R. (1961). *J. Amer. Chem. Soc.* 83, 3884, 3890.
10. Gold, V. (1963). *Proc. Chem. Soc.* 141.
11. Kresge, A. J. & Allred, A. L. (1963). *J. Amer. Chem. Soc.* 85, 1541.
12. More O'Ferrall, R. A. (1969). *Chem. Commun.* 114.
13. Gold, V. & Grist, S. (1971). *J. Chem. Soc. (B)* 1665.
14. Heinzinger, K. & Weston, R. E. (1964). *J. Phys. Chem.* 68, 744.
15. Gold, V. (1969). *Adv. Phys. Org. Chem.* (Gold, V. ed.) 7, 259. Academic Press, London.
16. Gold, V. & Lowe, B. M. (1963). *Proc. Chem. Soc.* 140.
17. Gold, V. & Lowe, B. M. (1967). *J. Chem. Soc. (A)* 936.
18. Gold, V. & Grist, S. (1972). *J. Chem. Soc. (Perkin II)* 89.
19. Gold, V. & Kessick, M. A. (1965). *Discuss. Faraday Soc.* 39, 84.
20. Kresge, A. J. (1964). *Pure Appl. Chem.* 8, 243.
21. Schowen, R. L. (1972). *Progr. Phys. Org. Chem.* (Streitwieser, A. & Taft, R. W. eds.) 9, 275.

22. Bigeleisen, J. (1955). *J. Chem. Phys.* 23, 2264.
23. Hibbert, F. & Long, F. A. (1971). *J. Amer. Chem. Soc.* 93, 2836.
24. Walters, E. A. & Long, F. A. (1972). *J. Phys. Chem.* 76, 362.
25. More O'Ferrall, R. A., Koeppl, G. W. & Kresge, A. J. (1971). *J. Amer. Chem. Soc.* 93, 9.
26. More O'Ferrall, R. A. & Kouba, J. (1967). *J. Chem. Soc. (B)* 985.
27. Bell, R. P., Fendley, J. A. & Hulett, J. R. (1956). *Proc. Roy. Soc. A* 235, 453.
28. Jones, J. R. (1969). *Trans. Faraday Soc.* 65, 2430.
29. Riley, T. & Long, F. A. (1962). *J. Amer. Chem. Soc.* 84, 522.
30. Long, F. A. & Watson, D. (1958). *J. Chem. Soc.* 2019.
31. Walters, E. A. & Long, F. A. (1969). *J. Amer. Chem. Soc.* 91, 3733.
32. Pocker, Y. (1959). *Chemy Ind. (London)* 1383.
33. Calmon, J. P., Calmon, M. & Gold, V. (1969). *J. Chem. Soc. (B)* 659.
34. Goodall, D. M. & Long, F. A. (1968). *J. Amer. Chem. Soc.* 90, 238.
35. Huang, H. H., Robinson, R. R. & Long, F. A. (1966). *J. Amer. Chem. Soc.* 88, 1866.
36. La Mer, V. K. & Greenspan, J. (1937). *Trans Faraday Soc.* 33, 1266.
37. Batts, B. D. & Gold, V. (1969). *J. Chem. Soc. (A)* 984.
38. Maron, S. H. & La Mer, V. K. (1938). *J. Amer. Chem. Soc.* 60, 2588.
39. Jones, P., Longridge, J. L. & Wynne-Jones, W. F. K. (1965). *J. Chem. Soc.* 3606.
40. Jones, J. R. (1965). *Trans. Faraday Soc.* 61, 95.
41. Halevi, E. A. & Long, F. A. (1961). *J. Amer. Chem. Soc.* 83, 2809.
42. More O'Ferrall, R. A. & Slae, S. (1970). *J. Chem. Soc. (B)* 260.
43. Gold, V. & Grist, S. (1971). *J. Chem. Soc. (B)* 2282.
44. Ford, W. T., Graham, E. W. & Cram, D. J. (1967). *J. Amer. Chem. Soc.* 89, 4661.
45. Streitwieser, A. Jr., Hudson, J. A. & Mares, F. (1968). *J. Amer. Chem. Soc.* 90, 648.
46. Andreades, S. (1964). *J. Amer. Chem. Soc.* 86, 2003.

11. Labelling of Molecules

In nearly all of the previous chapters reference has been made to the use of carbon acids labelled in a specific position with either deuterium or tritium. More frequently than not one has been concerned with the stability of the label under various conditions of solvent, temperature and catalyst. As the stability of the label is related to the ease with which it can be inserted it should be possible to apply some of the knowledge gained from these studies to devising successful methods of synthesis.

11.1. VARIOUS METHODS OF LABELLING[1,2]

Although deuterium and tritium are both isotopes of hydrogen there are important differences arising from the fact that the latter is radioactive when it comes to preparing deuterium and tritium labelled compounds. In particular the presence of radioactive impurities, sometimes at high activity and low concentration, renders difficult radiochemical as distinct from chemical purification of the compound. In addition the deuterium labelled compound is usually required at a high deuterium content in the required position whereas the corresponding tritiated compound is usually employed at trace concentrations of tritium. This means that the process of preparing the deuteriated compound sometimes requires a number of equilibrations which may lead under certain circumstances to the formation of appreciable concentrations of dimer.[3]

Although not widely used for the preparation of tritium labelled carbon acids there are several methods based on the weak β radiation emitted by tritium. The method of recoil labelling,[4,5] frequently associated with the name of Wolfgang, involves irradiation in the neutron flux of a nuclear reactor of an intimate mixture of a lithium salt (usually the carbonate) and the material to be labelled; recoil tritons produced by the Li (n, α) reaction combine with the excited organic molecule. The neutron flux is of the order of $10^{10}-10^{12}$ neutrons/cm^2 s and the time involved is usually between 2 and 4 days. Unfortunately the degree of radiation damage is high and consequently, purification difficult.

The Wilzbach method[6] involves the exposure of a small quantity of the material (0·1–1 g) in a finely divided form to tritium gas (activity 1–10 curies) for a period of time in the region of 7–20 days. Since its introduction in 1956 the method has been used to synthesise a diverse range of compounds varying in complexity from methane to ribonucleic acid and including sugars, steroids and polypeptides. The method, despite its inherent simplicity suffers from several disadvantages common to the recoil labelling method. Radiation damage is usually high, the product is labelled at random and the specific activity of the product can not be reliably estimated in advance. The high concentration of tritium necessary is also a drawback.

Several modifications[7,8] of the Wilzbach method based on the need to increase the degree of tritium incorporation whilst using a lower T_2 concentration and a shorter exposure time have been reported. This is usually done by supplying an additional source of energy. The technique developed by Wilzbach and Dorfman[7] involves the spreading of 0·5 g of the compound in a glass vessel in which are inserted two electrodes; the tritium gas is admitted to a pressure of 5–14 mm, one electrode is connected to a Tesla coil leak detector and the other to earth and a discharge of 1000 V passed for a few minutes. The product is relatively free from impurities and has an activity comparable to that obtained by the original exposure method.

In recent years heterogeneous methods of exchange involving a catalyst have been used for incorporating tritium (and deuterium) into organic compounds. One of the first to be reported[9] and subsequently employed by Evans and co-workers[10] for the synthesis of labelled adenine, quanine and some polycyclic aromatic hydrocarbons involved the use of tritiated acetic acid. Platinum oxide which had been pre-reduced with hydrogen, the hydrocarbon (0·3 g) and 70% acetic acid were heated in a sealed tube at a temperature of c. 150° for between 16 and 24 h.

More recently Garnett and co-workers[11,12] have made an extensive study of metal catalysed exchange. They found platinim to be the most active of the transition metals and a critical evaluation of the various methods used for its preparation was made.[13] By carefully controlling the different variables the reproducibility of the catalyst was much improved. In a typical procedure the organic compound together with tritiated water (1–10 μc/mg) is vacuum sealed in an ampoule with an activated transition metal catalyst such as pre-reduced PtO_2 and shaken for several hours at a temperature of between 30 and 150°C. For compounds such as benzene which are easily labelled refluxing is usually sufficient.

The method is a convenient one step process in which the organic compound need not be water soluble and where a solvent is not necessary. The level of radioactivity required is low and the product is usually radiochemically pure. The organic compound need not exchange with tritiated water as tritiated benzene can be used instead. This has been done in some cases in order to measure the change in the rate of exchange on inserting another compound. A reduction in rate indicates that a poisoning effect is operative; for sulphur containing compounds as well as others which contain groups such as iodide or nitro, capable of strong chemisorption at the catalyst surface, this seems to be important. Experience has shown that on the whole the method works better for aromatic compounds than it does for aliphatic compounds.

Although the method leads to a generally labelled compound it can be used in conjunction with other techniques to label a specific portion of a molecule. Thus to prepare aniline labelled in both meta positions it can first of all be catalytically labelled to give $C_6T_5NH_2$. Acid catalysed detritiation using Ingold's procedure[14] then yields $C_6H_3T_2NH_2$, only the meta positions being labelled. Similarly, catalytically labelled tetralin yields essentially $(5,6,7,8\text{-}^3H]$-tetralin which can be readily dehydrogenated to give $[1,2,3,4\text{-}^3H]$-naphthalene, a compound that is difficult to obtain readily by other procedures.

Garnett[15] has also developed a homogeneous method of studying metal catalysed exchange which is basically the analogue of the heterogeneous method. In a typical experiment a solution of acetic acid (1 mole), D_2O(1 mole), HCl($1\cdot5 \times 10^{-3}$M), the organic compound and disodium platinum tetrachloride ($1\cdot5 \times 10^{-3}$M) is allowed to react for up to 4 h in an evacuated sealed tube at a temperature within the range $25\text{-}120°C$. Acetic acid is essential to the medium to ensure homogeneity of phase and the concentration of hydrochloric acid is sufficient to stabilise the catalyst complex against reduction and thus prevent precipitation of the platinum. Too high an acid concentration inhibits the homogeneous metal catalysed process and only acid catalysed exchange will take place, if this is at all possible.

For many mono substituted benzenes there is a remarkable similarity in isotope orientation between the homogeneous and heterogeneous methods implying that the chemistry of adsorbed molecules and inorganic co-ordination compounds are intimately related, probably through π complex formation. The homogeneous method has been used to label phenanthrene and pyrene as well as naphthalene, bromobenzene, nitrobenzene and acetophenone.[16] The latter compounds are difficult to prepare by the heterogeneous method and it seems that the method will be replaced in the passage of time by this new development.

Of the various methods employed to label carbon acids, that of isotopic hydrogen exchange in solution is the most widely used. For relatively acidic compounds such as β-diketones exchange can be achieved in the presence of D_2O (or HTO) alone. For some investigations the need to prepare and isolate a compound that is fully deuteriated in a specific position can be avoided. Bell and co-workers,[17] for example, in their studies on rates of halogenation of β-ketoesters have allowed the compounds to exchange with a large excess of D_2O for 7–10 half lives as estimated from the rates of bromination. The reaction can then be initiated by adding a small volume of this solution to a much larger volume of bromine solution in H_2O. In this way the reaction velocity measured is that of the ionisation of the deuterium compound, provided the anion formed reacts with bromine much more rapidly than it picks up hydrogen from the solvent to form the undeuteriated compound. This assumption is usually justified by the observation that the reactions are always kinetically of zero-order with respect to bromine and that secondly no acceleration in rate due to replacement of deuterium by hydrogen occurs.

For less acidic compounds it is customary to use the hydroxide ion as a base. In this way a large number of labelled carbon acids have been prepared. If the rate of incorporation of label under these circumstances is inconveniently slow highly basic media may be employed.[18]

A useful one-step method of preparing α-deuterio carboxylic acids from which a number of other compounds such as alcohols, amines and halides can be prepared has been developed by Atkinson and co-workers.[19] Refluxing a solution of potassium acetate, for example, in basic D_2O causes ready exchange of the protons of the methyl group with a half-life of 3–5 h at 85°. Despite the fact that aliphatic substitution on the alpha–carbon of acetic acids slows the exchange rate several fold repeated exchange brings the isotopic content at the α carbon up to 98 atom % deuterium. The results for several phenylacetates[20] support a mechanism in which the carbon–hydrogen bond is cleaved by OH^- in the rate determining step leading to the formation of an α carbanion carboxylate intermediate:

$$Ar - \underset{\underset{H}{|}}{CH} - CO_2^- + OD^- \xrightarrow{\ s\ } Ar - \bar{C}H - CO_2^- + HDO \xrightarrow[D_2O]{\ f\ }$$

$$ArCHD . CO_2^- + O\bar{D} \quad (11.1)$$

Chemical methods of labelling take advantage of the characteristic reactions of compounds with the difference that at some stage a labelled reactant is introduced. Reaction of an aryl halide (usually the bromide) with magnesium followed by decomposition of the complex with D_2O or HTO is a widely exployed procedure. A similar method involves treating the bromo-compound with butyl–lithium, followed by quenching in D_2O or HTO. A method which is particularly useful for synthesising labelled heterocyclic compounds is the catalytic halogen–hydrogen exchange reaction.[21] Thus [6-^{2}H]-purine was prepared by suspending 1 gram of the 6-chloro compound in 25 ml of D_2O and shaking for 30 min with 0·5 g of 10% palladium on charcoal catalyst after the high pressure apparatus had been charged to 7 lb/in^2 with deuterium. After filtering off the catalyst the solution was neutralised by careful addition of sodium peroxide and the solvent removed by freeze drying. The labelled compound was obtained by sublimation.

11.2. APPLICATION OF HIGHLY BASIC MEDIA[18]

In the case of those carbon acids which exhibit little or no tendency to ionise in aqueous hydroxide solutions it has been customary to prepare the labelled compounds by synthetic routes. Recent developments however show that isotopic hydrogen exchange in highly basic media may be employed for such a purpose. Instead of using the hydroxide ion the more powerful alkoxide bases may be employed; the base strengths increase in the order OH^- in $H_2O <OMe^-$ in MeOH $< OEt^-$ in EtOH $< OB\bar{u}$-t in t-BuOH. Alternatively advantage may be taken of the fact that whilst heavy solvation of the hydroxide ion inhibits its ability to abstract a proton the addition of dipolar aprotic solvents which effectively desolvate the anion make it a considerably more powerful base (Chapter 6). In this way very weak carbon acids can be labelled, the limit being set by the fact that the dipolar aprotic solvents themselves contain ionisable protons and may be preferentially labelled. Even here the range can be extended by using a labelled aprotic solvent as the source of either deuterium or tritium.

The amide ion in liquid ammonia[22] as well as lithium or cesium cyclohexylamide in cyclohexylamine[23] are both highly basic systems (for the same concentration of base the reaction between H_2 and KND_2 in ND_3 is faster by a factor of 10^{14} than that between H_2 and KOD in D_2O) that have been frequently used to label weak carbon acids. Only their well-known sensitivity to moisture and oxygen have curtailed their use in this area.

The advantages of using dipolar aprotic solvents such as dimethyl sulphoxide to induce rapid exchange are many. Firstly, the labelled compound is obtained by a reaction the mechanism of which is usually well established and in a pure form or at worst in a condition where little radiochemical purification is necessary. Secondly, dimethyl sulphoxide is a very good solvent for a large number of organic compounds and is stable over long periods of time. In most cases the reaction can be carried out either at or close to room temperature. Finally, depending on the carbon acid either a specifically or generally labelled product may be obtained. On the other hand it is necessary to bear in mind that dimethyl sulphoxide can behave as an oxidising agent[24] and also act as a source of free radicals by interaction with suitable substrates.[25] Most important of all it is a potential health hazard[26] in view of its ability to confer greater penetrative power into tissue for many organic compounds.

Some of the advantages of using highly basic media in the synthesis of labelled carbon acids can be illustrated by reference to the preparation of aromatic compounds containing CD_3 groups. Other methods are available but each has serious limitations. Thus one could start with a compound containing a carboalkoxy group which in turn could be reduced with lithium aluminium deuteride to the alcohol and converted into the chloride or bromide by the action of concentrated acid. Formation of the Grignard reagent from the halide and decomposition with D_2O gives the required product.[27] The method however depends on the ready availability of the esters and whilst this presents no serious problem in the benzene series there are relatively few of the naphthalene and phenanthrene type available.

An alternative approach[28] would be to employ the trichloromethyl derivative and dechlorinate it using zinc dust and CD_3COOH. Here again the method is severely restricted by the fact that the starting materials are not readily available. The same criticism applies[29] if the bromo or iodo compound is used and the lithio-derivative formed using n-butyl-lithium; addition of CD_3Br or CD_3I would then give the necessary product.

In view of these difficulties Leitch and co-workers[29] investigated the possibility of promoting exchange in toluene, for example, by using $[^2H_6]$ dimethyl sulphoxide in the presence of the dimsyl anion:

$$C_6H_5 . CH_3 + CD_3SOCD_2^- \rightarrow C_6H_5 . CH_2^- + CD_3SOCD_2H \qquad (11.2)$$

$$C_6H_5CH_2^- + CD_3SOCD_3 \rightarrow C_6H_5 . CH_2D + CD_3SOCD_2^- \qquad (11.3)$$

Repeated (2 or 3 times) exchange at 150–160°C did in fact lead to the formation of $C_6H_5 . CD_3$ (atom % D > 99) and the method was extended to xylenes, durene, mono- and poly-methylnaphthalenes and phenanthrenes with success.

11.3. LABELLED CARBON ACIDS

Acetylacetone, ethylacetoacetate, ethylmalonate,[17] 2-carbethoxy-cylopentanone,[30] tricarboxymethane and 2-acetylcyclohexanone[31] are but a representative few of the many compounds than can be easily labelled by dissolving the compounds in either D_2O or HTO. A similar method can be used for many heterocyclic compounds— thiazole[32] and benzimidazole[33] are labelled in the 2-position on heating in D_2O and the equivalent 8 position in purine,[21] adenine,[34] adenosine,[35] guanosine[35] and hypoxanthine[36] can also be labelled in a similar manner. Methylation of the N-7 position of guanine derivatives renders the C-8 hydrogen so labile that exchange proceeds quite rapidly even under physiological conditions.[37] The great accelerating effect of added electronegative atoms can also be used to incorporate deuterium and tritium as, for example, in various tetra-zolium salts.[38]

Malononitrile can also be labelled by exchange in water[17] but the less acidic 1,4-dicyano-2-butene[39] and t-butylmalononitrile[40] like many other carbon acids require the presence of base. Deuteriated diethyl ketone ($[2,2,4,4,-^2H_4]$pentan-3-one) for example can be prepared[41] by refluxing the ketone in a $D_2O-NaOD$ mixture. Repeating the process several times gave a product containing 99·9 atom % deuterium in the specified positions. Hexadeuterio-acetone[42] as well as the corresponding dimethyl sulphoxide[43] (CD_3SOCD_3) have been prepared in this way; so also have methoxy-acetone[44] ($CH_3COCD_2OCH_3$) and $[2-^2H]$-isobutyraldehyde.[45] The preparation of several of the corresponding tritiated compounds have been reported.[46,47]

The phenylacetylenes are of similar acidities to these ketones and can be prepared by similar means.[48,49] Although aliphatic nitro-compounds are considerably more acidic than either the phenyl-acetylenes or the ketones the rates of ionisation are of the same order of magnitude. $[^2H_3]$-nitromethane is therefore prepared by[50] refluxing a mixture of the ordinary compound, D_2O and KOD. The process was repeated 4 times, the deuterium content of the heavy water being increased in each stage starting at 87% and ending with 99·5%. $[1-^2H_2]$-nitroethane, $[1-^2H]$-nitrocyclohexane and $[2-^2H]$-nitropropane were all prepared in a similar manner.[50] $[1-^2H]$-nitroethane was prepared by a slightly different scheme:

$$CH_3.CH_2.NO_2 \xrightarrow{OD^- - D_2O}$$

$$CH_3.CH.NO_2^- \xrightarrow{NH_3OD^+Cl^-, D_2O} CH_3.CHD.NO_2 \qquad (11.4)$$

The second stage requires a weak acid in order to minimise the decomposition of nitroethane in acid solution to form acetaldehyde and nitrous oxide (Nef reaction). The choice of the hydroxylamine cation was based on the observation of Kornblum and Graham[51] that by destroying nitrous acid formed in the Nef reaction it also minimises side reactions to give $CH_3CH(NO)NO_2$ and $CH_3C(NO_2):NO_2H$.

$[\alpha\text{-}^2H_3]$-2,4,6-trinitrotoluene[52] has been prepared by exchange in a D_2O-OD^- mixture containing a small amount of aprotic solvent; the reaction was virtually complete after 4 h at room temperature. The deuteriation of 4,4'4''-trinitrophenylmethane and 4,4'-dinitro-diphenylmethane has been achieved in a similar manner.[53] In the case of 1,3,5-trinitrobenzene[54] exchange was allowed to proceed for 3 h at 100°C; 1,3-dinitrobenzene was found to exchange its 2-H under similar conditions.[55] $[\alpha\text{-}^2H_2]$-Nitrobenzylcyanide was prepared[56] by exchange with $NaOD-D_2O$ in the presence of a little dioxan at room temperature.

$[^2H]$-Triphenylmethane can be prepared by isotopic exchange in highly basic media[18] or by reacting the ordinary compound with butyl-lithium, followed by addition of D_2O.[49] This latter method has been used to prepare $[^2H]$-p-biphenylyldiphenylmethane[49] as well as many aromatic hydrocarbons—$[9\text{-}^2H]$-phenanthrene, $[9\text{-}^2H]$-anthracene, $[2\text{-}^2H]$-biphenyl, $[4\text{-}^2H]$-biphenyl, $[6\text{-}^3H]$-chrysene, $[1\text{-}^3H]$-pyrene, $[3\text{-}^3H]$-fluoranthene and $[2\text{-}^3H]$-triphenylene are just a few of the examples.[57,58]

Fluorene labelled in the 9 position can be obtained[59] by metallation with butyl-lithium in hexane. Direct quenching of the 9-fluorenyllithium with D_2O however gives variable and substantial amounts of $[9\text{-}^2H_2]$-fluorene. The preferred method in these circumstances is to convert the fluorenyllithium into the Grignard reagent before quenching. Many labelled hydrocarbons have been prepared by reacting the appropriate aryl bromide (or chloride) with magnesium to form the Grignard reagent and the ethereal solution subsequently quenched with D_2O or HTO. In some cases the addition of a small amount of ethyl bromide prior to the deuteriation (or tritiation) helps to remove any residual water.[60] Compounds that have been prepared in this way include $[\alpha\text{-}^2H]$-m-xylene, $[\alpha\text{-}^2H]$-2-methylnaphthalene, $[2\text{-}^2H]$-toluene, $[2\text{-}^3H]$-anthracene and $[3\text{-}^2H]$-fluorobenzene.[60−63]

REFERENCES

1. Evans, E. A. (1966). *Tritium and its Compounds*, Butterworths, London.
2. Thomas, A. F. (1971). *Deuterium Labelling in Organic Chemistry*. Appleton-Century-Crofts, New York.
3. Calf, G. E. & Garnett, J. L. (1969). *Chem. Commun.* 373.

4. Wolfgang, R., Rowland, F. S. & Turton, C. N. (1955). *Science* 121, 715.
5. Rowland, F. S. & Wolfgang, R. (1956). *Nucleonics* 14, 58.
6. Wilzbach, K. E. (1957). *J. Amer. Chem. Soc.* 79, 1013.
7. Wilzbach, K. E. & Dorfman, L. (1959). *J. Phys. Chem.* 63, 799.
8. Ghanem, N. A. & Westermark, T. (1960). *J. Amer. Chem. Soc.* 82, 4432.
9. Eidinoff, M. L. & Knoll, J. E. (1953). *J. Amer. Chem. Soc.* 75, 1992.
10. Crowter, D. G., Evans, E. A. & Rasdell, R. (1962). *Chemy Ind. (London)* 1622.
11. Garnett, J. L. (1962). *Nucleonics* 20, 86.
12. Garnett, J. L. & Sollich, W. A. (1961). *Aust. J. Chem.* 14, 441.
13. Garnett, J. L. & Sollich, W. A. (1963). *J. Catalysis* 2, 339.
14. Ingold, C. K., Raisin, C. G. & Wilson, C. L. (1936). *J. Chem. Soc.* 1643.
15. Garnett, J. L. & Hodges, R. J. (1967). *J. Amer. Chem. Soc.* 89, 4546.
16. Garnett, J. L. & Hodges, R. J. (1967). *Chem. Commun.* 1001.
17. Bell, R. P. & Crooks, J. E. (1965). *Proc. Roy. Soc. Ser. A* 286, 285.
18. Jones, J. R. (1968). *J. Labelled Compounds* 4, 197.
19. Atkinson, J. G., Csakvary, J. J., Herbert, G. T. & Stuart, R. S. (1968). *J. Amer. Chem. Soc.* 90, 498.
20. Balenger, P., Atkinson, J. G. & Stuart, R. S. (1969). *Chem. Commun.* 1067.
21. Bullock, F. & Jardetzky, O. (1964). *J. Org. Chem.* 29, 1988.
22. Shatenshtein, A. I. (1963). *Adv. Phys. Org. Chem.* (Gold, V. ed.) 1, 156. London, Academic Press.
23. Streitwieser, A. Jr., Van Sickle, D. E. & Langworthy, W. C. (1962). *J. Amer. Chem. Soc.* 84, 244.
24. Amonoo-Neiza, E. H., Ray, S. K., Shaw, R. A. & Smith, B. C. (1965). *J. Chem. Soc.* 6250.
25. Russell, G. A. & Janzen, E. G. (1967). *J. Amer. Chem. Soc.* 89, 300.
26. Buckley, A. (1965). *J. Chem. Educ.* 42, 674.
27. Dizabo, P. & Leitch, L. C. (1962). *Bull Soc. Chim. Fr.* 574.
28. Renaud, R. N. & Leitch, L. C. (1956). *Can. J. Chem.* 34, 98.
29. Chen, T. S., Wolinska-Mocydlarz, J. & Leitch, L. C. (1971). *J. Labelled Compounds* 6, 285.
30. Bell, R. P., Fendley, J. A. & Hulett, J. R. (1956). *Proc. Roy. Soc. Ser. A* 235, 453.
31. Barnes, D. J. & Bell, R. P. (1970). *Proc. Roy. Soc. Ser. A* 318, 421.
32. Breslow, R. (1958). *J. Amer. Chem. Soc.* 80, 3719.
33. Fritzsche, H. (1967). *Biochim. Biophys. Acta* 149, 173.
34. Elvidge, J. A., Jones, J. R., O'Brien, C. & Evans, E. A. (1971). *Chem. Commun.* 394.
35. Shelton, K. R. & Clark, J. M. (1967). *Biochemistry* 6, 2735.
36. Bergmann, F. B., Lichtenberg, D. & Neiman, Z. (1969). *Chem. Commun.* 992.
37. Tomatz, M. (1970). *Biochim. Biophys. Acta* 18, 199.
38. Rochat, A. C. & Olofson, R. A. (1969). *Tetrahedron Lett.* 39, 3377.
39. Walters, E. A. & Long, F. A. (1969). *J. Amer. Chem. Soc.* 91, 3733.
40. Hibbert, F., Long, F. A. & Walters, E. A. (1971). *J. Amer. Chem. Soc.* 93, 2829.
41. Calmon, J. P., Calmon, M. & Gold, V. (1969). *J. Chem. Soc. (B)* 659.
42. Condon, F. E. (1951). *J. Amer. Chem. Soc.* 73, 4675.
43. Buncel, E., Symons, E. A. & Zabel, A. W. (1965). *Chem. Commun.* 173.
44. Hine, J., Hampton, K. G. & Menon, B. C. (1967). *J. Amer. Chem. Soc.* 89, 2664.

45. Hine, J., Houston, J. G., Jensen, J. H. & Mulders, J. (1965). *J. Amer. Chem. Soc.* 87, 5050.
46. Jones, J. R. (1965). *Trans. Faraday Soc.* 61, 95.
47. Albagli, A., Jones, J. R. & Stewart, R. (1970). *J. Chem. Soc. (B)* 1509.
48. Halevi, E. A. & Long, F. A. (1961). *J. Amer. Chem. Soc.* 83, 2809.
49. Pocker, Y. & Exner, J. H. (1968). *J. Amer. Chem. Soc.* 90, 6764.
50. Bell, R. P. & Goodall, D. M. (1966). *Proc. Roy. Soc. Ser. A* 294, 273.
51. Kornblum, N. & Graham, G. E. (1951). *J. Amer. Chem. Soc.* 73, 4041.
52. Buncel, E., Norris, A. R., Russell, K. E. & Tucker, R. (1972). *J. Amer. Chem. Soc.* 94, 1646.
53. Bowden, K. & Stewart, R. (1965). *Tetrahedron* 21, 261.
54. Buncel, E. & Symons, E. A. (1967). *Chem. Commun.* 771.
55. Buncel, E. & Zabel, A. W. (1967). *J. Amer. Chem. Soc.* 89, 3082.
56. Caldin, E. F. & Tomalin, G. (1968). *Trans. Faraday Soc.* 64, 2814.
57. Streitwieser, A. Jr., & Lawler R. G. (1965). *J. Amer. Chem. Soc.* 87, 5388.
58. Streitwieser, A. Jr., Lewis, A., Schwager, I., Fish, R. W. & Labana, S. (1970). *J. Amer. Chem. Soc.* 92, 6525.
59. Streitwieser, A. Jr., Hollyhead, W. B., Pudjaatmaka, A. H., Owens, P. H., Kruger, T. L., Rubenstein, P. A., MacQuarrie, R. A., Brokaw, M. L., Chu, W. K. C. & Niemeyer, H. M. (1971). *J. Amer. Chem. Soc.* 93, 5088.
60. Streitwieser, A. Jr. & Van Sickle, D. E. (1962). *J. Amer. Chem. Soc.* 84, 249.
61. Streitwieser, A. Jr. & Langworthy, W. C. (1963). *J. Amer. Chem. Soc.* 85, 1757.
62. Streitwieser, A. Jr. & Ziegler, G. R. (1969). *J. Amer. Chem. Soc.* 91, 5081.
63. Streitwieser, A. Jr., Lawler, R. G. & Perrin, C. (1965). *J. Amer. Chem. Soc.* 87, 5383.

Author Index

Subject Index

Chemical Compound Index